The Immune System

A COURSE ON THE
MOLECULAR AND CELLULAR BASIS
OF IMMUNITY

To our wives and families

The Immune System

A COURSE ON THE
MOLECULAR AND CELLULAR BASIS
OF IMMUNITY

I. McConnell
MA, PhD, BVMS
Medical Research Council
Centre, and Honorary Associate
Lecturer in Pathology
University of Cambridge

A. Munro
MA, PhD
Reader in
Immunology
Fellow of Christ's College
University of Cambridge

H. Waldmann
MB, BChir, PhD, MRCP
Lecturer in
Pathology
University of Cambridge

Second edition

Blackwell Scientific Publications
Oxford London Edinburgh
Boston Melbourne

© 1975, 1981 by
Blackwell Scientific Publications
Editorial offices:
Osney Mead, Oxford, OX2 0EL
8 John Street, London, WC1N 2ES
9 Forrest Road, Edinburgh, EH1 2QH
52 Beacon Street, Boston
    Massachusetts 02108, USA
99 Barry Street, Carlton
    Victoria 3053, Australia

First published 1975
Reprinted 1976, 1978
Second edition 1981
Reprinted 1982, 1983, 1984

Italian edition 1979

Printed and bound in Great Britain
at The Alden Press, Oxford

DISTRIBUTORS

USA
    Blackwell Mosby Book Distributors
    11830 Westline Industrial Drive
    St Louis, Missouri 63141

Canada
    Blackwell Mosby Book Distributors
    120 Melford Drive, Scarborough,
    Ontario, M1B 2X4

Australia
    Blackwell Scientific Book
    Distributors
    31 Advantage Road,
    Highett, Victoria 3190

British Library
Cataloguing in Publication Data

McConnell, Ian
    The immune system.—2nd ed.
    1. Cellular immunity
    I. Title   II. Munro, A   III. Waldmann, H
    574.2'9   OR185.5

ISBN 0-632-00626-9

Contents

Preface to the Second Edition

The second edition is based on an advanced course in immunology for third year undergraduates taught in the Department of Pathology, University of Cambridge.

The considerable advances made in immunology since the first edition have led to the second edition being completely rewritten. Nevertheless, the style and structure of the first edition have been maintained. In the first two sections we emphasize the new information on immunoglobulin genes, the genetics and biochemistry of the major histocompatibility systems and their rôle in lymphocyte differentiation and interactions in the immune response. In the last section we stress those areas of immunopathology where basic principles have improved the understanding of disease or where clinical problems have added to basic immunological knowledge. The book provides a synthesis of the experimental work on which current concepts and discoveries in immunology are based. This approach has been adopted because we feel that teaching at the advanced level should not be entirely didactic.

We thank all those who contributed to the success of the first edition, particularly Mike Hobart who has since chosen to apply his efforts to molecular genetics rather than immunology. We have missed his energies but his spirit remains in much of the text. To maintain uniformity in content some of the chapters from the first edition have not been repeated. They nonetheless remain excellent synopses of particular areas of immunology.

We gratefully acknowledge the help and advice of many of our colleagues in Cambridge. We are grateful to David Franks and Robin Coombs who were responsible for establishing the Immunology course in Cambridge in its present form. We thank Arnold Feinstein for his contribution to the chapter on immunoglobulin structure, Peter Lachmann for permission to use much of his review and teaching material on the complement system and Anthony Butterworth for his help with the chapter on effector mechanisms in immunity and hyersensitivity. We are indebted to Helgi Valdimarsson, David Brown and Sue Bright for providing material which formed the basis of the chapters on 'Immunity Deficiency', 'Auto-allergic Diseases' and 'HLA and Disease' respectively. Finally we thank Neil Gorman, Jeremy Pearson and David Secher for reading and criticizing the text, our secretaries Jane

Pearson and Gill Habicht for tolerating countless drafts and the Part II students in the Department of Pathology for being responsive guinea-pigs.

As in the first edition we have been selective in our choice of references and apologize to the many immunologists whose work we admire but mention without reference.

Finally we thank our publishers especially John Robson and his colleagues for producing the book.

Acknowledgements

We are grateful to authors, editors and publishers for permission to reproduce the following figures and tables:

Fig. 1.3   from Secher D. (1979) *Int. Rev. Biochem.* **23**, 1, Fig. 7.

Fig. 1.4   from Weigert M. *et al.* (1978) *Nature* **276**, 285, Fig. 2.

Fig. 2.1   from Feinstein A. & Rowe A.J. (1965) *Nature* **205**, 147, Figs 3 & 4.

Fig. 2.2   from Valentine R.C. & Green N.M. (1967) *J. Molec. Biol.* **27**, 615, Fig. 1 plates 3, 4.

Fig. 2.3   from Feinstein A., Munn E.A. & Richardson N.E. (1971) *Ann. N.Y. Acad. Sci.* **190**, 104, Figs 1, 7, 8.

Fig. 2.7   from Deisendorf J. *et al.* (1976) *Hoppe-Seyler Z. Physiol. Chem.* **357**, 435.

Fig. 2.8   from Feinstein A. & Beale D. (1977) In *Immunochemistry: An Advanced Textbook* (eds Glynn L.E. & Steward M.W.), p. 263, Fig. 13. John Wiley & Sons, Chichester.

Fig. 2.9   from Davies R.D. *et al.* (1975) *Contemp. Topics in Molecular Immunol.* **4**, 127, Fig. 8.

Fig. 2.11a   from Amzel L.M. *et al.* (1974) *Proc. Nat. Acad. Sci. U.S.A.* **71**, 1427, Fig. 4.

Fig. 2.11b   from Segal D.M. *et al.* (1974) *Proc. Nat. Acad. Sci. U.S.A.* **71**, 4298, Fig. 5.

Fig. 2.17   from Eisen H.N. (1973) *Immunology* 2nd ed. (eds Davis *et al.*). Harper & Row, New York.

Fig. 3.2   from Knofel H.R. *et al.*. (1975) *Eur. J. Immunol.* **5**, 78, Fig. 1; and Reid K.B.M. & Porter R.R. (1976) *Biochem. J.* **155**, 19, Fig. 3.

Fig. 3.5   Harrison R.A. & Lachmann P.J. (1975) *Mol. Immunol.* **17**, 219.

Fig. 4.3   from Sanger F. *et al.*(1977) *Proc. Nat. Acad. Sci. U.S.A.* **74**, 5463, Fig. 1.

Fig. 4.6   from Siedman J.G. & Leder P. (1978) *Nature* **276**, 790, Fig. 4.

Fig. 4.8   from Cohn M. *et al.* (1974) In *The Immune System* (eds. Sercarz E.E. *et al.*), p. 89, Fig. 1. Academic Press, New York.

Table 5.1.   from Milstein C.P. & Feinstein A. (1968) *Biochem. J.* **107**, 449, table 2.

Table 5.2   from Secher D.S. (1979) *Int. Rev. Biochem.* **23**, 1, table 9.

Fig. 6.5   from van Rood *et al.* (1980) In *The Role of the Major Histocompatibility*

Complex in Immunobiology (eds Dorf M. & Benacerraf B.). Garland Press Publishing, New York.

Table 6.5   from Albert *et al.* (1980) *Tissue Antigens* **16**, 113, table 5.

Fig. 6.6   from Bodmer W.F. & Bodmer J.G. (1978) *Brit. Med. Bull.* **34**, 309, Fig. 3.

Fig. 6.7   from Singer S.J. & Nicholson G.L. (1972) *Science* **175**, 720, Fig. 3.

Table 6.7   from Nathanson S.G. *et al.* (1980) In *Trends in Histocompatibility* (eds Reisfeld R.A. & Ferreira S.O.); and Kohn H.I. *et al.* (1978) *Immunogenetics* **7**, 279.

Fig. II.1   from Milstein C. *et al.* (1979) *Ciba Found. Symp.* **66**, 251, Fig. 3.

Fig. II.2   from Unanue E.K. *et al.* (1972) *J. exp. Med.* **136**, 885, Figs 1–5.

Fig. 8.4   from Lydyard P.M. *et al.* (1976) *J. exp. Med.* **144**, 79, Fig. 2.

Fig. 8.6   from Dintzis H.M. *et al.* (1976) *Proc. Nat. Acad. Sci., U.S.A.* **73**, 3677, Fig. 4.

Fig. 9.1   from Le Dourain N.B. *et al.* (1976) In *Phylogeny of Thymus and Bone Marrow Bursa Cells* (eds Wright R.K. & Cooper E.I.). Elsevier, North Holland.

Fig. 9.2a   from Weiss L. (1972) In *The Cells and Tissues of the Immune System. Structure, Function and Interaction*, p. 81. Prentice-Hall, New York.

Fig. 9.4c   from Reinhertz E.L. & Scholssomann S.F. (1980) *Cell* **19**, 821, Fig. 2.

Fig. 10.6   from Rosenthal A.S. *et al.* (1976) In *Immunobiology of the Macrophage* (ed. Nelson D.S.). p. 131. Academic Press, New York.

Fig. 12.1   from Shevach E.M. & Rosenthal A.S. (1973) *J. exp. Med.* **138**, 1213, Fig. 2.

Fig. 13.4   from Weigle W.O. (1971) *Clin. exp. Immunol.* **9**, 437, Fig. 1.

Table 13.2   from Desaymard C. (1977) *Eur. J. Immunol.* **7**, 647, table 3.

Fig. 14.6   from Ford W.L. (1975) *Progr. Allergy* **19**, 1, Fig. 4; and Nieuwenhuis P. & Ford W.L. (1976) *Cell. Immunol.* **23**, 254, Fig. 9.

Figs. 14.8b, c, g,   from Andrews P. *et al.* (1980) *Ciba Found. Symp.* **71**, 211, Figs 1, 4.

Fig. 14.9   from Drexhage H.A. *et al.* (1975) *Cell and Tissue Res.* **202**, 407.

Fig. 14.10   from McConnell *et al.* (1980) *Ciba Found. Symp.* **71**, 211, Fig. 1.

Fig. 15.3   from Glauert A.M. *et al.* (1978) *J. Cell Science* **34**, 173.

Fig. 15.4   from Sanderson L.J. & Glauert A.M. (1979) *Immunology* **36**, 119, Fig. 1.

Fig. 15.5   from Gell P.G.H., Coombs R.R.A. & Lachmann P.J. (1975) In *Clinical Aspects of Immunology* 3rd ed., p. 761, Fig. 25.1. Blackwell Scientific Publications, Oxford.

Advice to Readers

This book presents data at a rather high density. Most people will find it necessary to read slowly and to be sure that they understand at each stage. The Glossary attempts to provide accurate or exemplary definitions for the special terms used in immunology. Consult it if you are not fully happy about the meaning of a term.

The book is divided into three sections covering Immunochemistry, Cellular Immunology and Immunopathology. Each section is preceded by a Preamble providing a directory of what is to be covered and in the case of Section II some background information. Readers with some knowledge of immunology may find these preambles unnecessary.

Section I
Molecules and Genes

There are two major molecular systems involved in antigen recognition. The first is the antibody molecules which belong to a class of serum proteins known as the immunoglobulins. Studies of their biology, structure and genetics have formed much of the discipline of immunology over the last 20 years. The second, initially discovered by Gorer in the 1930s, is known as the major histocompatibility system or MHS. In recent years it has become clear that the MHS is not just a stumbling block to transplantation but is involved in lymphocyte function in the immune response.

The molecules and genes of these two systems are discussed in this section. Rather than give an exhaustive review we have restricted our discussion to those areas of current interest where new information at the biochemical, structural and DNA level highlights particular aspects of the immunoglobulins or the products of the MHS. For example, in Chapter 1 (a kind of shortened Gray's Anatomy of the immunoglobulins) we emphasize current studies on immunoglobulin variable regions since here new information on the amino acid sequence data of the variable region has aided our understanding of the three-dimensional structure of immunoglobulin domains (Chapter 2) and the genes which code for them (Chapters 4 and 5). Similar emphasis has also been placed on idiotypes. The reader is advised to pay particular attention to idiotypes since these are now recognized as important to the understanding of the generation of antibody diversity and to regulatory cell interactions in the immune response. Chapter 2 discusses the three-dimensional structure of the antibody molecule and the chemistry and properties of the antibody combining site. We hope those with Cyclopean vision will appreciate the three-dimensional pictures. The complement system (Chapter 3) is a good example of a third molecular system of much interest to the immunologist. Recent advances in the structure of certain complement components and of the homeostasis of complement activation reveal that complement is not entirely witchcraft. Chapter 4 describes the impact which studies on genetic engineering have made to our understanding of the arrangement and structure of immunoglobulin genes. As this is a fast moving and exciting field, we provide for the non-molecular biologist a simple overview of the elegant methodologies currently being used to study immunoglobulin DNA. It seems that immunoglobulins continue to break the rules and you may be surprised to read that there are at least four genes for one polypeptide chain. Studies at the DNA level have added much to the speculations on the evolution of the genes for immuno-globulin and complement (Chapter 5). The concluding chapter in this section reveals our bias for the MHS and summarizes the current state of play with respect to the biochemistry and genetics of this important system of cell surface molecules.

Note. To avoid ambiguity when discussing genes and their products, we have used italics to denote a gene or loci (e.g. *HLA-A, B or C*) and normal lettering for the products of loci (HLA-A, B or C).

Chapter 1
Immunoglobulins as Proteins

1.1 Introduction

The complexities of any biological system are best understood in molecular terms. In the immune system the best characterized molecules are the antibodies which occur in the globulin fraction of serum and are known as the immunoglobulins. In the early 1950s a knowledge of their different physical and biological properties permitted their isolation and characterization and there is now such a vast and comprehensive literature that to repeat much of it in detail would be redundant. Rather, the emphasis in this chapter will be on summarizing the salient features of immunoglobulins and in discussing their more interesting aspects.

1.1.1 Basic structure

Immunoglobulins are made up of equal numbers of heavy and light polypeptide chains (general formula $(H_2L_2)_n$), held together by non-covalent forces and usually by interchain disulphide bridges. Each chain contains two or more runs of amino acid sequence approximately 110 residues in length and containing one intrachain disulphide bond (Fig. 1.1). There is considerable amino acid homology between these various runs and they are all folded into a three-dimensional structure or domain of similar dimensions held together by a disulphide bridge (Chapter 2, Fig. 2.2). In any one molecule all the light chains are identical as are the heavy chains and in the H_2L_2 unit the molecule is symmetrical about its long axis.

The N-terminal domain of each chain shows much more variation in amino acid sequence than the other domains and is known as the variable region to distinguish it from the relatively invariant constant regions.

Native immunoglobulins are rather resistant to proteolytic digestion but certain enzymes have been useful in elucidating immunoglobulin structure (Fig. 1.1). Most immunoglobulins can be cleaved about half-way along the heavy chain. Papain cleaves the molecule into three fragments of similar size:

(a) *Two* Fab fragments of approximately 50,000 M.W. each carrying a single antigen-combining site and comprising the variable regions of both chains, the constant region of the light chains and the first constant domain ($C_H I$) of the heavy chain. Univalent Fab fragments combine with but do not precipitate antigen.

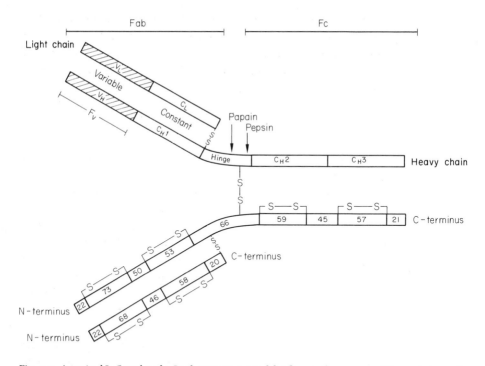

Fig. 1.1. A typical IgG molecule. In the upper part of the figure, the names of the various parts of the molecule are given. The lower part of the figure shows the arrangements of the intrachain disulphide bridges.

(b)   An Fc fragment that readily crystallizes, composed of the C-terminal halves of the heavy chains.

If pepsin is used the digestion occurs a little closer to the C-terminus than with papain, the interheavy-chain disulphide bridges are preserved and a large F(ab')$_2$ fragment (approximately 100,000 M.W.) is released. Being divalent this fragment will combine with and precipitate antigen. Pepsin extensively degrades the Fc fragment. The region joining the Fab and Fc parts of the molecule is known as the hinge region. Using careful conditions, it is sometimes possible to split off the variable regions, known as Fv.

1.2 Heterogeneity of immunoglobulins

Antibody molecules have two functions. Their prime function of antigen recognition is dictated by the primary amino acid sequence of the variable region. The secondary functions of antibodies, such as complement fixation and interaction with a variety of tissue cells, are mediated by the constant regions of heavy chains. Tissue cells which interact with antibody do so via membrane receptors for the Fc region.

The normal antibody response involves the activation of a large number of different clones of antibody-secreting cells (i.e. polyclonal). This is reflected in the marked heterogeneity of specific serum antibodies and limits their use for amino acid sequence studies. Homogeneous immunoglobulin is the product of a single clone of antibody-secreting cells and is ideal for biochemical analysis.

1.2.1 Homogeneous immunoglobulins

There are two sources of homogeneous immunoglobulin suitable for structural and amino acid sequence studies.

(a) *Myelomas.* Neoplastic antibody-secreting plasma cells (plasmacytomas) continuously synthesize a single molecular species of immunoglobulin. Serum concentrations of the abnormal protein in patients (or mice) with plasmacytomas can be in excess of 10 mg/ml, and it is readily identified as a single sharp spike in the serum electrophoretic profile. Specificities of myelomas are usually unknown but can be determined by screening them for reactivity with large numbers of different antigens (Potter, 1972 and 1977). Myelomas of known specificities have been of great value in understanding the relationship between the amino acid sequence of the combining site and antigen specificity.

(b) *Monoclonal antibodies.* Homogeneous antibodies occasionally arise after immunization with certain antigens (Krause, 1970). However, it is now possible to make monoclonal antibodies by cell fusion techniques (Köhler & Milstein, 1975). The possibility of making antibodies *à la carte* in unlimited amounts is revolutionizing immunology and has widespread application in many fields of biology and medicine.

In this technique (Fig. 1.2) spleen cells from immunized animals are used as a source of antibody-secreting cells of known specificity. These are fused with plasmacytoma cells to produce hybrid cells, some of which will secrete immunoglobulins with specificities present in the antibody-producing cell population. The fusion mix at first contains unfused normal cells and plasmacytoma cells as well as the desired hybrids. The latter are selected by appropriate tissue culture conditions which permit only the hybrid cells to survive. By repeated subculture and dilution, single clones of antibody-secreting cells are eventually established.

Most sequence work so far has been done with myeloma proteins from mouse and man, although more recently some sequences have been determined for monoclonal antibodies.

1.2.2 Light-chain types and subtypes

There are two types of light chain, κ and λ, whose multiple structural differences are reflected in antigenic differences. Although they are molecules of apparently similar

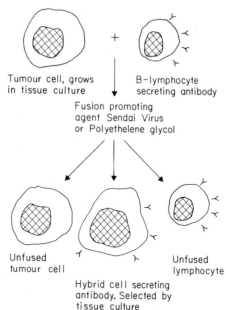

Fig. 1.2. Cell fusion to produce monoclonal antibodies. For description, see text.

Tumour cell, grows in tissue culture

B−lymphocyte secreting antibody

Fusion promoting agent Sendai Virus or Polyethelene glycol

Unfused tumour cell

Hybrid cell secreting antibody. Selected by tissue culture techniques

Unfused lymphocyte

function it is surprising that the sequence homology between κ and λ should only be 40 per cent. In fact there is far greater homology between human and mouse κ chains, suggesting that during evolution light-chain divergence preceded speciation (see Chapter 5). The proportion of κ to λ varies between species with the $\kappa:\lambda$ ratio being 2:1 in man; 25:1 in mice and 1:25 in horses.

In man there are four distinct λ-chain subtypes which are the products of tandem gene duplication (Chapter 5). These subtype differences reflect amino acid substitu-

Table 1.1. Amino acid substitution in the constant region of human λ chains correlated with λ-chain subtypes

	Serological markers			Critical amino acid residues				
	Mcg	Oz	Kern	112	114	153	163	190
$C_{\lambda1}$	−	+	−	Ala	Ser	Ser	Thr	Lys
$C_{\lambda2}$	−	−	+	Ala	Ser	Gly	Thr	Arg
$C_{\lambda3}$	−	−	−	Ala	Ser	Ser	Thr	Arg
$C_{\lambda4}$	+	+	−	Asn	Thr	Ser	Lys	Lys

The serological markers Kern and Oz correspond to amino acid replacements at positions 153 and 190 respectively. The pattern of substitutions would suggest that $C_{\lambda1}$ after duplication and mutation gave rise to $C_{\lambda3}$ and $C_{\lambda4}$. $C_{\lambda2}$ possibly arose from a duplication of $C_{\lambda3}$. Adapted from Fett and Deutsch (1975).

tions at different positions in the λ-chain constant region (Table 1.1). The Oz and Kern markers, antigenic determinants first detected on myeloma proteins, were originally believed to be allotypes but this is not the case since both markers simultaneously occur in all normal sera. There are no subtypes of human κ chains.

1.2.3 Heavy-chain classes

There are five distinct heavy-chain classes: μ, γ, α, δ, and ε. The heavy chain determines the immunoglobulin class and each combines with either κ or λ light chains. For example, two μ chains with either two κ or λ chains constitute a 7S IgM subunit, there being five such subunits per whole IgM molecule. Table 1.2 shows the different physiochemical and biological properties of the immunoglobulin classes.

1.2.4 Heavy-chain subclasses

In many species there are several versions of both the γ and α heavy-chain classes. By various criteria, such as antigenicity, sequence homologies and carbohydrate content the subclasses are more related to each other than to the other classes. In man, sequence studies show a 95 per cent homology between different subclasses compared with a 45 per cent homology between classes. The biological and physical characteristics of the IgG subclasses in various species are detailed in Table 1.3.

1.2.5 Structural differences between immunoglobulin classes and subclasses

Gross structural differences between immunoglobulin classes and subclasses are seen in the number of domains, the number and arrangement of disulphide bridges and in overall carbohydrate content. These differences for human immunoglobulin are schematically outlined in Fig. 1.3. There are three constant region domains in γ, α and probably δ (C_H1, C_H2 and C_H3) and four in μ and ε. The C_H3 domains in μ and ε correspond to the C_H2 domains of the γ chain. This suggests that in IgM and IgE the extra domain is C_H2 which is probably where the hinge region would be in IgG. The position of the light to heavy-chain bridge also varies between classes. μ, α, δ, ε and γ chains apart from $\gamma1$ have this bridge between V_H and C_H1 whereas in IgG1 and possibly in some IgA2 molecules the light to heavy bridge occurs between C_H1 and C_H2. Alternatively, in IgA2 the light chains are covalently linked to one another forming a light-chain dimer and there is no disulphide bond to the α chain. The interheavy-chain disulphide bridges also vary between the various IgG subclasses. IgG1 and 4 have only two interchain disulphide bridges, IgG2 has four and IgG3 has 11. The μ and ε chains have the largest number of carbohydrate residues which are attached such that in the fully assembled molecule they are present on the outer surface of the domains.

Table 1.2. Physiocochemical and biological properties of immunoglobulin classes

Class		Heavy chain		Whole molecule (H$_2$L$_2$)$_n$				Placental transfer	Complement fixation (classical pathway)	Serum conc. (mg/ml)
		M.W.	Domains	Sedimentation coefficient	M.W.	n	Carbohydrate content (%)			
IgM	μ	70.000	5	19S	900.000	5	12	–	+	0.6–2.0
IgG	γ	50.000	4	7S	150.000	1	3	+	+	8–16
IgA	α	55.000	4	11S	300.000	2	7.5	–	–	1.5–4
IgD	δ	~65.000	4	7S	~180.000	1	12	–	?	0.03
IgE	ε	65.000	5	8S	180.000	1	12	–	–	0.0003

Table 1.3. IgG subclasses in man and animals

Species	IgG subclasses	γ chains	Relative electrophoretic mobility pH 8.6	Relative conc. as % serum IgG	Complement activation		Placental transfer	Heterologous skin sensitizing	Other
					Classical	Alternative			
Human	IgG1	γ1	slow	70	++		+	+	binds to macrophages
	IgG2	γ2	slow	20	±		±	−	
	IgG3	γ3	slow	7	+++		+	+	binds to macrophages
	IgG4	γ4	fast	3	−	+?	+	+	
Mouse	IgG1	γ1	fast		−			−	
	IgG2a	γ2a	slow		+				
	IgG2b	γ2b	slow						
Guinea-pig	IgG1	γ1	fast	app. 25	−	+		+	
	IgG2	γ2	slow	app. 75	+++			−	
Cow/Sheep	IgG1	γ1	fast	app. 75	+++	(+)	−	+	in colostrum
	IgG2	γ2	slow	app. 25	−	+	−	−	

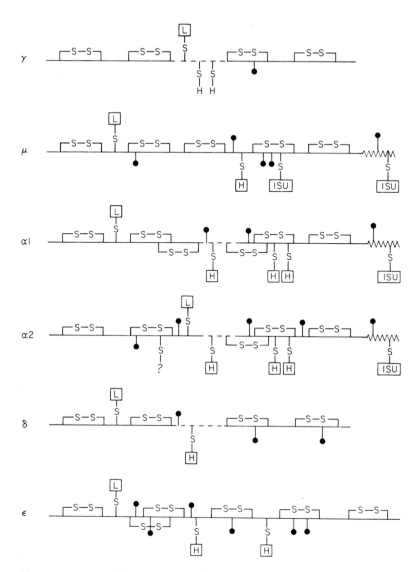

Fig. 1.3. The arrangement of the *intrachain* and *interchain* disulphide bridges and carbohydrate on human heavy-chain classes. IgG is represented by IgG1. The other subclasses of IgG differ in the number and position of the interchain disulphide bridges. The extra residues at the end of the α and μ chains form a tail piece containing the SH group which can either form an intersubunit (ISU) disulphide bridge in polymeric immunoglobulins or which reacts with J chain. (From Secher, 1979.)

Key   S   S   = interchain disulphide bridge to other heavy (H) or light (L) chain
       | or |
      [H]   [L]

       ┌ˢ⁻ˢ┐   = intrachain disulphide bridge   ♦ = carbohydrate

1.2.6 Light-chain allotypes

Allotypes are variants which are inherited as alternatives (i.e. alleles, see §4.1). The various allelic forms of the human κ chain are known as the Km (formerly Inv) allotypes (Table 1.4). These differences are serologically detectable and correlate with simple amino acid substitutions at approximately the same position as the Oz markers (which are not alleles) on the λ chain.

	Amino acid at position no.:	
Km allotype	153	191
1, 2	Ala	Leu
3	Ala	Val
1	Val	Leu

Table 1.4. Sequences correlated with Km (formerly Inv) allotypes   Data from Milstein *et al.* (1974).

In rabbits the *b* locus allotypes of the κ chain do not represent simple amino acid substitutions as the constant region of the κ chains in *b4* and *b9* rabbits show only 65 per cent homology. The possible evolutionary origins of complex and simple allotypes is discussed later (see §5.4).

1.2.7 Heavy-chain allotypes

In rabbits, mice and humans there are a variety of heavy-chain allotypes (Mage *et al.*, 1973). In humans the Gm markers on the different subclasses of IgG and Am markers on IgA often represent single amino acid substitutions (see Table 5.2). In mice allotypic markers have been described for α, $\gamma 1$, $\gamma 2$, $\gamma 2a$ and, more recently, μ and δ chains. In the latter case these allotypic differences were detected on IgD present on lymphocytes (see Chapter 8). Finally in rabbits there is a remarkable situation with respect to the *a* locus allotypes. The same allotypic determinants are present on IgM, IgA and IgG molecules and correlate with multiple differences in the amino acid sequence in the V_H regions. This was the first indication that the same V_H region appeared in different classes of immunoglobulin (see §4.3).

1.3 The variable regions

Sequence studies of V regions show that they consist of a single domain with an intrachain disulphide bridge. The first few N-terminal amino acids indicate whether the V region being sequenced belongs to κ, λ or heavy chain and so far no V_κ, V_λ or V_H sequences have been found associated with the wrong constant region. This implies that there are three different groups of V-genes coding for the variable regions.

1.3.1 V-region subgroups

The classification of variable regions does not stop at these three major groups. Within each group there are clearly defined subgroups where the members of each subgroup are more similar to each other than to any other variable region sequence (Milstein & Pink, 1970). The number of subgroups in mice and man is discussed in §4.7. It is generally accepted that for each well-defined subgroup there is at least one gene and that the subgroups are not alleles of each other. This has been shown in man where every individual has representatives of each subgroup amongst his immunoglobulins. In mice the number of subgroups of V_κ and V_H is so large that the total number is not known (Hood et al., 1976). In addition, comparisons of amino acid sequences within one subgroup show that subgroups can be further subdivided into sub-subgroups (Fig. 1.4). It is unlikely that V regions carrying the same substitutions in three or more positions could have arisen by a process of random mutation. It has thus been assumed that for each sub-subgroup there is a separate gene (McKean et al., 1978) (see §4).

There is a minor nomenclature problem for V regions. In man the terms group, subgroup and sub-subgroup are used as defined above. In mice the word group has been used for the equivalent of subgroup in man and subgroup for sub-subgroup (Potter, 1977). We have used the human nomenclature for V regions from all species.

1.3.2 J segments

Detailed analysis of V_κ regions showed that the definition of sub-subgroups could be clearly made when the first 100 amino acids of the V-region sequence were considered. Positions 101–113 inclusive also showed variants but the sequences in this region appeared to be varying independently of the sequences in the first part of the chain (Fig. 1.4). This would be explained if the DNA coding for this part of the chain was independent of the DNA coding for the rest of the variable region. In Chapter 4 we describe that this is indeed the case and the run of amino acids from 101 to 113 has come to be called the J segment and is coded for by J segment genes. (It is not to be confused with J chain—see 1.5.1.)

1.3.3 Hypervariable residues

Some positions in the variable region appear much more variable than others. A plot

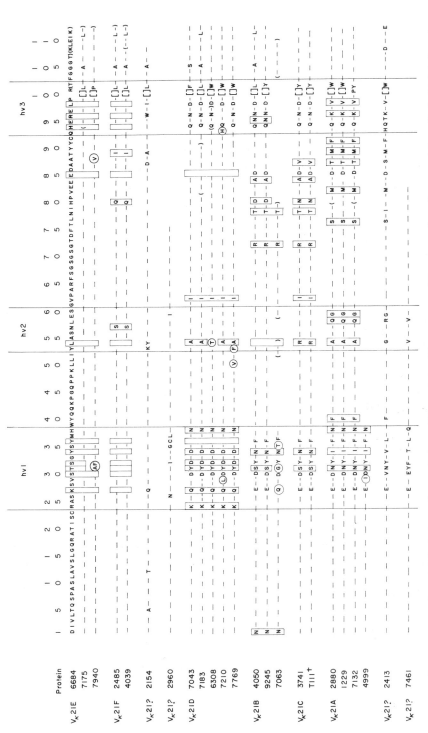

Fig. 1.4. The sequences of mouse V_κ regions of one subgroup. The amino acid sequences of V regions of myeloma proteins, all of which belong to the $V_\kappa 21$ subgroup. The sequences are divided into sub-subgroups $V_\kappa 21A$–$V_\kappa 21F$. $V_\kappa 21$? are unassigned to sub-subgroups. The $T111$ is a BALB/c protein. The rest are from NZB mice. The unique substitutions are circled, while the sub-subgroup associated residues found in one, two or three sub-subgroups are boxed. The three hypervariable regions, which contribute to the antigen-binding site are marked hv1, hv2 and hv3. The J segment extends from residue 101 to 113 (see Chapter 4). For key to the one-letter amino acid code see the Glossary. (Adapted from Weigert et al., 1978.)

of variation versus position shows that the hypervariable residues tend to form clusters (Fig. 1.5) and X-ray crystallography confirms that the amino acids in most of these clusters are close to the antigen-combining site (see §2.5.2). These clusters of hypervariable residues have also been called hypervariable regions or complementarity-determining residues as opposed to the other residues in the V region which have been referred to as framework residues. These names imply structure or function which have not necessarily been proven. From the figures it can be seen that V_L has three hypervariable regions while V_H has four. This extra cluster of hypervariable residues, 81–85, is not involved in the antigen-combining site.

1.4 Idiotypes

The term idiotype was originally defined as a unique antigenic determinant found on the variable regions of antibody molecules from a single clone of antibody-secreting cells (Oudin, 1966). This determinant can be recognized by antibodies (anti-idiotypic antibodies) in much the same way as amino acid sequences which define class, subclass and allotype are recognized. Idiotypes are not a nightmarish invention of the immunochemist but are central to our understanding of the interaction between lymphocytes in the immune system (see Chapters 7, 9 and 10). In addition they provide an invaluable tool for analysing genetic aspects of the immune response and for studying the structure of antigen receptors on cells.

1.4.1 Idiotypes in theory

Since its original definition the term idiotype has been used to describe many different phenomena. A broad view would be that an idiotype is a set of idiotypic determinants or idiotopes and an idiotope is any antigenic determinant on V_H, V_L, or formed by the interaction of V_H with V_L. This definition of an idiotype is in some ways unsatisfactory as the antigenicity of a molecule depends on how it is used to induce an immune response so that different antisera may detect different idiotopes on the same molecule. Nevertheless, if the sequence defining an idiotype has arisen by somatic mutation then it is unlikely to have occurred again in another individual. Such idiotypes fit the original definition and have been denoted as individual idiotypes or IdIs. These idiotypes are likely, but are not necessarily, defined by hypervariable residues. Alternatively, if the sequence defining the idiotypes is coded for by a germ line gene (see Chapter 4) then one would expect to find the idiotypes in other individuals of the same inbred strain or in other strains carrying that gene. These inherited idiotypes have been called IdXs or cross-reacting idiotypes. If a cross-reacting idiotype is defined by amino acids in the hypervariable region then in addition to being carried by molecules with the same antigen-combining site, the idiotype will also be found on antibody molecules with different specificities but

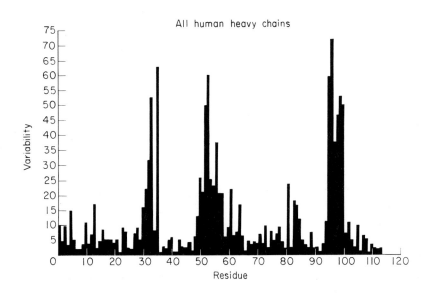

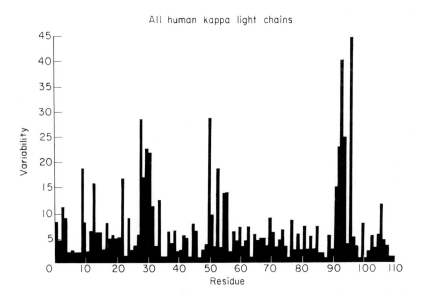

Fig. 1.5. A plot of the variability of the different residues in human V_H and V_K regions. Variability has been calculated as the number of different amino acids found in a particular position divided by the frequency of the most common residue in that position. (Adapted from Kabat *et al.* 1979.)

which use the idiotype-defining residues in their combining sites. If the amino acids defining the idiotype are amongst the framework residues then the idiotypes will occur on molecules with many different specificities. In this case an anti-idiotypic serum would define a V-region subgroup or an allelic form of a subgroup like the *a* locus in rabbits. In some cases it is possible to show that the idiotype is defined by idiotopes in the antigen-combining site as the reaction of the anti-idiotypic anti-serum with the idiotopes is prevented if the combining site has first bound specific antigen.

1.4.2 Idiotypes in practice

There are two types of anti-idiotypic reagents. First, antibodies to individual idiotypes (anti-IdIs) have been of limited value as the idiotopes they identify appear in only one individual. They have been used to confirm that identical V regions are used in different classes of immunoglobulin and to estimate the size of the immunoglobulin universe (see Chapter 7). The second type of reagent, antibodies to inherited idiotypes (anti-IdXs), has proved to be much more useful. The idiotypes they recognize occur in all individuals or strains carrying the appropriate gene thus allowing the anti-idiotypic antisera to be used in a much wider range of experimental protocols (see section 2). In addition the products of the genes can be easily followed in genetic experiments. Some of the commonly used IdXs are listed in Table 1.5.

Anti-idiotypic antibodies can be raised to myeloma proteins or monoclonal antibodies in animals of a different species; in individuals of the same species but of a different strain; in animals of the same strain and even in the same individual who has made the idiotype (see Chapter 10). In the latter case they are known as auto-anti-idiotypic antibodies. Prior to immunization in different species the animals have to be made tolerant to the immunoglobulin of the species against which the anti-idiotypic antibodies are to be raised. Antibodies to constant regions or inappropriate anti-idiotypic specificities must be removed by absorption, or avoided by prior induction of tolerance (see Chapter 13).

1.5 Other polypeptide components of immunoglobulins

1.5.1 J chain

The J chain is a 15,000 M.W. polypeptide rich in cysteine which is structurally unrelated to the basic immunoglobulin domain. It is invariably found in association with the polymeric immunoglobulins IgM and IgA and is not to be confused with J segment (see § 1.3.3). In both the IgM pentamer and the IgA dimer, there is one J chain covalently linked via a disulphide bridge to the tail piece of an α or μ chain

Table 1.5. Commonly used cross-reacting idiotypes of mice

Idiotype	Locus symbol	Reference antibody or myeloma protein	Reference strain
A5A	*Igh-Sal*	Antibodies to group A carbohydrate on streptococci	A/J
T15	*Igh-PC*	Myeloma protein TEPC 15 and antibodies to phosphoryl choline	BALB/c
J558	*Igh-Dex*	Proteins J558 and MOPC 104E and anti-dextran antibodies	BALB/c
ARS	*Igh-Ars*	Antibodies to p-azo-phenyl arsonate	A/J
NP	*Igh-NP*	Heteroclitic antibodies to NP	C57Bl

Adapted from Weigert and Potter (1977) and Green (1979).

(Fig. 1.3). The J chain is synthesized by the antibody-forming cell, and is even made by those cells which are secreting non-polymeric immunoglobulins such as IgG. The secretion of unpolymerized IgM and IgA in mouse mutant plasmacytomas is associated with a failure of J-chain synthesis. The J chain is evolutionarily highly conserved.

1.5.2 Secretory component

The IgA dimers of the external secretions (gut, saliva and milk), carry a 60,000 M.W. polypeptide, secretory component, which is not synthesized by the antibody-forming cell but by epithelial cells and becomes attached during immunoglobulin secretion. The exact function of the secretory component is not known but it retards the proteolysis of IgA by digestive enzymes.

1.6 Biological activities of immunoglobulins

Most of the biological activities of immunoglobulin other than antigen-binding are mediated via the Fc region of the molecule. Activation of the classical pathway of complement is initiated by the binding of C1q (the first component) to IgM or IgG. IgA, IgD and IgE do not bind C1q (see § 2.6.1 and Table 1.3).

The Fc part also plays a crucial rôle in the movement of IgG across epithelial surfaces. In man the placental transfer of immunoglobulins is subclass-specific but in ruminants the placenta is impermeable to IgG. Ruminants receive most of their maternal immunoglobulins via the colostrum.

Finally a wide variety of cells of the lympho-myeloid series bind immunoglobulins via Fc receptors. Polymorphonuclear leucocytes, monocytes, macrophages, K cells and lymphocyte subpopulations all express Fc receptors albeit for different immunoglobulin classes and subclasses. Binding to Fc receptors can initiate the intrinsic activities of cells, for example phagocytosis, or release of vasoactive amines from mast cells and eosinophils. Most of the consequences of these biological processes are more fully described in later chapters.

1.7 Synthesis, assembly and secretion

Like other secreted proteins immunoglobulins are synthesized on the ribosomes of the endoplasmic reticulum (ER). The chains are synthesized separately and since synthesis starts with the N-terminus this is the first part of the chain to appear in the lumen of the ER. For many secreted and membrane proteins the first 15–30 N-terminal residues do not appear in the final product. This happens for both light and heavy chains. It is suggested that the reason for making a precursor with this extra leader sequence is to direct the passage of the growing chain through the membrane of the ER (Milstein *et al.*, 1972; Blobel & Dobberstein, 1975). These leader or signal sequences vary in length and amino acid sequence but they are all characteristically hydrophobic. The leader sequence is normally removed from the growing polypeptide chain before the chain has been completed.

The completed heavy and light chains initially interact non-covalently and then interchain disulphide bridges form to yield the structure H_2L_2. Intermediate forms H_2, H_2L and HL can be detected but the formation of large H_n aggregates is prevented by the presence of a pool of excess light chains. Allelic exclusion (see § 4.5) ensures that assembled immunoglobulin molecules will contain two identical antigen-combining sites—an essential requirement for antibody function.

Carbohydrate residues are first attached to the nascent chains shortly after synthesis. All the necessary glycosylating enzymes occur within the lumen of the ER and there is sequential attachment of carbohydrate to the assembled molecules during their sojourn within the ER. The first attachment of galactosamine to aspartic acid residues occurs rapidly while attachment of sialic acid and other terminal residues proceeds just prior to the final process of secretion and release from the cell.

The polymeric forms IgM and IgA assemble themselves shortly before secretion, the J chain being attached at this time. It seems that the J chain has an initiating function during polymerization though subunits derived from polymers can re-assemble in the absence of J chains.

1.8 Membrane-bound immunoglobulins

Immunoglobulins are not only found in plasma and tissue fluids but also on the surface of cells. The amino acid sequence of serum immunoglobulin is such that it would be very unlikely for the molecule to interact with the membrane to become an integral transmembrane protein. Consequently if membrane immunoglobulin is to signal the antigen-binding event to the cell it must either interact with a special membrane receptor, or contain an additional hydrophobic region to allow it to traverse the membrane lipid. There are many cells such as macrophages and mast cells which do not synthesize immunoglobulin but yet carry surface immuno-

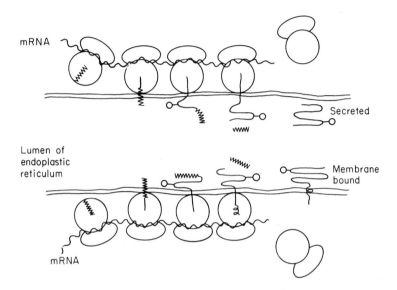

Fig. 1.6. Diagrammatic representation of the synthesis of heavy chains of secreted and membrane immunoglobulin. Once the leader or signal sequence has been synthesized the ribosomes bind to the endoplastic reticulum (ER) and the nascent chain passes through the membrane. The ribosome leaves the ER after chain termination has occurred. For a secreted protein the C-terminal end of the chain passes right through the membrane of the ER and it can then be secreted from the cell without having to cross another membrane. For certain membrane proteins the completed chain remains embedded in the membrane with the C-terminus on the inside of the cell. -o represents carbohydrate attached to the nascent chain, ᴡᴡᴡ the leader sequence and ᴧᴧᴠ a run of hydrophobic residues.

globulin on their membranes. These cells have receptors specific for Fc that absorb immunoglobulins from the tissues fluids and it is via these receptors that signalling occurs. In the case of a B cell the surface immunoglobulin is not absorbed from the tissue fluids but is synthesized by that cell (see Chapter 8). Recent evidence suggests that the surface IgM on B cells has a different composition from serum IgM containing some 10–20 extra hydrophobic residues at the C-terminal end of the heavy chain (Williams et al., 1978). There is still some doubt about the exact arrangement of these extra residues. Figure 1.6 shows a possible scheme for the synthesis of heavy chains of secreted and membrane immunoglobulin.

References

BLOBEL G. & DOBBERSTEIN B. (1975) Transfer of proteins across membranes. *J. Cell Biol.* **67**, 835.

FETT J.W. & DEUTSCH H.F. (1975) A new λ-chain gene. *Immunochemistry* **12**, 643.

GREEN M.C. (1979) Genetic nomenclature of the immunoglobulins loci of the mouse. *Immunogenetics* **8**, 89.

HOOD L., LOH E., HUBERT J., BARSTAD P., EATON B., EARLY P., FUHRMAN J., JOHNSON N., KRONENBERG M. & SCHILLING J. (1976) The structure and genetics of mouse immunoglobulins: an analysis of NZB myeloma proteins and sets of BALB/c myeloma proteins binding particular haptens. *Cold Spr. Harb. Symp. Quant. Biol.* **41**, 817.

KABAT E.A., WU T.T. & BIOLOFSKY H. (1979) *Sequences of immunoglobulin chains*. U.S. Public Health Service, National Institute of Health publication No. 80-2008.

KÖHLER G. & MILSTEIN C. (1975) Continuous cultures of fused cells secreting antibody to predefined specificity. *Nature* **256**, 495.

KRAUSE R.M. (1970) The search for antibodies with molecular uniformity. *Adv. Immunol.* **12**, 1.

McKEAN D.J., BELL M. & POTTER M. (1978) Mechanism of antibody diversity: multiple genes encode structurally related mouse κ variable regions. *Proc. Nat. Acad. Sci. U.S.A.* **75**, 3913.

MAGE R., LIEBERMAN R., POTTER M. & TERRY W.D. (1973) Immunoglobulin Allotypes. In SELA M. (ed.), *The Antigens*, Vol. 1, p. 299. Academic Press, New York.

MILSTEIN C. & PINK J.R.L. (1970) Structure and evolution of immunoglobulins. *Prog. Biophys. Molec. Biol.* **21**, 209.

MILSTEIN C., BROWNLEE G.G., HARRISON T.M. & MATTHEWS M.B. (1972) A possible precursor of immunoglobulin light chain. *Nature (New Biol.)* **239**, 117.

MILSTEIN C.P., STEINBERG A.G., McLAUGHLIN C. & SOLOMON A. (1974) Amino acid sequence change associated with genetic marker Inv 2 of human immunoglobulins. *Nature (Lond.)* **248**, 160.

OUDIN J. (1966) The genetic control of immunoglobulin synthesis. *Proc. Roy. Soc. Lond.* B **166**, 207.

POTTER M. (1972) Immunoglobulin-producing tumors and myeloma proteins of mice. *Physiol. Rev.* **52**, 631.

POTTER M. (1977) Antigen-binding myeloma proteins of mice. *Adv. Immunol.* **25**, 141.

SECHER D.S. (1979) Structure of immunoglobulins. *Int. Rev. Biochem.* **23**, 1.

WEIGERT M. & POTTER M. (1977) Antibody variable region genetics. *Immunogenetics* **5**, 491.

WEIGERT M., GATMAITAN L., LOH E., SCHILLING J. & HOOD L. (1978) Rearrangement of genetic information may produce immunoglobulin diversity. *Nature* **276**, 785.

WILLIAMS B.P., KUBO R.T. & GREY H.M. (1978) μ-Chains from a non-secretor B cell line differ from secreted μ-chains at the C-terminal end. *J. Immunol.* **121**, 2435.

Further reading

EDELMAN G.M. (1973) Antibody structure and molecular immunology. *Science* **180**, 830.

EICHMANN K. (1978) Expression and function of idiotypes on lymphocytes. *Adv. Immunol.* **26**, 195.

GLYNN L.E. & STEWARD M.W. (eds) (1977) *Immunochemistry. An Advanced Textbook*. John Wiley & Sons, Chichester.

KABAT E.A. (1976) *Structural Concepts in Immunology and Immunochemistry*, 2nd ed. Holt, Rinehart & Winston, New York.

NISONOFF A., HOPPER J.E. & SPRING S.B. (1975) *The Antibody Molecule*. Academic Press, New York.

PORTER R.R. (1973) Structural studies of immunoglobulin. *Science* **180**, 713.

Chapter 2
Immunoglobulin Structure

2.1 Introduction

This chapter is concerned with the three-dimensional structure of immunoglobulins and how this relates to their ability to bind antigen and initiate secondary phenomena such as complement activation. Two direct methods are available to investigate three-dimensional structure: electron microscopy and X-ray diffraction crystallography. The former has been used since the early 1960s, while the latter has produced high resolution results only in the 1970s. For the interpretation of the data much use is made of the chemical structure and biophysical properties of immunoglobulins.

2.2 Electron microscopy

Studies of the structure of immunoglobulins started with the electron microscopic examination of antigen–antibody complexes using negative staining. The molecules and particles under investigation are embedded in an electron dense stain, for instance sodium phosphotungstate, and are visualized because they exclude stain to present a less opaque path for the electron beam.

The earliest electron micrographs of immunoglobulins were of virus particles linked by antibody. They were followed by the use of ferritin–IgG anti-ferritin complexes made under controlled conditions (Fig. 2.1). The antibody molecule was seen to be Y-shaped with a variable angle between the arms. When pepsin-digested antibody was used F(ab′)₂, the stem of the Y-shaped molecule was absent, and the precipitates redissolved on reduction.

Valentine and Green (1967) introduced the elegant technique of using a bi-functional hapten as antigen. The haptenic determinants are separated by a short aliphatic chain, about 20 Å in length, and with specific antibody can form cyclic oligomers. Two, three, four and sometimes more IgG molecules linked together by the hapten via their combining sites are usually seen (Fig. 2.2). The principal advantage of this system is the absence of bulky antigen molecules, around which the stain accumulates, leading to better resolution and contrast.

These studies illustrate two important points: first the antigen-combining site is on the end surface of the Fab arms and second, in IgG, there is freedom of movement

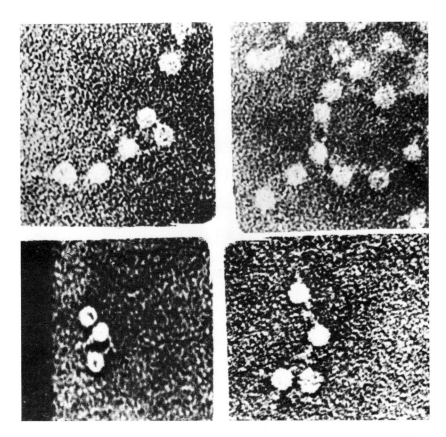

Fig. 2.1. Complexes of IgG and F(ab')$_2$ antibody with ferritin. Note that the angle between the Fab arms is variable; the Fc in the IgG complexes in the lower pictures and the cyclic oligomers. (Taken from Feinstein & Rowe, 1965.)

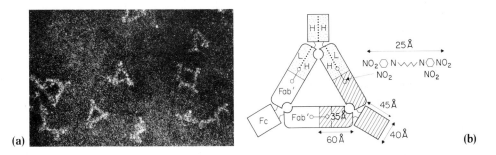

(a)

(b)

Fig. 2.2. Electronmicrographs of IgG antibodies specific for DNP complexed with a divalent ligand (DNP-NH-(CH$_2$)$_8$-NH-DNP). Fig. (a) shows complexes using whole IgG, the Fc part of IgG protrudes from the corners of the cyclic complexes. Fig. (b) is a diagrammatic representation of the complex formed with three IgG molecules similar to the one seen in the centre of Fig. (a). (From Valentine and Green, 1967.)

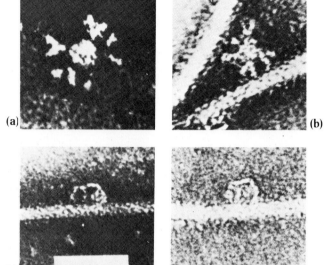

Fig. 2.3. Electronmicrographs of IgM antibodies (a) unbound IgM; (b) IgM cross-linking two bacterial flagella; (c) examples of IgM attached to a single flagella with the central disc in Fig. (a) now seen in profile. (From Feinstein *et al.*, 1971.)

of the Fab arms with respect to each other and the Fc portion. This latter has been confirmed by depolarization of fluorescence and other physical measurements.

IgM is a pentamer constructed from five identical basic units and has a characteristic starfish-like appearance when examined in the electron microscope (Fig. 2.3). In some molecules the five arms are seen to be bifid and these are the Fab parts, which are attached to a central disc-like structure about 100 Å in diameter. When complexed with antigen, for instance the flagella of *Salmonella*, the IgM molecules assume a variety of shapes (Fig. 2.3). Where they are cross-linking widely separated flagella, the characteristic star shape is seen, but when many combining sites are attached to a single flagellum, the molecule has a staple appearance. Transitional forms are also seen. The staple form shows a highly contrasted bar, representing the central disc in profile, held some 100 Å away from the surface of the flagellum by the Fab arms which are bent down from the plane of the central disc. It should be noted that the Fab arms have the facility to bend either up or down, and in IgM, unlike in IgG, they have a distinct tendency to move together as a rigid F(ab')$_2$* pair with a fixed angle being maintained between them. The observation that IgM seems to have only five effective antibody-binding sites when it interacts with polymeric antigens can probably be explained by the lack of flexibility of the Fabs with respect to each other in the F(ab')$_2$ arms. Even when two antigenic determinants are sufficiently close to be reached by both combining sites in a F(ab')$_2$ arm, divalent-binding is likely to be prevented owing to the absence of rotational flexibility of the Fabs.

* In this chapter F(ab')$_2$ designates the bivalent arms of IgM.

The IgA 7S subunit appears indistinguishable from IgG in the electron microscope, but pictures of the dimeric form show that this is constructed from two identical basic units joined via the ends of the Fc portions. Again the antigen-binding sites are on the ends of the Fab arms and the arms can assume multiple configurations (Fig. 2.4).

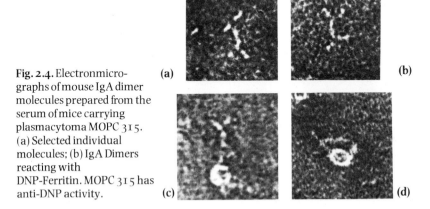

Fig. 2.4. Electronmicro-graphs of mouse IgA dimer molecules prepared from the serum of mice carrying plasmacytoma MOPC 315. (a) Selected individual molecules; (b) IgA Dimers reacting with DNP-Ferritin. MOPC 315 has anti-DNP activity.

(a)   (b)

(c)   (d)

2.3 X-ray crystallography

In the EM individual molecules are photographed and can be studied separately. X-ray crystallography permits far greater resolution but integrates the common features of molecules held in a regular crystalline array. The interaction between adjacent molecules in the crystal required to build up a crystal lattice may stabilize the molecules in a confirmation that would occur rarely in free solution. So far it has proved difficult to obtain high resolution information from the crystals of whole immunoglobulin molecules, but the data which have been obtained confirm and extend the information from the EM. The molecule has a two-fold rotational axis of symmetry with the Fc portion on, and parallel to, the axis.

2.4 High resolution of immunoglobulin domains

X-ray studies at high resolution have been successful on crystals of various fragments of mouse and human myeloma proteins, particularly Fab, Fc and light-chain dimers. The most obvious feature of this work is that the polypeptide chains of any domain have a characteristic pattern of folding which is essentially similar, irrespective of their origin (Fig. 2.5). For much of its length the chain is thrown into a series of folds that form two surfaces of anti-parallel β-pleated sheets which are stabilized by an intrachain disulphide bridge. For C domains one surface is made up of three

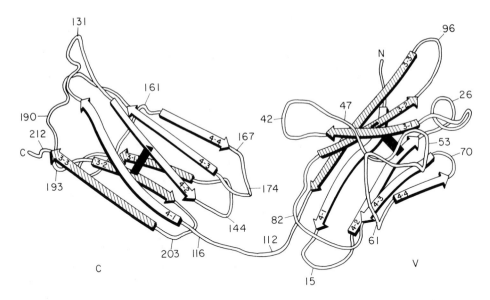

Fig. 2.5. The folding of C and V region domains in crystals of a light-chain dimer. The white arrows (4-1 to 4-4) correspond to segments of the four-chain surface and the striated arrows (3-1 to 3-3) represent segments of the three-chain surface. The arrows point from N- to C-terminus. The black bar represents the disulphide bridge. (Adapted from Schiffler *et al.*, 1973.)

runs of the chain and the other of four. Adjacent runs on each surface are anti-parallel (see Fig. 2.5), and the space between the surfaces is filled with hydrophobic side groups. Although X-ray crystallography data is lacking for many of the C domains it seems likely that irrespective of class or subclass they will all be similarly folded. There is striking sequence homology in the residues which form the two anti-parallel β-pleated sheets and there is a marked tendency to conserve hydrophobic and non-polar residues, particularly those that fill the space between the β-pleated sheets (Feinstein & Beale, 1977). The folding of $C_{\gamma}2$ is noticeably different from $C_{\gamma}1$ and $C_{\gamma}3$. From the conservative replacement at critical residues $C_{\gamma}2$ is likely to correspond to $C_{\mu}3$, $C_{\varepsilon}3$ and $C_{\alpha}2$ (see Chapter 5).

As one would predict from amino acid sequence data, the three-dimensional structures of V domains or C domains are more similar to each other than any V domain is to any C domain. The V domains have an additional loop and a less well defined bilayer structure than C domains (Davies *et al.*, 1975). The V domains of light and heavy chains interact with each other through their three-chain surfaces which allows residues in the hypervariable regions around residues 26, 53 and 96 to form the antigen-combining site (see Fig. 2.9).

2.4.1 Domain interactions

Certain pairs of domains are held together by non-covalent forces. V-region domains interact with each other through the apposition of their three-chain or (y) surfaces. This results in both the N- and C-terminal ends of the domain being well apart in space. On the other hand C-region domains, when they interact, do so through their four-chain or (x) surfaces and this allows their C-terminal ends to approach each other with the N-terminal ends held far apart. In Fab the different modes of interaction of the V and C domain allow the V_H–V_L interaction to be immediately followed by the C_H–C_L interaction. However, the structure of C-region domains and the mode of their pairing would not allow all the sequential heavy-chain domains to interact with their corresponding partners without the addition of further amino acids.

In IgG, the $C_\gamma 1$ domain interacts with the C domain of the light chains and the $C_\gamma 3$ domains interact with each other. $C_\gamma 1$ is attached to $C_\gamma 2$ through the additional sequence forming the hinge region which contains all the interheavy-chain di-sulphide bonds. The two $C_\gamma 2$ domains do not interact with each other, thus allowing the $C_\gamma 3$ domains to do so. The carbohydrate which is attached to the $C_\gamma 2$ domains lies directly over the four-chain surfaces and would in any case prevent them from interacting (Figs 2.6 and 2.7).

With IgM the situation is more complex. However, by using the available data from X-ray crystallography and knowledge of the arrangements of carbohydrate and interchain disulphide bridges, Feinstein has developed a hypothetical model for IgM which is very likely to represent the actual structure.

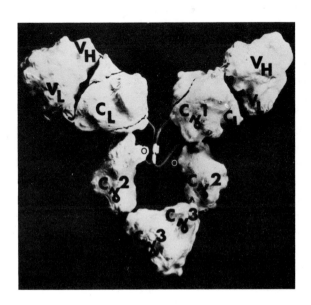

Fig. 2.6. A plaster model of human IgG1. ○ marks the sites of attachment of oligosaccharide to $C_\gamma 2$. (From Feinstein & Beale, 1977.)

L   R

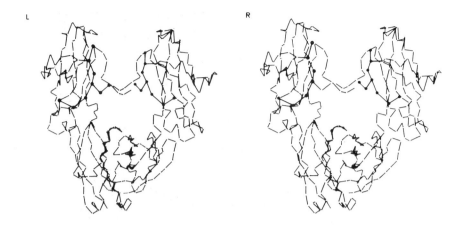

Fig. 2.7. Stereo representation of the α-carbon backbone of the Fc fragment from human IgG. The $C_\gamma2$ domains are at the top and do not interact. The carbohydrate unites attached to $C_\gamma2$ are represented as (●). (From Deisenhofer *et al.*, 1976.)

Models for IgM are shown in Fig. 2.8. IgM, compared to IgG, has an additional domain and the central disc of the IgM molecule is made up of a densely packed complex of the $C_\mu3$ and $C_\mu4$ domains. The $C_\mu3$ domains are circumferentially arranged around the disc almost enclosing their maximum circle. Both the inter-heavy-chain bridges between the C-terminus of the $C_\mu2$ domains and the inter subunit bridges between the C-terminal of the $C_\mu3$ domains are close to the periphery of the disc. The spatial position of the single J chain is not known but it is attached to the most C-terminal cystein (the penultimate residue in the tail piece of the $C_\mu4$ domain) and joins heavy chains probably from adjacent subunits.

2.5 The antibody-combining site

Much of the knowledge of the antibody-combining site arose from chemical and amino acid sequence analysis of the variable regions. More recently X-ray diffraction data on combining sites with and without their respective antigen have yielded precise information on the structural details.

2.5.1 Chemical information

Amino acid sequence data on the variable regions of both heavy and light chains have revealed hypervariable residues; these occur in clusters around residues 24–34, 50–56 and 89–97 in the light chains and 31–35, 50–65 and 90–102 in the heavy

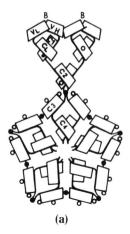

(a)

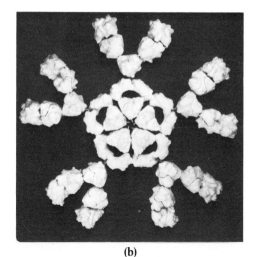

(b)

Fig. 2.8. Models of IgM. (a) Diagram of the arrangement of the domains in IgM showing only one of the (Fab)₂ arms.
● Interchain disulphide bridge; ○ carbohydrate; B antigen-binding site. (b) A plaster model of IgM showing all five F(ab)₂ arms. (c) The dislocated form of IgM corresponding to the 'staples' in the electron micrographs of Fig. 2.3c. (Adapted from Feinstein & Beale, 1977).

(c)

chains (see Chapter 1, Fig. 1.5). A fourth hypervariable region may exist in the heavy chains (residues 82–89) but this part of the V region has nothing to do with the antigen-combining site. Convincing evidence that the other hypervariable residues or residues close to them are involved in the combining site comes from affinity labelling studies. In this approach chemically reactive haptens first bind specifically (and non-covalently) to their combining site and being chemically reactive then form a stable covalent bond with neighbouring residues in the combining site. If the affinity label is radioactive then the amount bound to the heavy and light chains can be determined by separating them and the position of binding defined by isolating the labelled peptides after cleavage of the whole chain. Most affinity labels will only form a covalent bond with tyrosines, histidines or lysines, although Fleet *et al.* (1972) have developed an affinity label based on aromatic azides which is ideal in not being residue specific. Their system depends on the fact that aromatic azides on exposure to light at 400 nm form chemically reactive nitrenes which can insert into any C–H bond.

2.5.2 *Structural information*

The location of the antigen-combining site on the end surface of the Fab arms of antibody molecules was first revealed by EM studies of antigen–antibody complexes (see Figs 2.1–2.4). High resolution X-ray crystallography has shown that the heavy- and light-chain variable regions are similarly folded such that the hypervariable regions correspond to the solvent accessible loops located on the end of the V-region domain away from the point of attachment of the C region. The combining site itself is a cleft approximately 16 Å long of variable width and depth lying in a flat surface defined by the hypervariable loops of each chain. Stereo pictures of one of the two Fab crystals with known ligands are shown in Fig. 2.9 and both the antigen-binding sites are diagrammatically represented in Figs 2.10 and 2.11. Substitutions, insertions and deletions in the hypervariable region can have profound effects on the shape of the combining site but it should be stressed that invariant residues also make contact with the antigen.

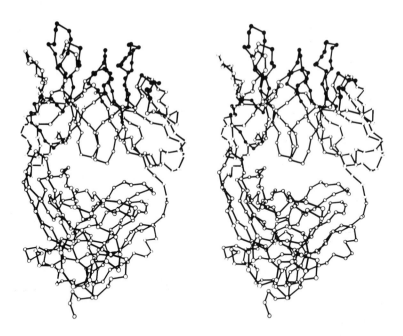

Fig. 2.9. Stereo representation of the mouse Fab prepared from the IgA myeloma McPc 603. The heavy chain is on the left side of the picture and the V domains are at the top. The residues in the hypervariable regions are shown as blackened circles. Note that in V_L the second hypervariable region L2 is masked from the binding site by the first hypervariable region L1. In the heavy chain the extra hypervariable region lies to one side at the back of the molecule in the orientation illustrated. Compare the stereo image of the antigen-binding site to the end on drawing in Fig. 2.11. (From Davies *et al.*, 1975.)

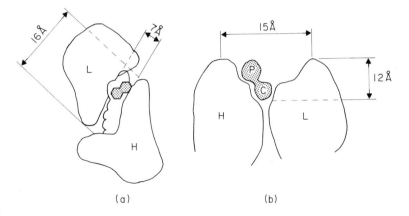

Fig. 2.10. A diagram of the antigen-combining sites of two crystaline myeloma proteins with known ligands (a) NEW, which binds vitamin K_1OH viewed end on and (b) McPc 603 binding phosphorylcholine viewed from the side.

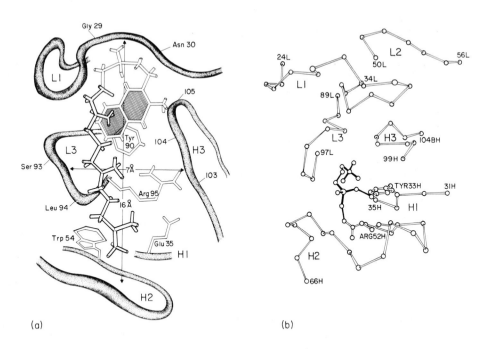

Fig. 2.11. Detailed drawing of the binding site viewed end on of (a) human IgG NEW and (b) McPc 603. The ligands vitamin K_1OH and phosphorylcholine are partially hatched or solid lines respectively. L1, L2, L3 and H1, H2 and H3, refer to the hypervariable regions of light and heavy chains. (From Amzel *et al.*, 1974; Segal *et al.*, 1974.)

The antigen-combining site is usually 'faithful' to its ligand and although a given combining site reacts with chemically related haptens, the affinities are normally quite different. It is theoretically possible that two separate, non-overlapping antigen-binding sites coexist on the same molecule (Richards et al., 1975). An example of this may be the mouse myeloma protein MOPC 460 which has comparable affinity for the two haptens DNP and menadione. Although one can modify the myeloma protein so that it will bind only one or the other of these haptens, they do in fact compete with each other for binding, showing that their binding sites are at least partially overlapping. Further, a small proportion of antibodies induced to DNP, bind menadione and a secondary challenge with menadione will preferentially stimulate these clones with apparent dual specificity. Space-filling models of the two haptens show that they share three-dimensional features and it is likely that the dual specificity of MOPC 460 is due to unexpected cross-reactivity. Even if such a situation were of common occurrence, as it probably is, it would not contradict the apparent specificity of antisera since a given antiserum will contain a heterogenous population of antibody molecules of which only a small proportion will share the same alternative specificity and therefore go undetected.

2.5.3. Affinity of antibody–hapten reactions

The binding of a hapten to the antigen-combining site is very similar to the binding of substrate to the active centre of an enzyme and can be treated mathematically the same way. If [Ab], [Ag] and [Ab/Ag] represent the concentration of free antibody, antigen and antibody–antigen complex at equilibrium the reaction

$$Ab + Ag \rightleftharpoons Ab/Ag. \tag{1}$$

can be expressed as

$$K = \frac{[Ab/Ag]}{[Ab] \times [Ag]} = \frac{k_{12}}{k_{21}} \tag{2}$$

where K is the equilibrium or affinity constant for the reaction of hapten to the antibody-combining site. Values of K for haptens vary from $10^{11}M^{-1}$ to $10^{5}M^{-1}$. The affinity constant is the ratio of the forward and reverse rate constants; $K = k_{12}/k_{21}$. Using techniques for fast reactions it is possible to show that the forward reaction (k_{12}) is always very fast in the order of $10^{8}M^{-1} sec^{-1}$, while the back reaction (k_{21}) is much more variable suggesting that the stability of a hapten–antibody complex is controlled by the rate of dissociation of the complex.

To derive a general equation for the reaction of haptens with antibodies one must take into account that the number of antigen-combining sites per molecule, usually expressed as n, depends on the class of antibody. Further, it is convenient to express the extent of the reaction as the average number of molecules of hapten bound to each molecule of antibody. This ratio will vary from zero, when no reaction has taken place, to n when all the antigen-combining sites are fully occupied (2 for IgG). If this ratio is expressed as r then by applying equation (2) for each step of the reaction of hapten with any antibody it is possible to show that at equilibrium

$$r = \frac{nK\,[Ag]}{1 + K\,[Ag]} \tag{3}$$

A derivation of this equation can be found in Eisen (1973). Equation (3) can be rearranged to

$$\frac{r}{[Ag]} = nK - rK \tag{4}$$

and a plot of $r/[Ag]$ versus r, the Scatchard plot, will be a straight line provided the value of K is the same for all the molecules of specific antibody in the antiserum. Except for monoclonal antibodies this is usually not the case and the Scatchard plot will be non-linear (Fig. 2.12).

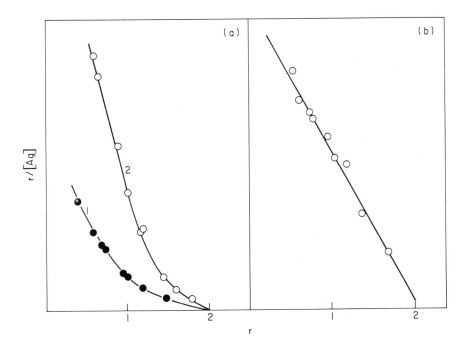

Fig. 2.12. Scatchard plots of haptens binding to antibodies. (a) Dinitroaniline binding to two different preparations of purified anti-DNP antibodies. (b) DNP–lysine binding to a myeloma protein with anti-DNP activity. Note the straight line of this plot compared to (a). (From Eisen, 1973.)

It can be seen from equation (4) that for IgG antibodies, when $r = 1$, i.e. when half the antigen-combining sites have reacted with hapten, then as n equals 2, K will equal $1/[Ag]$ or in other words the average affinity constant is the reciprocal of the concentration of free hapten required to fill half the antigen-combining sites.

2.5.4 Measurement of affinity constants of haptens by equilibrium dialysis

To determine the affinity constants one must measure at equilibrium the concentrations of free hapten and the amount bound to a known amount of antibody. The simplest and most general way to do this is by equilibrium dialysis (Eisen, 1973). The principle relies on the use of dialysis membranes which are freely permeable to hapten but impermeable to antibodies. At the start of the experiment antibody is placed in one chamber and hapten in the other. After the system has come to equilibrium at a fixed temperature (the affinity of antibodies is temperature dependent, increasing with lower temperatures) the concentration of the hapten in the two chambers is measured. This can be done conveniently if the hapten is radioactive or coloured. It is usual to set up several chambers with different concentrations of the hapten and provided a known amount of pure antibody has been used, it is then possible to calculate the moles of hapten bound to each mole of antibody (r) and to plot $r/[Ag]$, the free hapten concentration, against r for the different experimental conditions (see equation (4)). It is also possible using this technique to determine the affinity of unpurified antibodies just from the equilibrium concentrations of free and bound hapten $[H_f]$ and $[H_b]$. If $[Ab_T]$ represents the concentration of free antigen-combining sites at the start of the experiment, then equation (2) can be expressed as

$$K = \frac{[H_b]}{[H_f]\,[Ab_T - H_b]} \tag{5}$$

This can be rearranged to:

$$\frac{1}{[H_f]} = K\,\frac{[Ab_T]}{[H_b]} - K \tag{6}$$

$[Ab_T]$ and K can be derived from a plot of $1/H_f$ versus $1/H_b$. Again for a monoclonal antibody this plot will give a straight line.

2.5.5 Antibody concentration, affinity and hapten binding

From equation (6) it can be seen that there is a relationship between the equilibrium concentration of free and bound hapten and the starting concentration and affinity constant of the antibody.

$$[Ab_T'] = \frac{[H_b]}{K[H_f]} + [H_b] \tag{7}$$

The concentration of antigen-combining sites in the antiserum must always be greater than the concentration of hapten finally bound to the antibody. The amount of excess antibody required depends on the affinity constant of the antiserum and the ratio of the concentration of free to bound hapten. In order to increase the amount of hapten bound starting with a particular concentration of antigen, one must use more antibody or antibodies of higher affinity.

2.5.6 *The binding of antibodies to complex antigens*

The binding of haptens to antibodies can be handled easily mathematically but the binding of antibodies to complex antigens, particularly those that have repeating antigenic determinants, is beyond useful analysis. The reason for this is that when two or more antigen-combining sites on one antibody molecule react with determinants held in a stable matrix either as part of a polymeric antigen or as part of an antigen–antibody complex, then the stability of the reaction is much greater. In crude terms it is much less likely that both arms of an IgG molecule will let go of the antigen simultaneously. The term avidity has come to be used for the overall strength of binding of antibody to a complex of antigenic determinants. The increase in stability by reacting through multiple combining sites is illustrated in Fig. 2.2 where IgG antibody molecules react with the bivalent hapten to form cyclic complexes. For IgG antibody to form a lattice with antigen, the antigen must be at least trivalent (Fig. 2.13); with IgM antibody divalent antigen will suffice.

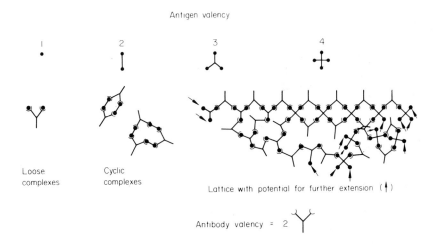

Fig. 2.13. The effect of antigen valency on complex size with IgG antibody. The capacity of a system to make an extended lattice depends on one of the reactants being at least divalent, and the other at least trivalent. Thermodynamic considerations limit the size of cyclic oligomers.

2.6 The structure of immunoglobulins in relation to their secondary functions

The ultimate aim of structural studies is to explain immunoglobulin functions in structural terms. Although the antigen-combining site is now quite well understood other functions of immunoglobulin molecules are proving harder to explain.

2.6.1 Immunoglobulin structure and complement activation

Activation of the classical pathway of complement is initiated by the binding of C1q (the first component of complement) to $C_\mu 3$ or $C_\mu 4$ domains of IgM and the $C_\gamma 2$ domains on IgG. The binding of C1q is polyvalent with the binding sites being located in the 'flower heads' of the C1q molecule (see Chapter 3, Fig. 3.1). Before C1q is activated at least two and probably more binding sites on C1q must simultaneously react with the appropriate site on immunoglobulin. The problem as far as the immunoglobulins are concerned is to explain why immunoglobulin in free solution does not activate C1q while antibody–antigen complexes do (see Chapter 3 for a discussion on complement activation). Three different mechanisms need to be considered:

(a)   Monomeric antigen bound in the antigen-binding site may induce a change in the C-region parts of the molecule. This is very unlikely as hapten–antibody complexes do not fix C1q.

(b)   Antibody bound to a polymeric antigen or to an antibody–antigen complex may be distorted compared to the antibody in free solution. This has been referred to as a dislocation of the antibody molecule.

(c)   The binding affinity of C1q may be increased through the formation of cyclic complexes. In §2.5.6 we discussed the increased avidity of binding of antibody to an array of antigenic determinants and the same would be true for the hexavalent C1q binding to aggregated immunoglobulin.

The activation of C1q by complexes of IgG as opposed to IgG in free solution is likely to be due to the increased binding affinity of C1q to cyclic complexes. C1q has a very low binding constant ($5 \times 10^4 \text{M}^{-1}$) for single molecules of IgG which does not result in complement activation. The binding is greatly stabilized (binding constant $1–3 \times 10^8 \text{M}^{-1}$) if C1q reacts with aggregated IgG either as a complex or bound to a cell surface (Hughes-Jones, 1977). To achieve this on a red cell surface requires about 1,000 molecules of IgG so that the gap between neighbouring IgG molecules is about 100 Å and is easily bridged by C1q.

With IgM the situation is different. The molecule is a pentamer and will contain sufficient C1q binding sites to be able to form stable complexes. This has been amply demonstrated by antibody titrations which show one molecule of IgM bound to the surface of a red cell is sufficient to cause C1q activation. Electron microscopy also shows that single IgM molecules act as the sites of initiation of complement fixation.

As with IgG, complement activation is not observed with hapten bound to IgM or when IgM is bound to a single determinant on a red cell. This latter situation is seen with IgM anti-Rhesus D antibody where there is such sparse distribution of the D antigen on the red cell that IgM may bind by only one of its binding sites. The rare reports of monovalent antigens causing IgM to fix complement can probably be explained by aggregation of the antigens (Metzger, 1978).

Electron microscopy provides the best evidence for the mechanism by which IgM binds C1q. When IgM reacts with a polymeric antigen, the F(ab')$_2$ arms are held bent away from the plane of the central disc of the molecule (see Figs 2.3 and 2.8). By using excess antigen one can control the number of IgM molecules which become dislocated and show that complement activation parallels the frequency of dis-located IgM molecules. The molecules reacting with antigen which retain the flat configuration do not activate complement (cf. hapten binding to IgM). The con-sequence of the dislocations could be either to uncover a pre-existing C1q binding site or to induce a shape change in the $C_\mu 3$ or $C_\mu 4$ domains (Feinstein et al., 1981). The central discs of IgM produced by a combination of trypsin and papain cleavage, which removes the F(ab')$_2$ arms, will fix complement in the absence of antigen. Again this could be either through uncovering C1q binding sites or through shape changes induced by removing the N-terminal parts of the molecule (Richardson et al., 1981).

2.6.2 Rheumatoid factor

Rheumatoid factors occurring in patients with rheumatic disease are IgM or IgG antibodies which preferentially bind to aggregated rather than soluble IgG. This property reflects the increased avidity of rheumatoid factor for complexes of IgG and is not related to a specificity in the rheumatoid factor for a determinant unique to aggregated IgG. Fab prepared from IgM rheumatoid factor has a low binding affinity $(10^4 - 10^5)M^{-1}$ for IgG which is the same irrespective of whether the antigen is soluble or aggregated.

A further illustration of the increased binding avidity of cyclic complexes is seen at the sites of synthesis of IgG rheumatoid factors where the rheumatoid factors react with themselves to form small precipitates. These can be dissolved by normal serum (non-rheumatoid) IgG.

2.6.3 Allotypes on immunoglobulins

In antigen–antibody reactions the antigenic determinants are likely to be on the surface of the molecule. For allotypic determinants on immunoglobulin molecules this is neatly confirmed by the fact that these determinants are all situated on the external or partially exposed parts of the chains (Fig. 2.14). Analysis of κ light-chain

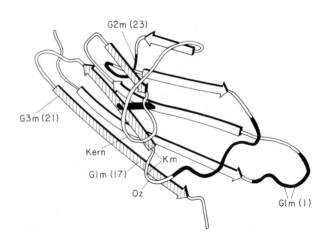

Fig. 2.14. The sites of the human allotypes on a three-dimensional model of a C domain. Allotypes from different domains are superimposed. Note particularly the Km allotype which is defined by aminoacids close to each other in space but widely separated in the sequence.

structures shows that residues 153 and 191, which are together responsible for the different Km allotypes, are close to each other in space. This is one of the best illustrations that antigenic determinants are formed by three-dimensional shapes and not sequences of amino acids.

References

AMZEL L.M., POLJAK R.J., SAUL F., VARGA J.M. & RICHARDS F.F. (1974) The three-dimensional structure of a combining region–ligand complex of immunoglobulin NEW at 3.5 Å resolution. *Proc. Nat. Acad. Sci. U.S.A.* **71**, 1427.

DAVIES R.D., PADLAN E.A. & SEGAL D.M. (1975) *Immunoglobulin Structure at High Resolution. Contemporary Topics in Molecular Immunology*, Vol. 4, p. 127. Plenum Press, New York.

DEISENHOFER J., COLMAN P.M., HUBER R., HAUPT H. & SCHWICK G. (1976) Crystallographic structural studies of a human Fc fragment. *Hoppe-Seyler's Z. Physiol. Chem.* **357**, 435.

EISEN H.N. (1973) *Immunology*, 2nd ed, p. 402. Harper & Row, New York.

FEINSTEIN A. & ROWE A.J. (1965) Molecular mechanism of formation of an antigen–antibody complex. *Nature (Lond.)* **205**, 147.

FEINSTEIN A., MUNN E.A. & RICHARDSON N.E. (1971) The three-dimensional conformation of IgM and IgA globulin molecules. *Ann. N.Y. Acad. Sci.* **190**, 104.

FEINSTEIN A. & BEALE D. (1977) Models of Immunoglobulins and Antigen–Antibody Complexes. In GLYNN L.E. & STEWARD M.W. (eds), *Immunochemistry: An Advanced Textbook*, p. 263. John Wiley & Sons, Chichester.

FEINSTEIN A. & RICHARDSON N. E. (1981) Tertiary structure of constant region of immunoglobulin in relation to function. *Monographs in Allergy*, EDEBO L. & STENDAHL, O. (eds), Karger, Basel.

FLEET G.W.J., KNOWLES J.R. & PORTER R.R. (1972) The antibody binding site labelling of a specific antibody against photo precursor of an aryl nitrene. *Biochem. J.* **128**, 499.

HUGHES-JONES N.C. (1977) Functional affinity constants of the reaction of ^{125}I-labelled C1q and C1q binders. *Immunology* **32**, 191.

METZGER H. (1978) The effect of antigen on antibodies: recent studies. *Contemp. Topics of Molec. Immunol.* **7**, 119.

RICHARDS F.F., KONIGSBERG W.H., ROSENSTEIN R.W. & VARGA J.M. (1975) On the specificity of antibodies. *Science* **189**, 130.

RICHARDSON N.E., MUNN E.A., REID K.B.M. & FEINSTEIN A. (1981) Tertiary structure of IgM in relation to function. *Molecular Immunol. In press.*

SCHIFFLER M., GIRLING R.L., ELY K.R. & EDMUNDSON A.B. (1973) Structure of a type Bence-Jones protein at 3.5 Å resolution. *Biochemistry* **12**, 4620.

SEGAL D.M., PADLAN E.A., COHEN G.H., RUDIKOFF S., POTTER M. & DAVIES D.R. (1974) The three-dimensional structure of a phosphorylcholine-binding mouse in immunoglobulin. *Proc. Nat. Acad. Sci. U.S.A.* **71**, 4298.

VALENTINE R.C. & GREEN N.M. (1967) Electron microscopy of an antibody–hapten complex. *J. Molec. Biol.* **27**, 615.

Further reading

DORRINGTON K.J. (1978) The structural basis of the functional versatility of immunoglobulin. *Canad. J. Biochem.* **56**, 1087.

GIVOL D. (1979) The antibody-combining site. *Int. Rev. of Biochem.* **23**, 71.

GLYNN L.E. & STEWARD M.W. (eds) (1977) *Immunochemistry: An Advanced Textbook.* John Wiley & Sons, Chichester.

KABAT E.A. (1976) *Structural Concepts in Immunology and Immunochemistry,* 2nd ed. Holt, Rinehart & Winston, New York.

NISONOFF A., HOPPER J.E. & SPRING S.B. (1975) *The Antibody Molecules.* Academic Press, New York.

Chapter 3
Complement

3.1 Introduction

Complement belongs to the group of plasma protein systems termed triggered enzyme cascades, which include the coagulation, fibrinolytic and kinin generating systems. The components of these systems circulate in an inactive form as pro-enzymes, awaiting the action of their predecessor in the sequence to convert them to their active form, frequently by a proteolytic step. They are all effector mechanisms which can produce a rapid and amplified response to a trigger stimulus. Such mechanisms have adaptive value if invoked in appropriate circumstances, but may be harmful if triggered in inappropriate circumstances. They are complex systems both in their reaction pathways and in the homeostatic mechanisms which control them.

3.1.1 Complement terminology

(a) C1–C9 represents the 'classical' complement components, i.e. those needed in the lysis of antibody-coated red cells using dilute serum (usually human, rabbit or guinea pig).

(b) B, D and P are the factors involved in the alternative pathway of complement activation.

(c) The bar over a component represents an activated state, usually enzymatic, generated during the complement sequence, e.g. $C\bar{1}$.

(d) An asterisk represents the presence of a short-lived binding site, e.g. C3b* (referred to as nascent C3b).

(e) A postscript 'i' represents the inactive state of a previously active component, e.g. C3bi.

(f) Fragments of a component derived by proteolytic cleavage are designated by postscripts a and b. The 'a' fragment is usually smaller, e.g. C3a and C3b. Fragments of C3b are designated 'c' or 'd' (see § 3.6.2). For historical reasons, the sub-components of C1 are represented by the use of the postscript letters q, r and s.

3.2 The complement components

The published approximate molecular weights, electrophoretic mobilities, serum concentrations and sites of synthesis of the major components of the complement system are shown in Table 3.1. It should be noted that most are fairly large proteins, and that C3 has a serum concentration in excess of 1 mg/ml. After immunoglobulins, albumin and transferrin, C3 is the most abundant of serum proteins. The complement components are not all synthesized by a single cell type.

3.2.1 *The organization of the complement system*

The complement system may conveniently be thought of as occurring in three main stages:

(a) Generation of C3-splitting enzymes. There are two distinct pathways for generating C3-splitting enzymes (C3 convertases) known as the classical and alternative pathways. These pathways can be triggered by a number of different mechanisms and involve quite distinct components.

(b) The cleavage of C3. This is the bulk reaction of the complement system and is analogous to the conversion of fibrinogen to fibrin in blood coagulation. Biologically it appears to be the most significant part of the sequence (see Chapter 15 and 16).

(c) The assembly of the lytic components. This step is initiated by the activation of C5 which seems to be the only enzymatic reaction in the lytic sequence. Thereafter the remaining components, C6–C9, combine to form a multimolecular complex which mediates the most characteristic action of the complement system—creation of membrane lesions and cell lysis.

3.3 The generation of C3 converting enzymes

Table 3.2 lists the enzymes known to be capable of splitting C3 to form C3b. The 'non-immunological' enzymes are serine/histidine esterases, sensitive to diisopropyl-fluorophosphate (DFP). They all seem to split the C3 molecule at the same point to yield C3a and C3b. The splitting of C3 *in vivo* by thrombin and plasmin, and especially by the leucocyte proteases, is probably important in antibody-independent inflammatory reactions (see Chapter 15). There are two immunological C3-converting enzymes which are generated by the classical and alternative pathways of

Table 3.2. C3 converting enzymes

Non-immunological	Immunological
Trypsin	$C\overline{42}$ Classical pathway C3 convertase
Thrombin	$C\overline{3b,Bb}$ Alternative pathway C3 convertase
Plasmin	$C\overline{VF,Bb}$ Cobra venom factor C3 convertase
Leucocyte cathepsins	

Table 3.1. Properties of complement components

Component	Approx. serum conc. (µg/ml)	Electrophoretic mobility pH 8.6	Molecular weight		Lability to		Synthesized by
			Whole molecule	Separate chains	Heat	NH_3	
CLASSICAL							
C1q	150	γ	400,000	6×22,000 6×23,000 6×24,000	+	–	Intestinal epithelium
C1r	50	β	166,000	2×83,000	++	–	Intestinal epithelium
C1s	50	α	83,000	83,000	–	–	Intestinal epithelium
C4	450	β	200,000	30,000 80,000 90,000	–	++	Macrophage. Synthesized as one chain
C2	30	β	100,000	100,000	++	–	Macrophage
C3	1,200	β	200,000	75,000 126,000	–	+	Liver and macrophages. Synthesized as one chain
ALTERNATIVE							
Factor B	200	β	90,000	90,000	+	–	Liver, macrophages and lymphocytes
Factor D	15	α2	23,000	23,000	–	–	
LYTIC							
C5	75	β	200,000	90,000 110,000	–	(+)	Spleen cells and macrophages. Synthesized as one chain
C6	60	β	130,000	130,000	+	–	Liver
C7	50	β	120,000	120,000	–	–	
C8	80	γ	154,000	14,000 63,000	+	–	Cells in spleen
C9	150	α	77,000 75,000	75,000	–	–	Liver
CONTROL PROTEINS							
C1 inhibitor	180	α2	100,000	100,000	–	–	
Factor I	25	β	100,000	55,000 45,000	–	–	
Factor H	700	β	150,000	150,000	–	–	
Properdin	25	γ	200,000	4×50,000	–	–	

Adapted from Porter (1979).

complement activation. They are designated immunological since they are initiated by antigen–antibody interactions.

3.3.1 The classical pathway C3 convertase

The components and reaction pathway which generate the classical pathway C3 convertase are shown in Fig. 3.1. In the presence of antigen–antibody complexes, C1 is converted to C̄1. C1 has three subcomponents, C1q, C1r and C1s. C1q binds to some antibodies, for instance IgM and some IgG subclasses but not to IgA, IgD and IgE. In man, IgG3 and IgG1 activate C1q. In the guinea pig only the IgG2 subclass acts on C1q, whereas IgG1 activates the alternative pathway. The reverse applies in ruminants.

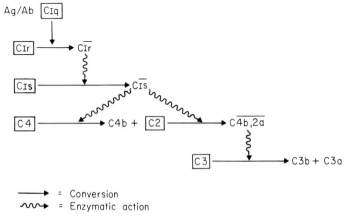

Fig. 3.1. The generation of the classical pathway C3 convertase has the characteristics of an enzyme cascade, the bulk product of which is C3b. ☐ = native component.

C1q has a characteristic appearance in the electron microscope which can be likened to a bunch of six tulips (Fig. 3.2). It is known that the molecule has six binding sites for IgG and the binding sites are located in the 'flower' heads (Reid & Porter, 1976). C1q has no described enzymatic activity and its interaction with immunoglobulin is discussed in Chapter 2. An extraordinary feature of C1q is the presence of a collagen-like amino acid sequence in each of the 18 polypeptide chains making up the whole molecule. These form six collagen-like fibril structures seen as the 'stalks' in the electron microscope. The mechanism of the conversion of C1 to C̄1 following the interaction of C1q with antibody involves the other two subcomponents C1r and C1s, together with calcium ions (Fig. 3.1). On activation both C1r and C1s are split into two chains of 56,000 and 27,000 M.W. held together by a disulphide bridge. The small chain of each carries the active site of a serine/histidine esterase. C̄1s splits lysine or tyrosine esters and in vivo acts on C4 and C2. The only known substrate of C̄1r̄ is C1s. How C1r is initially activated as a consequence of C1q

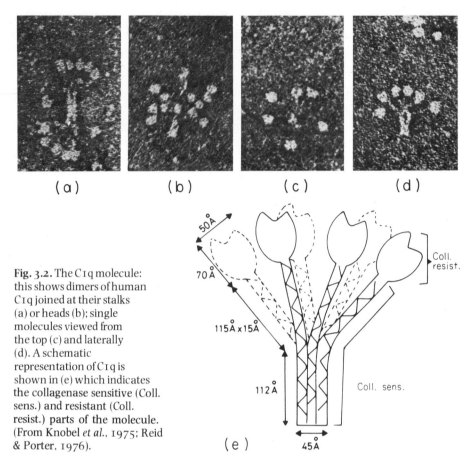

Fig. 3.2. The C1q molecule: this shows dimers of human C1q joined at their stalks (a) or heads (b); single molecules viewed from the top (c) and laterally (d). A schematic representation of C1q is shown in (e) which indicates the collagenase sensitive (Coll. sens.) and resistant (Coll. resist.) parts of the molecule. (From Knobel *et al.*, 1975; Reid & Porter, 1976).

binding to antibody–antigen complexes is not known, but it requires the presence of C1s.

C1̄ acts on C4 to split an 8,000 M.W. fragment (C4a) from the N-terminal end of the α or heavy chain. This exposes a short-lived hydrophobic binding site on the remaining larger fragment, C4b*. Some 10–15 per cent of C4b* binds hydrophobically to cell membranes in the vicinity of the antibody or antibody–antigen complex thereby localizing subsequent complement activation. The C4b* which fails to bind, loses its hydrophobic binding site to become C4b and remains in free solution. C4b, either on the membrane or in free solution, interacts reversibly with C2 in the presence of magnesium ions. A large fragment of 74,000 M.W. (C2b)† is released into free solution and the remaining C2a fragment remains complexed to C4b to form C4̄b2̄a—the classical pathway C3 convertase. This convertase is unstable and has a half-life of about 5 minutes at 37°C. After the formation of C4̄b2̄a, C1 and antibody are no longer required for the completion of the complement sequence.

† The 74,000 M.W. fragment is now called C2a and the remaining fragment C2b!

$C\bar{1}$ can also be activated by a variety of non-immunological mechanisms. Many acidic polymers (acidic mucopolysaccharides, heparin, protamine, DNA) can interact directly with $C1q$. Endotoxins from rough strains of gram-negative bacteria lacking the O antigen, do so via their lipid A component which by itself can activate the classical pathway. This is in contrast to endotoxin from smooth strains which are potent activators of the alternative pathway. Certain tissue proteases (plasmin, leucocyte cathepsins) also activate $C1$ not through their action on $C1q$ but following enzymatic cleavage of $C1r$ or $C1s$. Classical pathway activation by these tissue proteases affords a mechanism for the recruitment of the complement system at inflammatory sites. Finally an envelope glycoprotein of certain oncornaviruses bind directly to human $C1q$ and activate the classical pathway without involving antibody.

The inhibitor of $C1$ is a glycoprotein with 40 per cent carbohydrate which acts stoichiometrically on $C\bar{1}\bar{r}$ and $C\bar{1}\bar{s}$. It also inhibits plasmin, kininogenase (kallikrein), activated Hageman factor (XIIa) and activated plasma thromboplastin antecedent (XIa). The inhibitor is important in preventing the unrestrained action of $C\bar{1}$ on $C4$ and $C2$ in free solution. Heterozygous genetic deficiency of the inhibitor in man produces the disease of hereditary angio-oedema which is due to extensive local activation of $C1$, and the production of pharmacologically active fragments from $C4$, $C2$, $C3$ and $C5$ (see Chapter 15).

3.3.2 The alternative pathway C3 convertase

There are certain substances which fix large amounts of the later components, $C3$–$C9$, but none of the early classical pathway components $C1$, $C4$ or $C2$. The best known of these substances are yeast cell wall polysaccharide (zymosan), gram-negative endotoxin and a factor from cobra venom, all of which are initiators of the alternative pathway. In addition, some antibody subclasses behave similarly (e.g. guinea pig $IgG1$ and ruminant $IgG2$) as do $F(ab')_2$ fragments of rabbit and ruminant antibodies (Table 3.3). The status of human IgG subclasses and of IgA in this respect is in doubt because of the difficulty in obtaining purified antibodies free of endotoxin. More recently it has been shown that many parasites (e.g. trypanosomes, schisto-somula) and virus infected of transformed human cells can spontaneously activate the alternative pathway by an antibody-independent mechanism.

It is now clear that the increased breakdown of $C3$ during activation of the alternative pathway is dependent upon the $C3b$ feedback cycle (Fig. 3.3). $C3b$, no matter how it is produced, will form a loose complex with Factor B in the presence of Mg ions. This complex $(C\overline{3b},B)$ is a weak $C3$ splitting enzyme but when the Factor B in the complex is cleaved by the enzyme Factor D (always present in serum in an active form), the complex becomes $C\overline{3b,Bb}$, which is a powerful $C3$-splitting enzyme.

Table 3.3. A comparison of the requirements for classical and alternative pathway complement activation

	Classical	Alternative (C3b feedback) pathway
Activating agents		
Aggregates of human	IgG1, 3 (&2)	IgA
rabbit	IgG	F(ab')$_2$
guinea pig	IgG2	IgG1
ruminant	IgG1	IgG2
	(Lipid A)	Inulin
	Oncornavirus	Zymosan
		Endotoxin LPS
		CVF
		Trypanosomes
		Schistosomula
		Virus-transformed cells
Factors required to generate C3 convertase		
	C1	Factor D
	C4	C3
	C2	Factor B
Total serum requirement		
	Dilute	Concentrated
Ion requirements		
	Ca and Mg	Mg
Capacity to generate $C\overline{56}$ in acute phase serum (reactive lysis)		
	Low	High

This will produce more C3b to react with further Factor B, pushing the cycle on 'another turn' (Müller-Eberhard & Götze, 1972).

It has been suggested (Nicol & Lachmann, 1973) that the C3b feedback cycle is always ticking over at a low level primed by C3b occurring either spontaneously or via proteases including those released during inflammatory reactions (e.g. plasmin, thrombin, leucocyte cathepsins). Whether this leads to a burst of C3 cleavage will depend on the level of the control proteins and associated factors in the microenvironment wherein the C3b has been generated. Thus C3 activation via the alternative pathway is not initiated by a single event but by any process which amplifies the C3b feedback loop.

Two important features of this reaction should be noted:

(a) It requires a homeostatic mechanism, otherwise the cycle would continue

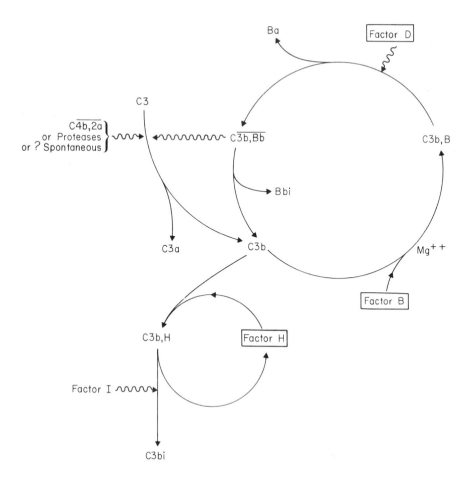

Fig. 3.3. The C3b feedback cycle. C3b generated either via the classical pathway C3 convertase or by other mechanisms combines with Factor B to initiate a self-amplifying feedback loop. Factor H (formerly β1H) and Factor I (formerly C3b inactivator or KAF) act as regulatory proteins to prevent exhaustive C3 activation. (Adapted from Lachmann, 1979.)

until one of the reactants has been exhausted. The control of the cycle is discussed below (§ 3.4).

(b) There is a strong analogy between the reaction of C3b with Factor B and the reaction of C4b with C2 (Fig. 3.4). There is also physicochemical similarity between C3 and C4, and C2 and Factor B—the evolutionary significance of this is discussed in Chapter 5.

3.4 The homeostasis of the C3b feedback cycle

Under normal circumstances the concentration of C3b,Bb regulates the extent of C3

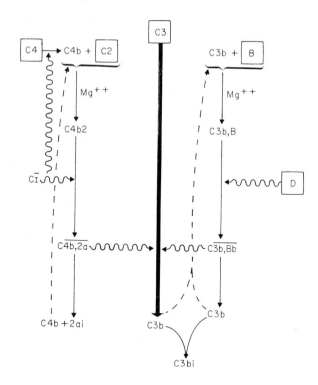

Fig. 3.4. Comparison of the classical and alternative pathways of complement activation. (Adapted from Lachmann & Hobart, 1979.)

breakdown mediated by the alternative pathway. Dissociation of $\overline{\text{C3b,Bb}}$ will lead to reduction of C3 cleavage while its stabilization will increase the rate of destruction of C3. Both types of event occur in the control of the alternative pathway.

3.4.1 Dissociation of $\overline{\text{C3b,Bb}}$

$\overline{\text{C3b,Bb}}$ dissociates to release C3b and inactive Bb (Bbi) which cannot be reutilized. The C3b is available to react with Factor B and form another complex of $\overline{\text{C3b,Bb}}$. Alternatively, the C3b can be destroyed through the action of a C3b splitting enzyme, Factor I (formerly C3b inactivator or KAF). This is present in active form in the plasma and its absence either *in vivo* (e.g. patients with Factor I deficiency) or *in vitro* by immunochemical depletion from serum, results in uncontrolled activation of the alternative pathway and exhaustion of native C3 (Alper *et al.*, 1972; Nicol & Lachmann, 1973).

The C3b is not itself susceptible to the action of the Factor I and only becomes so once it has formed a complex with Factor H (formerly β1H) (Whaley & Ruddy, 1976). Thus, the feedback cycle is controlled by the competition of Factor B and Factor H for C3b (Fig. 3.3). This competition appears to be weighted in favour of

Factor H since this can interact sequentially with many C3b molecules and Bb once dissociated cannot be reutilized. It may be that the depletion of Factor B from the immediate surroundings of a complement activation site is the critical factor in controlling the amount of C3 cleaved. It is interesting that Factor H, which is reutilized, should exist at such a high concentration in serum (700 μg/ml).

3.4.2 Stabilization of C$\overline{3b,Bb}$

Two serum factors stabilize C$\overline{3b,Bb}$: properdin and C3 nephritic factor (NeF). Properdin is a normal serum component first described by Pillemer et al. (1954) which in its activated state ($\overline{P}$) interacts with C3 in C$\overline{3b,Bb}$ (and presumably C3b,B) to stabilize the complex. The molecular events involved are obscure but it has been suggested that the change from P to $\overline{P}$ is non-proteolytic and involves a conformational change in properdin.

NeF is an autoantibody found in high concentrations in the serum of patients with mesangiocapillary glomerulonephritis and some patients with partial lipodystrophy. It reacts with C$\overline{3b,Bb}$ to stabilize the complex but does not prevent its enzymatic action. Interestingly the Fab fragment of NeF has the same activity as the whole molecule showing that divalent binding is not necessary for stabilizing the complex (Scott et al., 1978). This is one of the few examples where monovalent and multivalent antibody molecules have the same biological activity in vitro. Being an autoantibody it seems unlikely that NeF represents a normal serum component although it is difficult to exclude the presence of trace amounts in normal serum. NeF is not necessary for the alternative pathway since the latter functions normally in totally agammaglobulinaemic serum.

An attractive new idea is that many alternative pathway activators, particularly the polysaccharides, may provide a 'protective surface' on which C$\overline{3b,Bb}$ enjoys a longer half-life than in free solution (Fearon & Austen, 1977). The mechanism is unknown but in the case of heterologous erythrocytes the level of protection is inversely correlated with the sialic acid content of the membrane.

3.4.3 Cobra venom factor

Cobra venom factor (CVF) is a 150,000 M.W. protein found in snake saliva which has the ability to produce exhaustive activation of the alternative pathway in mammalian serum. CVF is in fact snake C3b, and complexes with mammalian Factor B to produce $\overline{CVF,Bb}$ which is a mammalian C3 convertase. However, CVF is not susceptible to mammalian Factor H and Factor I so that when CVF is added to serum (in vitro or in vivo) it results in complete depletion of C3. This phenomenon has been used to study the biological rôle of C3 in vivo.

3.5 The cleavage of C3

The activation of C3 is quantitatively the major event of the complement sequence. C3 is most readily cleaved at a particularly sensitive site on the N-terminal end of the α chain releasing a 9,000 M.W. fragment (C3a) (Fig. 3.5). C3a is a potent anaphyla-toxin and chemotactic factor. The larger C3b* fragment is unstable and possesses a highly labile binding site (half-life of milliseconds) which can form strong hydro-phobic interactions with cell surfaces, antigen–antibody complexes, yeast cell walls, etc. It has been shown that C3b* can form a covalent ester bond with the surface to which it binds (Law *el al.*, 1979). If C3b* fails to bind, the molecule undergoes secondary changes to form C3b and the binding site is lost. C3b either in the fluid phase or bound to cell membranes retains all its other biological activities. These include adherence reactions to receptors on cells and activation of the alternative pathway.

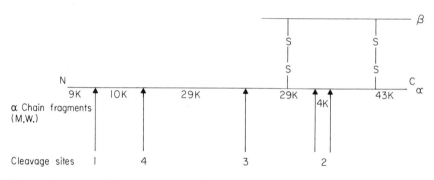

Fig. 3.5. Location of cleavage points on the α chain of C3.

1. C3 convertase cleavage site producing 9,000 M.W. C3a fragment.

2. Factor I and Factor H dependent cleavage site, producing a 4,000 M.W. fragment. The remaining part of the molecule is inactive C3bi.

3 and 4. Further cleavage sites by unidentified proteases. The fragment between cleavage sites 3 and 4 corresponds to C3d. (From Harrison & Lachmann, 1979a, b.)

Detailed studies on the proteolytic breakdown of C3b (Harrison & Lachmann, 1979a, b) have shown that the initial cleavage by Factor I and Factor H involves the removal of a 4,000 M.W. fragment from the α chain. The two parts of the cleaved chain remain attached to the β chain by disulphide bridges (Fig. 3.5). This inactive form of C3b is known as C3bi. By itself Factor H is not proteolytic. The events which follow are complex but breakdown of the chain continues, involving more than one unidentified protease resulting in the formation of C3c and C3d. The latter fragment is biologically inactive but can bind to C3d receptors on B lymphocytes.

3.6 The lytic complement sequence

The lytic or terminal pathway of complement is not an enzyme cascade but a series of self-assembling components (Fig. 3.6). C5 is split into C5a (15,000 M.W.) and C5b, which has a weak binding site for membranes. The C5 convertase of the classical pathway is formed by $\overline{C4b,2a}$ + one molecule of C3b; that of the alternative pathway is $\overline{C3b,Bb}$ + one molecule of C3b. C5b has for a short time the capacity to react with C6 to form the complex $\overline{C56}$, which can be released from complement-binding sites. It binds C7 stoichiometrically to give the trimolecular complex $\overline{C567}$* which will bind firmly to membranes and has a measurably long half-life in free solution at 37°. As a result there is significant 'contagion' of complement activity from the initial activation site and innocent bystander cells may become involved in the terminal lytic events.

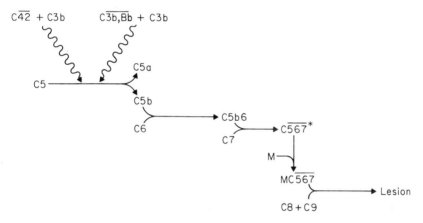

Fig. 3.6. The lytic complement sequence. Only the first stage, C5→C5b, is enzymatic. The remaining part of the reaction involves the self assembly of C6→C9. M=membrane. (Adapted from Lachmann & Hobart, 1979.)

3.6.1 Reactive lysis

It is possible to generate free $\overline{C56}$ in solution by the action of zymosan on sera with a relative excess of C5 and C6. Such sera include the sera of patients in the 'acute phase' of inflammation, for example those who have recently had major surgery or given birth. When activated, there is an excess of production of $\overline{C56}$ over the available C7, and this excess remains in the fluid phase, while the $\overline{C567}$* is bound or decays. The $\overline{C56}$ may be isolated and used with C7 to generate the $\overline{C567}$ on red cells or on liposomes having neither antibody nor C1–C3 on them. This is the phenomenon underlying reactive lysis (Thompson & Lachmann, 1970).

3.6.2 The lytic event

Membrane-bound C$\overline{567}$ interacts with one molecule of C8 and six molecules of C9 producing a complex of about 10^6 M.W. which mediates cell lysis (Kolb & Müller-Eberhard, 1973). The lytic event has been investigated both by electron microscopy and by functional studies. EM studies (Humphrey & Dourmashkin, 1969) first showed that complement-lysed cells contained 'holes' or 'lesions' which appeared as circular defects on the membrane, each measuring about 100 Å in diameter. These are stable structures, can often be dissociated from the membrane, cannot be detected on cells carrying C$\overline{567}$ and appear only after the addition of C8 and C9. They do not represent membrane proteins as they are seen after complement-mediated lysis of liposomes made solely of lecithin (Fig. 3.7). It is now accepted that the structures are in fact an annular arrangement of the components C5–C9 in the complex.

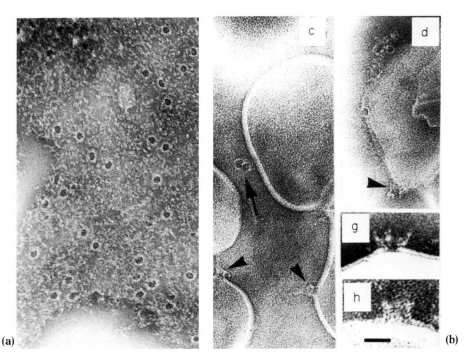

(a)   **(b)**

Fig. 3.7. (a) Complement lesions in erythrocyte membrane. (b) Electron micrographs of liposomes bearing C5–C9 complexes. The characteristic annular-shaped lesions are seen both in top view and in profile. E.M. pictures by courtesy of Dr. E. A. Munn.

At the functional level Mayer and his colleagues have shown that the lytic event is a single hit phenomenon and that the lipid bilayer is the site of attack (see Mayer, 1973; 1977a). From their studies it seems that the hydrophobic regions of C5b, C6, C7, C8 and C9 become inserted into the lipid bilayer and create a transmembrane channel. The pore size of this channel increases with each successive addition of a component of the lytic pathway, finally resulting in a channel of some 25 Å diameter formed by the complete C5–C9 complex. These channels lead to cell lysis by the following sequence of events. First the ions and low molecular weight substances equilibrate across the cell membrane. Since the higher molecular weight substances remain inside the cell, water is drawn in and the cell goes on swelling until the membrane ruptures. This can be shown by labelling red cells with a small radio-active marker such as ^{86}Rubidium (diameter 4 Å) and showing that the release of rubidium precedes the release of haemoglobin (diameter 60 Å) during complement-mediated lysis.

3.7 Complement and cell membranes

The discovery that C2, C4 and Factor B are coded by genes in the MHS has stimulated a search for membrane-associated complement components. There are two difficult-ies in this work. First, it is important to show that the membrane-associated complement components are not derived from the plasma. Second, although the membrane components may be evolutionarily related to the serum complement system, they may now be coded for by separate genes and retain functional but not antigenic similarities. Thus the conventional approach of using antibodies against the serum components as probes may not work. So far Factor B is the only component which is synthesized and expressed as a membrane component by human and mouse lymphocytes (Halbwachs & Lachmann, 1976; McConnell & Lachmann, 1976). This has largely been detected by a functional assay using CVF as a specific probe.

Finally, for many years it has been hypothesized that complement plays a rôle in various cell-mediated cytotoxic reactions. Although there are many similarities between complement-mediated lysis and cell-mediated lysis (Mayer, 1977b) this cannot be regarded as a strong argument in favour of a membrane-associated lytic pathway. Evidence for or against this idea must await the isolation of the effector molecules of cell-mediated cytotoxic reactions.

References

ALPER C.A., ROSEN F.S. & LACHMANN P.J. (1972) Inactivator of the third component of complement as an inhibitor of the properdin pathway. *Proc. Nat. Acad. Sci. U.S.A.* **69**, 2910.

AMOS N., SISSONS J.G.P., GIRARD J.-F., LACHMANN P.J. & PETERS D.K. (1976) The cofactors required by C3 nephritic factor to generate a C3 convertase *in vitro. Clin. exp. Immunol.* **24**, 474.

FEARON D.T. & AUSTEN K.F. (1977) Activation of the alternative complement pathway with rabbit erythrocytes by circumvention of the regulatory action of endogenous control proteins. *J. exp. Med.* **146,** 22.

HALBWACHS L. & LACHMANN P.J. (1976) Factor B of the alternative complement pathway on human lymphocytes. *Scand. J. Immunol.* **5,** 697.

HARRISON R.A. & LACHMANN P.J. (1980a) The physiological breakdown of the third component of human complement. *Mol. Immunol.* **17,** 9.

HARRISON R.A. & LACHMANN P.J. (1980b) Novel cleavage products of the third component of human complement. *Mol. Immunol.* **17,** 219.

HUMPHREY J.H. & DOURMASHKIN R.R. (1969) The lesion in cell membrane caused by complement. *Adv. Immunol.* **11,** 75.

KNOBEL H.R., VILLEGAR U. & ISLIKER H. (1975) Chemical analysis and electron microscopy studies of human C1q prepared by different methods. *Eur. J. Immunol.* **5,** 78.

KOLB W.P. & MÜLLER-EBERHARD H.J. (1973) The membrane attack mechanism of complement. Verification of a stable C5–9 complex in free solution. *J. exp. Med.* **138,** 438.

LACHMANN P.J. (1979) Complement. In SELA M. (ed.), *The Antigens,* Vol. V, p. 284. Academic Press, New York.

LACHMANN P.J. & HOBART M.J. (1979) The genetics of the complement system. In *Human Genetics: Possibilities and Realities. CIBA Symposium* **66** (NS), Excerpta Medica.

LAW S.K., LICHTENBERG N.A. & LEVINE R.P. (1979) Evidence for an ester linkage between the labile binding site of C3b and receptive surface. *J. Immunol.* **123,** 1388.

McCONNELL I. & LACHMANN P.J. (1976) Cell membrane associated complement components. *Transplantation Rev.* **32,** 72.

MAYER M.M. (1973) The complement system. *Sci. Amer.* **229,** 54.

MAYER M.M. (1977a) The cytolytic attack mechanism of complement. *Monogr. in Allergy* **12,** 1.

MAYER M.M. (1977b) Mechanism of cytolysis by lymphocytes; a comparison with complement. *J. Immunol.* **119,** 1195.

MÜLLER-EBERHARD H.G. & GÖTZE O. (1972) C3 proactivator convertase and its mode of action. *J. exp. Med.* **135,** 1003.

NICOL P.A.E. & LACHMANN P.J. (1973) The alternate pathway of complement activation: the role of C3 and its inactivator (KAF). *Immunology* **24,** 259.

PILLEMER L., BLUM L., LEPOW I.H., ROSS O.A., TODD E.W. & WARDLAW A.C. (1954) The properdin system and immunity. I. Demonstration and isolation of a new serum protein and its role in immune phenomena. *Science* **120,** 279.

PORTER R.R. (1979) Complement. *Int. Rev. Biochem.* **23,** 177.

REID K.B.M. & PORTER R.R. (1976) Subunit composition and structure of subcomponent C1q of the first component of human complement. *Biochem. J.* **155,** 19.

SCOTT D.M., AMOS N., SISSONS J.G.P., LACHMANN P.J. & PETERS D.K. (1978) The immunoglobulin nature of nephritic factor. *Clin. exp. Immunol.* **32,** 12.

THOMPSON R.A. & LACHMANN P.J. (1970) Reactive lysis: the complement-mediated lysis of unsensitized cells. I. The characterization of indicator factor and its identification as C7. *J. exp. Med.* **131,** 629.

WHALEY K. & RUDDY S. (1976) Modulation of the alternative complement pathway by β_1H globulin. *J. exp. Med.* **144,** 1147.

Chapter 4
The Immunoglobulin Genes

4.1 Introduction

The immunoglobulins are a very unusual family of polypeptide chains. In any one individual there are a vast number of different heavy and light chain V-region sequences associated with a small number of different C-region sequences that trigger the biological functions of the immunoglobulin molecules. In this way a limited number of biological effector functions can be directed at a large number of different pathogens.

This situation raises a number of interesting questions regarding the genes which code for immunoglobulin. First, can all the required V-region genes be inherited or are they derived by somatic mutation? Second, can *different* V-region genes become associated with the same C-region gene and conversely how can the *same* V region become associated with different C regions as must occur in heavy-chain switching? Since immunoglobulin chains are synthesized as complete poly-peptides and DNA is a linear array of information then clearly something special must happen between the information stored in DNA and the final polypeptide chain.

Both classical and molecular genetics have been applied to these problems. We now have considerable information on the number of the variable and constant region genes and of their arrangement in embyronic DNA and in the DNA of antibody-secreting plasma cells. This chapter is concerned with the experimental basis for this information.

4.2 The gross arrangement of immunoglobulin genes

Linkage studies have shown that the inherited V_H- and C_H-region genes, although not adjacent to each other, are closely linked. In rabbits the *a* locus allotypes which correlate with amino acid sequences in the V_H framework shows a recombination frequency of 0.4 per cent with respect to heavy chain C-region markers. Similarly, in mice the recombination frequency observed between V_H-region markers (the cross-reacting idiotypes, see §1.4), and heavy chain C-region markers varies from 0.4 to 4 per cent. In some cases the cross-over lies within the V-region cluster (Weigert & Riblet, 1978). The V and C genes for each type of light chain are similarly arranged.

In contrast the genes for κ, λ and heavy chains occur as three separate unlinked gene clusters. For example, in rabbits the allotypes $b4$ (a C_κ marker) and $d11$ (a $C_{H\gamma}$ marker) segregate independently. They both segregate independently from $c21$—a λ-chain C-region marker. Within each cluster the C-region genes are closely linked and different classes and subclasses of immunoglobulins are so close together that no recombinants have been observed in more than 5,000 mice. We know that recombinants can occur between C_H regions since rare cross-overs arise between the Gm markers in man.

From linkage studies the overall picture of the inherited genes for each immuno-globulin chain is of a larger cluster of V-region genes separated by about 10^5 base pairs or more from a small but extremely closely linked cluster of C-region genes occupying approximately 20,000 base pairs or less.

4.2.1 V and C genes from the same chromosome function together

In rabbits the presence of allotype markers in the V_H and C_H genes allows one to determine if heavy chains contain genetic information from only one chromosome or if molecules can be constructed by combining the genetic information from the two homologous chromosomes (Kindt, 1975). If an $a1/1,d11/d11$ homozygous buck is crossed with an $a2/2,d12/12$ doe all the offspring will be $a1/2,d11/12$ hetero-zygotes with $a1$ and $d11$ on one chromosome and $a2$ and $d12$ on the other. Analysis of the IgG from such animals shows that essentially all the molecules are either of allotype $a1$–$d11$ or $a2$–$d12$ and no molecules are found coded for in part by each chromosome (e.g. $a1$–$d12$ or $a2$–$d11$).

4.2.2 Chromosomal assignment of immunoglobulin gene clusters

One way to assign genes to chromosomes is by cell hybridization studies. Cells from two different species can be fused to form hybrid cell lines. With human–mouse hybrids, human chromosomes are gradually lost from the hybrid cells and a tentative assignment can be made correlating loss of expression with loss of a particular human chromosome. Using this technique heavy chain genes have been assigned to chromosome 14 in man (Croce et al., 1979) and chromosome 12 in mice. Kappa light chain genes are on chromosome 6 in mice (Hengartner et al., 1978).

4.3 Methods used to study gene structure

In recent years the technology for isolating and cloning mammalian genes together with the advent of rapid DNA sequencing techniques has been applied to immuno-globulin genes and has resulted in an explosion of information. To appreciate this work an understanding of the methodologies is useful.

4.3.1 Annealing of nucleic acids

The identification of particular genes in fragments of DNA is based on annealing studies. The crucial first step is to isolate mRNA which is either used itself as a probe in the annealing experiments or used as a template to form complementary DNA (cDNA) which is then used to detect the gene. The principle in annealing studies is that the complementary strands of DNA separate on heating and precisely recombine (anneal) on cooling. If radioactive cDNA or mRNA is added during this reaction it combines with any complementary base sequences and by using single-strand specific nucleases it is possible to determine the extent of the incorporation of the single-stranded probe into a double-stranded structure. In this way the genes in DNA fragments can be identified.

4.3.2 Restriction enzymes

These enzymes cleave DNA at defined sites yielding unique DNA fragments which can be separated according to size or base content. Fragments containing a particular gene can be identified by annealing experiments (Fig. 4.1).

4.3.3 DNA cloning

Fragments of DNA can be spliced into a bacteriophage genome which is then permitted to replicate in its host bacterium. The phage DNA recovered contains copies of the inserted DNA as well as the phage genome. The sources of DNA used for cloning are either double-stranded DNA made from single-stranded cDNA or alternatively purified restriction enzyme fragments of DNA carrying the appropriate gene. After replication, the DNA from many different clones of phage has to be screened to find a clone carrying the gene of interest (e.g. an immunoglobulin gene). DNA cloning is used for purifying DNA fragments and for producing sufficient quantities of genes for sequencing studies.

4.3.4 Electron microscopy of DNA

The ease with which double-stranded and single-stranded nucleic acid can be distinguished in the electron microscope has been of great value in visualizing gene arrangement. When DNA is reannealed in the presence of mRNA the RNA binds more firmly than DNA to the complementary bases on the DNA and displaces a single strand of homologous DNA which can be seen as a single-stranded loop (R loops) (Fig. 4.2). In many instances the bases in the DNA which are complementary to those in the mRNA probe do not form one continuous sequence but are interrupted by stretches of untranslated nucleotides known as intervening sequences.

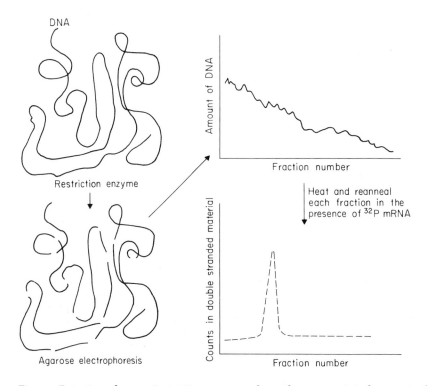

Fig. 4.1. Detection of genes. Restriction enzymes cleave the genome into fragments of DNA of unique molecular weight. These fragments can be partially separated by electrophoresis and the fractions containing a particular gene identified by an annealing reaction. Alternatively the separated fragments can be transferred as single strands to a cellulose nitrate filter paper (Southern Blot technique). The filter is then hybridized with a radioactive probe and after washing, the gene is located by radioautography.

These can be visualized in the EM since if mRNA anneals to two non-contiguous parts of a DNA strand the unannealed intervening DNA sequences will be seen as additional loops (Fig. 4.2).

4.3.5 DNA-sequencing techniques

DNA nucleotide sequences can be determined in several ways. The more powerful of these techniques are based on the ease with which different sized oligonucleotides are separated by electrophoresis. One procedure developed by Sanger depends on the use of didesoxynucleotides or other chain-terminating inhibitors of DNA synthesis (Sanger *et al.*, 1977). The DNA to be sequenced must be single-stranded, either as cDNA or prepared by strand separation. DNA synthesis is initiated using small

(a)

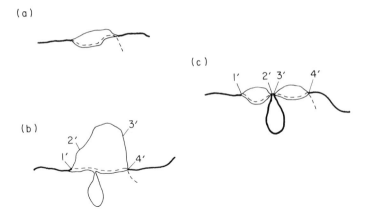

(c)

(b)

Fig. 4.2. Diagrammatic representation of the various R loops that can be formed. (a) A simple R loop where the mRNA has displaced a DNA strand which is seen as a single-stranded loop. Often it is possible to see a tail of single-stranded material at one end of the R loop which corresponds to the poly A tail on the mRNA. (b) An R loop of a gene which contains an intervening sequence of DNA not present in the mRNA. The smaller loop of single-stranded DNA has been formed by the mRNA bringing together two non-continuous sequences of DNA. In the larger loop the sequences 1′ to 2′ and 3′ to 4′ have been displaced by the mRNA but the sequence 2′ to 3′ is complementary to the sequence in the smaller R loop. These regions of complementary DNA can re-anneal to form structures like the one shown in (c). In all the figures dotted line represents RNA. In the electron microscope the double strands will appear as thicker lines than the single strands.

restriction enzyme fragments as primers, and the single-stranded DNA as template. The synthesis is allowed to proceed in the presence of radioactive nucleotides and a single dideoxynucleoside triphosphate which acts as a nucleotide specific chain-terminating inhibitor of DNA synthesis. For example, dideoxyadenosine phosphate added to the growing 3′ end of the chain prevents further addition to this chain as there is no free hydroxyl group to react with the next nucleotide. If the inhibitor of DNA synthesis is present in limited amounts, chains of different length will be synthesized, each one terminating with a dideoxyadenosine. The lengths of the chains synthesized will depend on the number of nucleotides from the primer to the complementary thymidine residues in the template. By analysing the chains made in four identical reaction mixtures, each of which contains a different site specific chain-terminating inhibitor, it is possible to read off a sequence of DNA for considerably more than 100 residues (Fig 4.3).

4.4 The immunoglobulin genes

Using the techniques described above it has been shown that the structure and

DNA template
(unknown sequence)   - - - G C G A A G C C G C A A T - - - - - - etc.

Synthesized DNA   - - - C G C T T C G G C G T T A - - - - - - etc.

Fragments synthesized in presence of:

    dideoxy C   - C, - C G C, - C G C T T C, etc.
    dideoxy T   - C G C T, - C G C T T, etc.
    dideoxy A   - C G C T T C G G C G T T A, etc.
    dideoxy G   - C G, - C G C T T C G, etc.

Fragments separated by size using acrylamide gel electrophoresis

    C T A G
    —   - C G C T T C
       —   - C G C T T
       —   - C G C T
       —   - C G C
           — - C G
       —   - C   **(a)**

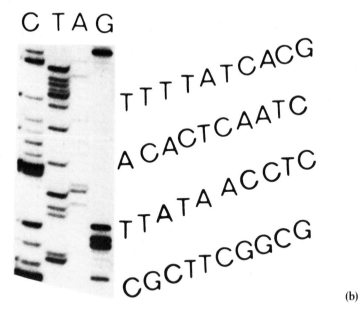

(b)

Fig. 4.3. (a) Technique for DNA sequencing. (b) An autoradiograph of an electrophoretic gel that has separated deoxyoligonucleotides by size. Each track contains the material synthesized in the presence of the same primer and single-stranded DNA. The difference in each track is due to the presence of different chain-termination inhibitors. The reaction mixture applied to each track contained different chain-termination inhibitors of DNA synthesis causing chain-termination at C, T, A and G on the template respectively. The sequence is shown at the side of the gel starting at the bottom. (Adapted from Sanger *et al.*, 1977.)

arrangement of immunoglobulin genes is different for genes isolated from embryonic tissue compared to genes obtained from cells synthesizing immunoglobulin. This is the first demonstration of the somatic rearrangement of genes. We will first describe the genes for mouse λ chains as these are the simplest and the most fully characterized.

4.4.1 λ-chain genes

Tonegawa and his colleagues have cloned and sequenced the $V_{\lambda 1}$ genes from embryonic tissue and from a λ chain secreting mouse plasmacytoma (Bernard *et al.*, 1978). Contrary to expectations the nucleotide sequence of the V_λ gene in embryonic DNA does not code for the complete V region of the λ light chain but it stops short after the codon for amino acid 97. The nucleotide sequence of the V_λ gene in its functional form (i.e. from the plasmacytoma) is the same as the inherited form except that the nucleotide sequence now terminates at a position corresponding to amino acid 109, the end of the variable region. The nucleotides coding for amino acids 98–109 represent the J-segment gene (see §1.3.2). These experiments provide formal proof that somatic cells can rearrange their inherited genetic information (Fig. 4.4). This confirms earlier studies by Tonegawa and others who used restriction enzymes to show that for both κ and λ chains in embryonic DNA the V- and C-region genes occurred in different DNA fragments whereas with plasmacytoma DNA they were in the same fragment.

From the distribution of the heavy-chain allotypes in rabbits we know that (see §4.2.1) gene rearrangement occurs intrachromosomally and rarely, if ever, involves

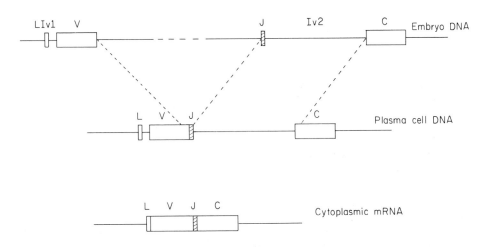

Fig. 4.4. Arrangement of mouse chain genes in embryonic and plasma cell DNA. Iv 1 and Iv 2 refer to intervening sequences of DNA, Iv 1 in the leader sequence of the V region and Iv 2 in between the J segment and C region genes. (Adapted from Brack *et al.*, 1978.)

genes on the other chromosome. This type of gene rearrangement is so far unique to immunoglobulin genes and studies with κ and λ chains suggest that the mechanism involves intrachromosomal deletion (see §4.4.2).

Nucleotide sequencing has also shown that in common with many eukaryotic genes the λ-chain genes contain two intervening sequences. One of these comprises 91 bases in the nucleotide sequence coding for the leader sequence of the V region and the other, about 1,250 nucleotides, lies between the end of the J gene and the start of the C gene. This latter intervening sequence is easily seen by using the R-loop technique (Fig. 4.5).

The J-segment gene is not transposed during differentiation of antibody-forming cells, as in embryonic tissue the J_λ gene is still 1,250 nucleotides 'upstream' from the C_λ gene. The distance between the V_λ gene and the J_λ gene in embryonic tissue is not known but is certainly several thousand nucleotides and probably much more. With the two λ subtypes there is only one V gene, one J gene and one C gene for each subtype.

4.4.2 κ-chain genes

Mouse κ-chain genes are arranged similarly to the λ-chain genes except there are many V_κ genes, five J_κ genes but only one C_κ gene. The five J-segment genes are separated from each other by about 300 nucleotides and form a cluster approximately 3,000 bases upstream from the C_κ-region gene. Again in the embryonic DNA

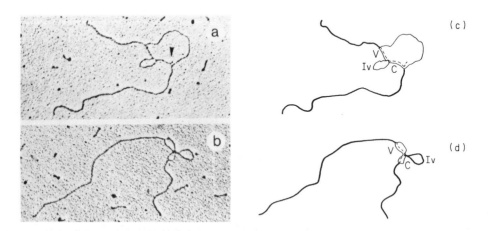

Fig. 4.5. R loops mouse of λ genes. (a) λ chain mRNA annealed to a cloned fragment of DNA isolated from a λ-chain secreting myeloma. (b) The same structure as in (a) but shown in a collapsed form (see Fig. 4.2c). (c) In the diagrams the thin line represents the displaced single strand of DNA and the dotted line represents the attached mRNA. Iv refers to the intervening sequences, and V and C to the V and C region genes. (Adapted from Brack & Tonegawa, 1977).

no V gene is adjacent to any of the J genes, while in the DNA from a cell synthesizing κ chains one V gene has been transposed to become continuous with one of the J-segment genes (Fig. 4.6). The amino acid sequence data discussed in §1.3.2 suggest that any one V gene can be transposed to any of the J-segment genes thus increasing the diversity of the V regions. Two groups have independently sequenced the region of DNA containing the cluster of J-segment genes (Sakano *et al.*, 1979b; Max *et al.*, 1979). Interestingly the product of one of the J-segment genes has not yet been found in a κ chain and it is suggested that this J-segment gene is defective in the signal used to excise the intervening sequence between the end of the J genes and the beginning of the C gene.

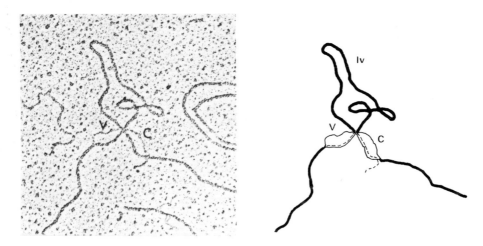

Fig. 4.6. An R loop of mouse K chain gene in its functional form (i.e. from a plasmacytoma). See Fig. 4.5 for the key to the diagram. (Taken from Seidman & Leder, 1978.)

Comparisons of the flanking sequences on the 3′ or downstream side of the V_κ and V_λ genes with those on the 5′ or upstream side of the J_κ and J_λ genes show that there are two short regions of highly conserved nucleotides. It has been proposed that these residues form an inverted repeat stem structure which acts as the recognition site for enzyme(s) to delete a piece of DNA and bring about the required intrachromosomal rearrangement (Fig. 4.7). This feature of the immunoglobulin genes has been conserved in evolution from the time of separation of the κ and λ chains and is likely to be found in the heavy-chain genes.

The exact number and arrangement of the V_κ genes is not known but examination of the V-region subgroups has shown that there are up to six to eight different genes for each subgroup (Siedman & Leder, 1978) and that within each subgroup

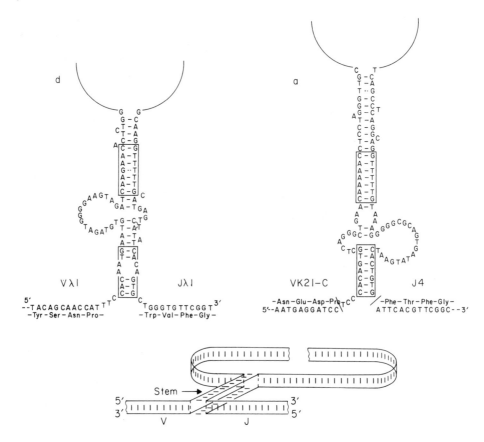

Fig. 4.7. The flanking sequences of J and V genes of K and λ chains arranged to form an inverted stem structure. Also shown is a hypothetical three-dimensional drawing of this stem structure. (Adapted from Sakano *et al.*, 1979b; Max *et al.*, 1979.)

the genes are very similar, possibly representing the sub-subgroups as defined by amino acid sequences (see §1.3.1). The homology in the V genes isolated from one of these subgroups extends over 2,000–3,000 nucleotides, nearly ten times larger than the V gene itself. The possible implications of this are discussed later in this chapter (see §4.8).

4.4.3 *Heavy-chain genes*

Much less is known about the mouse heavy-chain genes. Almost certainly they will have the same overall arrangement as the light-chain genes but for the heavy chain there are several C_H genes as well as multiple V_H and J_H genes (Roa *et al.*, 1979). The mechanism for joining V_H to J_H is likely to be the same as for light chains but the number of V_H and J_H genes is not known. At present the available information on the heavy-chain C-region genes shows that intervening sequences break up these genes into coding sequences corresponding to domains and that the hinge region behaves as a separate domain (Sakano *et al.*, 1979a; Early *et al.*, 1979). This finding possibly explains the unusual structure of immunoglobulin variants isolated from myeloma cells (see §5.4.4).

The expression of heavy-chain genes is more complex than light-chain genes. During clonal expansion of antibody-producing B cells the same V_H region is always expressed but can be associated with different classes of heavy chain. In fact at certain stages of their development B cells can synthesize three different classes of immunoglobulin each bearing the same identical V_H region though ultimately they become restricted to making only one immunoglobulin class. The mechanism for this complex expression (referred to as heavy-chain switching, see Chapter 8) is unknown and may involve different processes for the different stages of B-cell maturation. The final stage of B-cell development involves a second gene rearrangement and loss of irrelevant C_H genes (Honjo & Katooka, 1978, Rabbits *et al.*, 1980).

4.5 Allelic exclusion

Individual antibody-synthesizing cells from animals heterozygous for immunoglobulin allotype make only one of the two allelic forms potentially available (allelic exclusion). While it is usual for a cell to use only a fraction of its genetic potential there is no other case known of allelic exclusion of autosomal genes. The significance of this is discussed in Chapter 7. The only possible parallel is the suppression of genes on one of the X chromosomes in female cells (the Lyon phenomenon), but this affects most of the genes on one chromosome and not specific genes. There is no evidence for allelic exclusion of other autosomal genes in antibody-synthesizing cells. At present much effort is being made to determine the arrangement of V, J and C genes on the excluded chromosome to see if allelic exclusion is due to selective inactivation or selective activation, but no uniform picture has emerged.

4.6 From immunoglobulin genes to immunoglobulin chains

The V- and C-region nucleotides in light-chain mRNA correspond exactly to the amino acid sequences of the light chain. The mRNA also includes nucleotides for the leader sequence found on nascent chains (see §1.6) and in addition a further 150–200 nucleotides on either end.

The mRNA does not have any of the intervening sequences which occur at the DNA level. There must, therefore, be a mechanism whereby the intervening sequences are omitted from cytoplasmic mRNA. The mRNA in the cytoplasm is derived from a much larger RNA transcript present only in the cell nucleus and known as heterogeneous nuclear RNA (hnRNA) (Rabbits, 1978). For murine light chains hnRNA is ten times larger than light-chain mRNA isolated from polysomes. It is thought that the hnRNA is a faithful transcript of the DNA and includes the intervening sequence. In the nucleus the hnRNA undergoes post-transcriptional modification, the intervening sequences are removed and poly A tails added to the 3′ end (see Chapter 8, Fig. 8.3).

By comparing the nucleotide sequences from a number of genes it seems that usually an intervening sequence begins with GU and ends with AG and all between is excised. For example, CAA G (GU . . . AG)GU ACC becomes CAA GGU ACC after post-transcriptional processing. This cannot be the only signal required and there must be additional information which determines the sequence to be removed (see Lerner *et al.*, 1980).

4.7 The number of immunoglobulin genes

There are two theories for the origin of the DNA coding for antibodies. The germ line hypothesis argues that all immunoglobulin genes are inherited and that antibody diversity has occurred by mutation and selection during evolution. The somatic mutation hypothesis argues that diversity is generated by somatic mutation from a small number of inherited V-region genes during the lifetime of an individual (see Chapter 7). Support for either hypothesis rests to some extent on estimating the number of inheritable V-region genes. Such estimates can be obtained from amino acid sequence data of immunoglobulin chains and DNA sequencing of immuno-globulin genes.

The specificity of individual antibody molecules is determined by the combina-tion of V_H and V_L. Thus the usual estimate of 10^6–10^8 antibody molecules per individual could be satisfied by 10^3–10^4 different V_H and V_L. This type of combina-torial amplification can also occur within a chain since V-region sequences can be found associated with different J-segment sequences in different cells (see §1.3.2). It is unknown to what extent these intrachain combinations can affect specificity as the J segment starts at the very edge of the antigen-binding site.

From the amino acid sequence it is argued that the well-defined subgroups (or sub-subgroups) of the variable region must be coded for by different genes. Since the subgroups occur in all individuals of the species then the subgroups can not be alleles and each must be represented by at least one inherited V gene. From this argument the minimum number of inherited genes in mice is more than 50 for V_κ and V_H, one for $V_{\lambda I}$ and one for $V_{\lambda II}$. In man there are at least four V_κ, five V_λ and three V_H genes. Comparison of amino acid sequences of 18 separate mouse λ-chain myelomas shows that 12 are identical; the remaining six are individually different with the differences clustering to the hypervariable regions (Fig. 4.8). This would be expected if antigen were selecting somatic mutants from a single germ line V-region sequence. This view

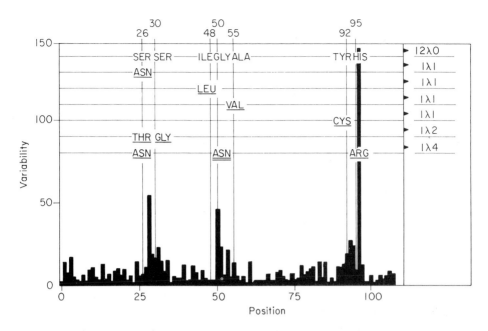

Fig. 4.8. The amino acid sequence differences of 18 mouse λ light chains myeloma proteins (12 identical λo) superimposed on the plot of variability (see Fig. 4.1). (From Cohn *et al.*, 1974.)

is confirmed by DNA studies which show that there are only two restriction enzyme fragments of DNA carrying the λ V gene—one for $V_{\lambda I}$ and the other for $V_{\lambda II}$.

In contrast there may be as many as 1,000 κ-chain genes in mice. Amino acid sequences have permitted the division of certain V κ subgroups into sub-subgroups (Weigert & Riblet, 1978, Fig. 1.6) and this is confirmed by DNA studies which reveal multiple subgroup genes. If there are 1,000 different κ V genes in mice, somatic variants probably contribute less to diversity in this species than they do in man where the number of V_κ subgroups is much smaller.

DNA sequence studies of mouse κ chains have revealed an interesting feature which might also contribute to κ-chain diversity. The extent to which multiple tandem gene copies are lost or altered through mismatched cross-over will depend on the homology of the intervening and flanking sequences associated with repeated genes; the greater the homology the more the chance of mismatched cross-over. The flanking sequences of the several V_κ genes belonging to one subgroup are homologous over a greater length than the flanking sequences surrounding genes for relatively invariant molecules such as the β chain of murine haemoglobin (Seidman *et al.*, 1978).

Finally it should be emphasized that the argument as to whether antibody diversity is germ line or somatic is not one of mechanism but one of time scale. It would be very surprising if different species had the same number of inherited genes. The number required for an adequate immune system will depend on a variety of factors such as the number of lymphocytes, the frequency of cell division, the time available for full lymphoid development, level of maternal immune protection and so on (see Chapter 7).

References

BERNARD O., HOZIUM N. & TONEGAWA S. (1978) Sequences of mouse immunoglobulin light-chain genes before and after somatic changes. *Cell* **15**, 1133.

BRACK C. & TONEGAWA S. (1977) Variable and constant parts of the immunoglobulin light-chain gene are 1,250 nontranslated bases apart. *Proc. Nat. Acad. Sci. U.S.A.* **74**, 5652.

BRACK C., HIRAMA M., LENHARD-SCHULLER R. & TONEGAWA S. (1978) A complete immuno-globulin gene is created by somatic recombination. *Cell* **15**, 1.

COHN M., BLOMBERG B., GECKELER W., RASCHKE W., RIBLET R. & WEIGERT M. (1974) First-order considerations in analysing the generator of diversity. In SERCARZ E.E., WILLIAMSON A.R. & FOX C.E. (eds), *The Immune System*, p. 89. Academic Press, New York.

CROCE C.M., SHANDER M., MARTINIS J., CICUREL L., D'ANCONA G.G., DOLBY T.W. & KOPROWSKI H. (1979) Chromosomal location of the genes for human immunoglobulin heavy chains. *Proc. Nat. Acad. Sci. U.S.A.* **76**, 3416.

EARLY P.W., DAVIS M.M., KABACK D.B., DAVIDSON N. & HOOD L. (1979) Immunoglobulin heavy-chain gene organization in mice. *Proc. Nat. Acad. Sci. U.S.A.* **76**, 857.

HENGARTNER H., MEO T. & MULLER E. (1978) Assignment of genes for immunoglobulin and heavy chains to chromosomes 6 and 12 in mouse. *Proc. Nat. Acad. Sci. U.S.A.* **76**, 4494.

HONJO T. & KATOOKA T. (1978) Organization of immunoglobulin heavy-chains genes. *Proc. Nat. Acad. Sci. U.S.A.* **75**, 2140.

KINDT T.J. (1975) Rabbit immunoglobulin allotypes. *Adv. Immunol.* **21**, 35.

LERNER M.R., BOYLE J.A., MOUNT S.M., WOLIN S.L. & STEITZ J.A. (1980) Are snRNPs involved in splicing? *Nature* **283**, 220.

MAX E.E., SEIDMAN J.G. & LEDER P. (1979) Sequences of five potential recombination sites encoded close to an immunoglobulin constant region gene. *Proc. Nat. Acad. Sci. U.S.A.* **76**, 3450.

RABBITTS, T.H. (1978) Evidence for splicing of interrupted immunoglobulins variable and constant region sequences in nuclear RNA. *Nature* **275**, 291.

RABBITS T.H., FORSTER A., DUNNICK, W. & BENTLEY D.L. (1980) The role of gene deletion in the immunoglobulin heavy chain switch. *Nature* **283**, 351.

ROA, D.N., RUDIKOFF S., KRUTZSCH H. & POTTER M. (1979) Structural evidence for independent joining region gene in immunoglobulin heavy chains. *Proc. Nat. Acad. Sci. U.S.A.* **76**, 2890.

SAKANO H., ROGERS J.H., HUPPI K., BRACK C., TRAUNECKER A., MAKI R., WALL R. & TONEGAWA S. (1979a) Domains and the hinge region of an immunoglobulin heavy chain are encoded in separated DNA segments. *Nature* **277**, 627.

SAKANO H., HUPPI K., HEINRICH G. & TONEGAWA S. (1979b) Sequences at the somatic recombination sites of immunoglobulin light-chain genes. *Nature* **280**, 288.

SANGER F., NICKLEN S. & COULSON A.R. (1977) DNA-sequencing with chain-terminating inhibitors. *Proc. Nat. Acad. Sci. U.S.A.* **74**, 5463.

SEIDMAN J.G. & LEDER P. (1978) The arrangement and rearrangement of antibody genes. *Nature* **276**, 790.

SEIDMAN J.G., LEDER A., NAU M., NORMAN B. & LEDER P. (1978) Antibody diversity. *Science* **202**, 11.

WEIGERT M. & RIBLET R. (1978) The genetic control of antibody variable regions in the mouse. *Springer Sem. in Immunopathol.* **1**, 33.

Chapter 5
The Evolution of Immunoglobulins and Complement

5.1 Introduction

The evolution of a system of adaptive immunity is a vertebrate characteristic, and represents a more sophisticated system of defence than that found in lower animals, which are equipped with phagocytes alone. The unique characteristics of the adaptive immune response are specificity, amplification and memory.

There is sufficient information to discuss the evolution of two components of the immune system—antibodies and complement. Complement is an effector mechanism triggered through the recognition of the constant regions of antibodies reacting with antigen (see §2.6.2). The selective pressures acting in favour of retaining the present interactions between antibody and complement are clear. It is less obvious by what mechanism the genetic potential for their synthesis arose.

5.1.1 Evolutionary origins

The evolutionary origin of a protein may be determined from a comparison of its amino acid sequence with that of structurally related proteins derived from living representatives of ancestral life forms. More precise information can be derived from a comparison of the nucleotide sequences of the corresponding genes including the intervening and flanking sequences. The immunoglobulins of mammals are among the most extensively studied of all proteins, but there are relatively little data on most complement components or primitive immunoglobulins.

Both antibody and complement are found in elasmobranch fishes. Efforts to find them in lower animals have given conflicting results, and the elasmobranchs will be taken as the most primitive possessors of both. IgM seems to have been the first class of immunoglobulin to have evolved and survived. It forms a plausible basis for the evolution of other classes and part of this chapter explains mechanisms whereby this could be achieved.

5.2 Gene duplication

Gene duplication is of widespread evolutionary and functional significance. In evolutionary terms it provides additional copies of a gene which can then safely undergo mutation and selection leaving one copy to maintain its original function. Functionally gene duplication provides large numbers of identical genes coding for cellular components made in bulk such as the genes for ribosomal RNA. It also permits the development of a small number of variant forms of a protein each with slightly different functions. Classic examples of such duplicates are the genes coding for the different chains of the immunoglobulins or haemoglobins. It has been argued by Harris (1979) that 50 per cent of all enzyme activities may be coded by duplicate sets of genes.

There are two types of mechanism for creating duplicate genes. Tandem duplication results in two copies of the gene occurring in close proximity on the same chromosome whereas chromosomal duplication results in the rearrangement of fragments of chromosomes or in gross changes in the chromosome number. In the latter case the two copies of the gene lie on different chromosomes.

5.2.1 Tandem duplication

Tandem duplication of genes involves the doubling of a stretch of DNA on a chromosome. It can give rise to a new gene which codes for a polypeptide chain larger than its parent, or to a complete identical duplicate gene. Unequal crossing over is probably the most common mechanism for tandem duplication. When the chromatids pair during meiosis, the DNA strands align themselves homologously. If the alignment is imperfect, crossing over will give rise to two daughter chromatids of unequal length, one with a gene, or part of it, deleted, and the other with a tandem duplicate. Surviving examples of both kinds of product are well known: haptoglobin 2 is a result of the fusion of a large part of the Hp^{1F} allele with the Hp^{1S} allele (Fig. 5.1a). Haemoglobin Lepore has an abnormal globin chain whose N-terminal sequence is that of the δ chain and C-terminal sequence of the β chain. The genetic event which led to this involved the deletion of a part of the gene cluster coding for the globin chains (Fig. 5.1b).

The presence of tandem gene copies permits mutation to occur without compromising the essential function of the gene but tandem duplication is not without risks. Since the net DNA content of the gametes is not altered by unequal crossing over, some will be deprived of the genetic potential which has gone into the duplicate. Duplication of the genes, to give a large number of homologous sequences of DNA closely arranged on the chromosome, increases the likelihood of non-homologous pairing and unequal cross-overs. In the case of the nucleolar organizer genes of the frog Xenopus laevus, the very large number of copies carried in the germ line (200–300) give rise to a grave instability in the numbers carried by each oocyte. A significant proportion of these are deficient mutants, becoming sterile ova, a situation tolerable only where a species is prolific (Brown & David, 1968).

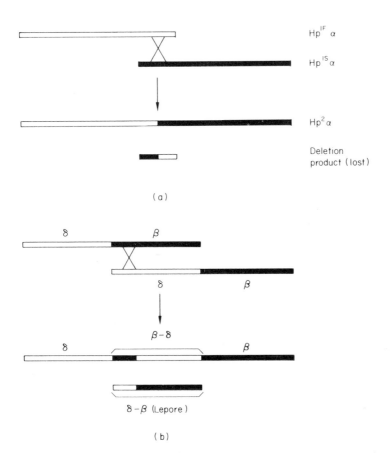

Fig. 5.1. Unequal crossing over. Unequal crossing over is the probable mechanism for the generation of the genes for $Hp^{2\alpha}$ and Hb Lepore. The first is an almost complete duplication product, the latter a deletion product.

5.2.2 Chromosomal duplication

There are many examples of related proteins being coded for by genes on different chromosomes. This can occur through chromosomal rearrangement by translocation of part of a chromosome either before or after tandem duplication, or by duplication of a whole chromosome by non-disjunction at meiosis. Indeed Ohno (1970) has argued that the development of individuals with a completely duplicated set of chromosomes (polyploidy) has been a crucial step in vertebrate evolution. Polyploidy is relatively common in fishes, but is incompatible with reproduction in species which use chromosomal sex determination, since XXXX, XXXY and XXYY individuals are sterile.

In chromosomal duplication the duplicate sets of genes are free to mutate to serve new functions and to evolve new control mechanisms different from those which operate on the parental genes.

The two types of gene duplication can be likened to features of a capitalist economy, which evolves by overproduction, adaptation and new overproduction. Tandem duplication is the stock-exchange bubble, confidence breeding over-confidence, then collapse. Chromosomal duplication is the opportunity for the tea-boy to make good, freed by emigration from old restraints and associations.

5.3 The evolution of immunoglobulins

The discovery that the genes for many proteins are split into several pieces by intervening sequences of untranslated nucleotides has important implication in understanding evolution (Crick, 1979). With the immunoglobulin chains the intervening sequences split the chains into pieces corresponding to individual domains and it is the evolution of domains that one has to consider (see Chapter 4). Both chromosomal and tandem duplication processes have been at work in the evolution of the immunoglobulins. We may imagine that a primordial immuno-globulin chain evolved by the tandem duplication of a gene which coded for a single domain. One of the copies specialized and may have reduplicated to provide a set of variable domains. The whole system seems to have undergone chromosomal duplication to give rise to κ-, λ- and heavy-chain precursor gene clusters on different chromosomes (Fig. 5.2).

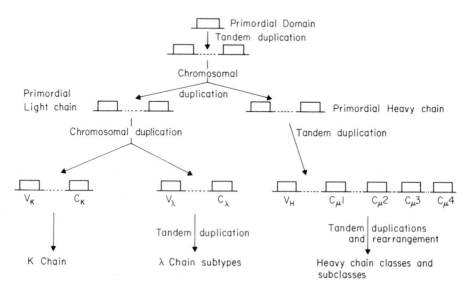

Fig. 5.2. The immunoglobulins seem to have evolved by a combination of tandem and chromosomal duplications of a gene which coded for a single domain. The scheme presented here is only one of a number of possibilities.

5.3.1 Evolution of heavy-chain classes

The complete amino acid sequences of at least one representative of α, γ, μ and ε classes have been determined. They show that it is impossible to construct a simple evolutionary tree for these chains. Comparison of the sequences, domain by domain, to determine the minimum number of mutations required to convert one sequence into another shows that the two most similar domains are the carboxy terminal domains of α and μ chains. Figure 5.3 shows the domains of each chain and indicates the domains closest in sequence. The problem in constructing a simple evolutionary tree can be appreciated from this figure and is most marked for the ε chain which appears to have domain similarities with three different chains. This would imply multiple recombination events between domains in the evolution of the molecule. In view of the intervening sequences between domains this is now a plausible explanation. The heavy-chain classes may represent a general phenomenon of new proteins evolving from parts of pre-existing genes (Tonegawa *et al.*, 1978).

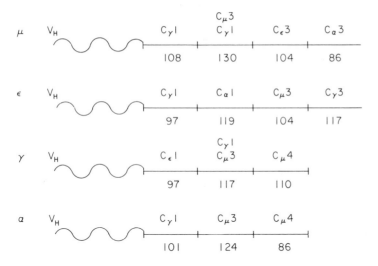

Fig. 5.3. Comparison of human C-region domains of different heavy-chain classes. For each chain the domain closest to it in sequence is shown above the line and the minimum number of mutations required to convert one domain to the other is shown below the line. (Adapted from Secher, 1979.)

5.3.2 Evolution of heavy-chain subclasses

As noted above (§ 5.2.1) tandem gene duplication is an unstable method for the generation of new genes. The existence of duplicates favours unequal crossing over, with consequent loss and duplication of genes. This effect is partially counteracted if the flanking and the intervening sequences of genes are not shared amongst the duplicated tandem copies (Seidman *et al.*, 1978) (see § 4.7). The number of sub-classes of IgG varies widely from species to species, with four in humans, two in guinea pigs and cows, and apparently only one in rabbits. This disparity in numbers itself suggests that the number of γ-chain genes fluctuates rapidly during evolution, and that speciation is often accompanied by either a collapse in the number of heavy-chain subclasses, or by the establishment of new subclasses. There is clear evidence for the recent evolution of subclasses in the case of the cow. The amino acid sequences of the two γ-chain subclasses are shown in Table 5.1. Since both chains have species-specific residues at positions 2 and 6 from the C-terminus, they must have a common cow-like ancestry. The $\gamma2$ subclass has a unique methionine residue at position 10, clearly indicating that this chain has evolved from a primordial cow-like $\gamma1$ chain. Subclasses seem to represent the 'current experiments' of immunoglobulin evolution and most are probably of neutral selective advantage. What is essential is that the capacity to synthesize subclasses of adaptive value is not lost.

5.3.3 *Evolution of light-chain subtypes*

As with the heavy chains the light-chain genes show evidence of current experiments in immunoglobulin evolution. In man the four λ C-region genes represent recent tandem gene duplication (see § 1.2.2) while in mice the whole of the DNA coding for V and C regions of the λ chain has been duplicated leading to a third light-chain type, called (unfortunately) λ_{II}.

5.3.4 *Immunoglobulin domains in other proteins*

Beta$_2$ microglobulin, a protein associated with several membrane glycoproteins (see § 6.11) has an amino acid sequence homology to a C-region domain and has clearly evolved from the same genes as the primordial immunoglobulin chain. One of the proteins that β_2 microglobulin associates with, HLA-B7, has been sequenced and part of the sequence has homology with an immunoglobulin C-region domain (see § 6.11). In this case the homologous region only represents one-quarter of the HLA molecule and it seems likely that this part of the molecule has evolved from the primordial immunoglobulin genes. The rest of the HLA molecule need not have evolved from the immunoglobulin genes, as intervening sequences in DNA favour evolution through rearrangement of fragments of DNA each coding for different successful structures (Blake, 1978). The immunoglobulin domain may represent such a structure and it is probable that it will appear in other proteins, particularly those associated with β_2 microglobulin. The nucleotides coding for the leader or signalling sequences on the N-terminal end of many secreted proteins may be another example of part of a protein with a separate evolutionary origin from the rest of the chain.

Table 5.1. C-terminal sequences of heavy chains

Chain	19	18	17	16	15	14	13	12	11	10	9	8	7	6	5	4	3	2	1
Sequence	(Met)	His	Glu	Ala	Leu	His	Asn	His	Tyr	Thr	Gln	Lys	Ser	Leu	Ser	Leu	Ser	Pro	Gly-COOH
Human γ1, γ2																			
Human γ3 Gm (−5)																			
Human γ4								Arg											
Rabbit γ																			Leu
Horse IgG(T) γ						Val	Glu					Ile	Asn-	Val		Arg			
Horse IgG γ														Val		His			
Bovine γ1											Met			Thr		Lys			Ala
Bovine γ2														Thr		Lys			Ala

All sequences identical to human γ1 except where shown. From Milstein and Feinstein (1968).

5.4 Allotypes and sporadic events

5.4.1 *Human heavy-chain allotypes*

These often cause confusion mainly because of lack of information and the fact that
the nomenclature keeps changing. The most recent nomenclature designates the
locus of the allotype but does not make clear what is an allele of what (see Table 5.2).

The latter is a real problem as well as a semantic one, since the Gm types usually
reflect single amino acid substitutions reflecting point mutations in the DNA
sequence coding for the γ chains (γ-chain cistrons). Intracistronic recombinations,
resulting from crossing over within the cistron, are rare events, and in their absence
mapping of markers by genetic methods is impossible. In classical genetic terms, any
unit which does not exhibit internal recombinations is a locus, and the markers in
the locus are alleles. In molecular terms this is not a very satisfactory definition, since
if one looks long enough, a recombination will be observed within the cistron,
provided that suitable markers are available with a space between them. The term
'homo-allele' has been used to describe the two DNA sequences which at a particular
point are mutually exclusive. In this sense G1m(3) and G1m(17) are homo-alleles
since they reflect two alternative amino acids at a single position (214) in the γ1
chain (Table 5.2). G1m(1) and nG1m(1) reflect two amino acid substitutions close
together. In practice, though we seek till Judgement Day, we shall probably never
observe the recombination of the sequences at this point because they are so close.

Table 5.2. Allotype-related
sequences in constant region
of human γ chains

Chain involved	Residue position	Residue	New nomenclature Numerical	New nomenclature Alphabetical
γ1	214	Arg	G1m(3)	G1m(f)
γ1		Lys	G1m(17)	G1m(z)
γ1	356/358	Asp/Leu	G1m(1)	G1m(a)
γ1, γ2, γ3		Glu/Met	nG1m(1)	nG1m(a)
γ3	296	Tyr	G3m(21)	G3m(g)
γ2, γ3		Phe	nG3(21)	nG3m(g)
γ3	436	Phe	G3m(11)	G3m(b⁰)
γ1, γ2, γ3		Tyr	nG3m(11)	nG3m(b⁰)
γ1, γ3, γ4	310	Leu	nG4m(a)	nG4m(a)
γ2, γ4		—*	nG4m(b)	nG4m(b)

* Residue deleted. Gm markers are on γ chains, G1m on γ1.
etc. From Secher (1979).

Since accurate location of the Gm markers is essentially impossible by genetic methods, they must be correlated with amino acid sequences. These will almost certainly have to be those of myeloma proteins, since homogeneity will be essential (see below). A number of proteins of each Gm type will have to be sequenced before the correlations can be regarded as firm, since individual proteins may have unique and unrepresentative point mutations. Few complete sequences are as yet available.

Allotypic markers and γ-chain subclasses are both relatively recent evolutionary events, and as a result, most of the individual Gm markers are confined to one subclass. Others, for instance nG1m(1) are expressed on all $\gamma 2$ and $\gamma 3$ molecules as well as on some $\gamma 1$ molecules. This arises because $\gamma 1$, $\gamma 2$ and $\gamma 3$ are tandem duplicates but in $\gamma 1$, a mutant has arisen, G1m(1), which is a true allele of nG1m(1) only in $\gamma 1$ chains. The nG1m(1) in $\gamma 2$ and $\gamma 3$ has been referred to as a non-antigen or isoallotype.

As a result of their recent evolution and close linkage, the heavy-chain allotypes tend to be inherited as groups of markers. Where a new mutant arises close to a pre-existing marker, it will be passed on in coupling linkage with that marker until a recombination occurs between them. There will be a tendency for the new marker to occur in the population in coupling rather than repulsion for many generations, a situation which makes the mapping problems severe throughout the system, but it does permit certain rare events to be very evident, for instance the discovery of the 'Lepore' immunoglobulins (see § 5.4.3).

5.4.2 Complex allotypes

With rabbits some of the allotypes represent single amino acid substitutions while the a and b locus allotypes are complex (Table 5.3) and due to multiple amino acid differences. The evolution of these complex allotypes is unlikely to be the same as the evolution of simple allotypes. Various schemes have been proposed: one is that the segregating gene is not a structural gene but a control gene which regulates the expression of one of a set of genes carried by all individuals; another is that sets of

Table 5.3. Commonly used allotypic markers on rabbit immunoglobulins

Ig chain	Locus	Alleles	Amino acid substitution (residue)
C_γ	d	11, 12	Met, Thr (225)
	e	14, 15	Thr, Ala (309)
C_κ	b	4, 5, 6, 9	Multiple
C_λ	c	7, 21	Unknown
V_H	a	1, 2, 3	Multiple

Adapted from Kindt (1975).

tandem genes have collapsed leaving a single representative of the set which is different in different individuals. For example, if there were a selective pressure to reduce the number of λ C-region genes in man (see Table 1.1) then in some individuals the remaining C_λ gene might be $\lambda 2$ while in others it could be $\lambda 4$, thus creating allotypes that had multiple amino acid substitutions. Gene collapse in this way could also be followed by further expansion.

5.4.3 'Lepore' heavy chains

'Lepore' heavy chains, like the classical haemoglobin Lepore, have the N-terminal sequence of the constant region of one subclass and the C-terminal sequence of another (Fig. 5.1). The 'Lepore' immunoglobulins are the best evidence that the human γ subclass genes are arranged in the order 4-2-3-1.

5.4.4 Structural variants of immunoglobulins

The most striking structural abnormalities are found in patients with heavy-chain disease proteins; these consist of part of an immunoglobulin heavy chain and no light chains. A large number of more subtle variant immunoglobulins have now been found in patients with plasmacytomas (Franklin & Frangione, 1975) or isolated as mutants of mouse plasmacytoma cell lines maintained *in vitro* (Adetugbo *et al.*, 1977; Secher *et al.*, 1977). A remarkable feature of many of these variants is that the deletions often involve entire domains, either a constant region domain or the hinge region, and deletions involving the V region terminate at the same position in the C region. The structure of the heavy-chain genes helps to explain the non-random nature of some of these deletions (Fig. 5.4) since a deletion starting anywhere in one intervening sequence and finishing anywhere in the next would remove a complete domain from the final protein (Sakano *et al.*, 1979). Alternatively, a mutation may cause the splicing enzymes to jump to the next intervening sequence and delete a domain sequence present in heterogeneous nuclear RNA from the mRNA (Frangione & Franklin, 1979).

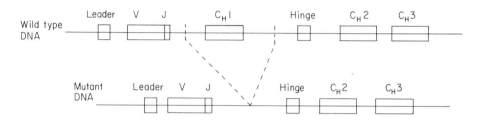

Fig. 5.4. A possible explanation for non-random mutation in immunoglobulin C regions. The figure shows the gene for a heavy chain in a cell making immunoglobulin of that class.

5.5 Complement

As indicated earlier (§ 5.1.1) there is a dearth of structural information on complement components. However, there is growing knowledge of their genetics. This will be covered first since speculation on their evolution derives from it.

5.5.1 Complement deficiencies

The known deficiencies of the human complement system are set out in Table 5.4. Their association with human disease is discussed further in Chapters 8 and 16.

Table 5.4. Complement deficiency in man

Component	Total no. of affected subjects	Healthy	Immune complex disease	Defects in bacterial immunity
C3	5	0	2	4
C3b inactivator	4	1	0	3
C5	4	1	1	2
C6	5	1	0	4
C6+C7	1	1	0	0
C8	9	4	3	2
C1r	3	0	3	2
C4	2	0	2	0
C2	>40	~20	~20	0
C1̄ inhibitor	many		18	0

Adapted from Lachmann and Hobart (1979).

Deficiencies are also found in experimental animals: C4 in guinea pigs, C5 in mice and C6 in rabbits and hamsters. Complete absence of a component does not necessarily imply that the gene is missing. The gene could be present but there may be a defect in gene expression or release of the product from the cell.

C1̄ inhibitor deficiency is expressed as a disease in heterozygotes and this is inherited as a dominant trait. There is no recorded case of a homozygous C1̄ inhibitor-deficient individual but this is not good evidence for it being lethal, since the frequency of the event must be very small, perhaps 10^{-7} or fewer zygotes, and would usually demand the union of two affected individuals.

Functional deficiency of complement components is the result of either lack of synthesis, hypercatabolism (which is usually a secondary phenomenon) or synthesis of a dysfunctional molecule. C1̄ inhibitor deficiency can be caused by genetic defects of the first or third kind, and can lead to deficiency of C4 and C2 of the second kind. In the cases of C6 deficiency in rabbits and C4 deficiency in guinea pigs, antisera against the missing component can be raised by immunizing the deficient animal. These antisera cross-react with the homologous component from a large number of species, indicating that the asynthetic defect is complete.

5.5.2 Complement polymorphisms

Genetically-determined charge polymorphisms have been demonstrated for many of the complement components (see Lachmann & Hobart, 1979). The less common alleles of Factor B represent mutants in a different part of the molecule from the common allelic differences, since on cleavage during activation, common alleles go with the Ba fragment, the rare ones with the Bb fragment.

The situation with C4 is complex. The two common electrophoretic variants, C4F and C4S, segregate differently in different individuals. In some heterozygotes C4F and C4S segregate independently as if they were true alleles, while in others they segregate together and behave as tandem genes. Until more is known about the DNA structure it is impossible to interpret unambiguously this finding but it may represent a relatively recent mismatch cross-over occurring in a heterozygous person. The red cell antigens, Rodgers and Chido, have been shown to be C4 (F and S respectively) adsorbed onto the surface of the red cells (O'Neill et al., 1978).

5.5.3 Genetic linkage of complement components

The most striking finding is the linkage of complement components to the MHS. In man, C2, C4 and Factor B lie close to HLA-B. In mice and guinea pigs C4 is linked to the MHS, and in rhesus monkeys Factor B is linked to the MHS. It is important to know if all three components associated with HLA are also associated with the MHS in other vertebrate species. Of the other complement genes C6 and C7 have been shown to be closely linked (Lachmann & Hobart, 1979).

5.5.4 The evolution of complement

The complement system divides into three groups of components involved in the classical, alternative and lytic or terminal pathways. It has been suggested (Lachmann & Hobart, 1979) that the original complement system, the 'archaeo-complement', consisted of C3 and Factor B. The functions of this primitive system might have been to augment inflammatory reactions following splitting of C3 to C3b by leucocyte enzymes and subsequent amplification via the C3b feedback cycle. The classical and lytic pathways as we now understand them are envisaged as being derived by gene duplication from this 'archaeo-system' (Fig. 5.5). The lack of detailed information on the structure of genes for complement components makes it difficult

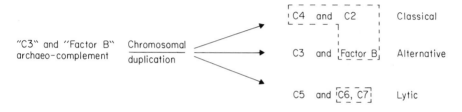

Fig. 5.5. A possible scheme for the evolution of complement. The broken boxes enclose genetically linked components. (Adapted from Lachmann & Hobart, 1979.)

to test this hypothesis but the physicochemical and biological similarities between the components are compatible with it. The three proteins C3, C4 and C5 are all made as a 200,000 M.W. precursor and function in the complement-reaction pathways after cleavage of a small 9,000 M.W. fragment from the N-terminal end of the α or heavy chain (see Chapter 3). The cleaved fragments interact with other components of the complement system giving rise to reactive complexes; C3b with Factor B forms C3b,Bb (the alternative pathway C3 convertase) and C4b with C2 generates C4b,2a (the classical pathway C3 convertase). Both are proteolytic enzymes but the third member of the set, C5b, which reacts with C6, is not proteolytic and initiates the self assembly of the terminal components leading to cell lysis. The properties of C2 and Factor B are also compatible with the relationship in Fig. 5.5. They are physicochemically similar and occupy a similar reaction position in the classical and alternative pathways respectively (see Chapter 3). However, there is at present no convincing evidence to relate C6 and C7 to Factor B as suggested in Fig. 5.5. Linkage studies are compatible with C3, C4 and C5 evolving as chromosomal duplications and with C6 and C7 and possibly C2 and Factor B evolving as tandem gene duplicates. The association of C4, C2 and Factor B with the MHS would require additional selective pressure to have brought these genes together.

Of the complement components not shown in Fig. 5.5, C1r, C1s and Factor D are probably evolutionarily related. All three are serine histidine esterases and in active form have molecular weights of 25,000. C1r and C1s have considerable sequence homologies but there is little sequence information for Factor D.

References

ADETUGBO K., MILSTEIN C. & SECHER D.S. (1977) Molecular analysis of spontaneous somatic mutants. *Nature* **265**, 299.

BLAKE C.C.F. (1978) Do genes in pieces imply proteins in pieces? *Nature* **273**, 267.

BROWN D.D. & DAVID I.B. (1968) Specific gene amplifications in oocytes. *Science* **160**, 272.

CRICK F.H.C. (1979) Split genes and RNA splicing. *Science* **204**, 264.

FRANGIONE B. & FRANKLIN E.C. (1979) Split immunoglobulin genes and human heavy-chain deletion mutants. *J. Immunol.* **122**, 1177.

FRANKLIN E.C. & FRANGIONE B. (1975) Structural variants of human and murine immuno-globulins. *Contemp. Topics of Molec. Immunol.* **4**, 89.

HARRIS H. (1979) Multilocus enzymes in man. *CIBA Symp.* (NS) **66**, 187.

KINDT T.J. (1975) Rabbit immunoglobulin allotypes: structure, immunology and genetics. *Adv. Immunol.* **21**, 35.

LACHMANN P.J. & HOBART M.J. (1979) The genetics of the complement system. *CIBA Symp.* (NS) **66**, 231.

MILSTEIN C.P. & FEINSTEIN A. (1968) Comparative studies of two types of bovine immuno-globulin G heavy-chains. *Biochem. J.* **107**, 559.

OHNO S. (1970) *Evolution by Gene Duplication.* Springer-Verlag, Berlin.

O'NEILL G.J., YANG S.Y., TIGOLI J., BERGER R. & DUPONT B. (1978) Chido and Rodgers blood groups are distinct antigenic components of human complement C4. *Nature* **273**, 668.

SAKANO H., ROGERS J.H., HUPPI K., BRACK C., TRAUNECKER A., MAKI R., WALL R. & TONEGAWA S. (1979) Domains and the hinge region of an immunoglobulin heavy chain are encoded in separate DNA segments. *Nature* **277**, 627.

SECHER D.S. (1979) Structure of immunoglobulins. *Int. Rev. Biochem.* **23**, 1.

SECHER D.S., MILSTEIN C. & ADETUGBO K. (1977) Somatic mutants and antibody diversity, heavy-chain disease variants. *Immunological Rev.* **36**, 51.

SEIDMAN, J.G., LEDER A., NAN M., NORMAN B. & LEDER P. (1978) Antibody diversity. *Science* **202**, 11.

TONEGAWA S., MAXAM A.M., TIZARD R., BERNARD O. & GILBERT W. (1978) Sequence of a mouse germ-line gene for a variable region of an immunoglobulin light chain. *Proc. Nat. Acad. Sci. U.S.A.* **75**, 1485.

Further reading

KLEIN J. (1977) Evolution and Function of the MHS: Facts and Speculation. In GOTZE D. (ed.), *Major Histocompatibility System in Man and Animals,* p. 339. Springer-Verlag, Berlin.

Chapter 6
The Major Histocompatibility System

6.1 Introduction

The major histocompatibility system (MHS) plays a major rôle in the immune response. It is known as the MHS for historical reasons since the molecules of this system were first recognized as classical transplantation antigens on the cell surface. Today most of our knowledge of the MHS in mice (*H-2*) is derived from studies on inbred and recombinant strains of mice. Studies of the MHS in man (HLA) originated with the discovery of antibodies in multigravid women or polytransfused individuals, which reacted with human white blood cells.

The products of the MHS occur as transmembrane proteins, and in vertebrates show striking similarities in their biochemistry, tissue distribution and function. This chapter is concerned with the serology, biochemistry and genetics of the MHS in mice and man.

6.2 Inbred and congeneic mouse strains

Inbred mice are derived by repeated brother–sister mating for at least 20 generations (5 years). The offspring finally arising from this incestuous effort are genetically homogeneous with differences between mice being 1.0 per cent or less. Different inbred strains of mice differ at many genetic regions and not solely at the MHS.

Coisogeneic mice differ only at a single locus and arise through a point mutation within an inbred strain. Congeneic mice on the other hand are bred to differ at any particular locus using the breeding programme outlined in Fig. 6.1. With all congeneic mice it is difficult to be precise about how much genetic information on either side of the marker gene has been transferred into the background strain and apparently identical congeneic lines prepared by separate breeding protocols may not be entirely the same. During the construction of *H-2* congeneic lines useful recombinants within *H-2* can sometimes be isolated.

6.3 The *H-2* complex

The *H-2* complex in mice is in the IX linkage group (17th chromosome) and the *H-2* genes carried on an individual chromosome form an *H-2* haplotype. Different

Fig. 6.1. A breeding regime for producing congeneic C57Bl mice. To construct a C57Bl mouse (*H-2^b*) carrying *H-2^d* from BALB/c; mice from each strain are mated with each other and the F1 offspring backcrossed on to C57Bl. Half the progeny of each backcross generation will be heterozygous *H-2$^{b/d}$* whilst the rest will be homozygous *H-2^b*. The *H-2* heterozygous mice are identified and mated to C57Bl so that at each successive backcross generation the *H-2$^{b/d}$* mice become more C57Bl like. After more than 10 backcross matings the heterozygous animals are mated with each other and 25 per cent of the offspring will be homozygous *H-2^d* (derived from BALB/c) carried in a C57Bl background. The bars under each mouse represent the part of 17th Chromosome carrying *H-2*.

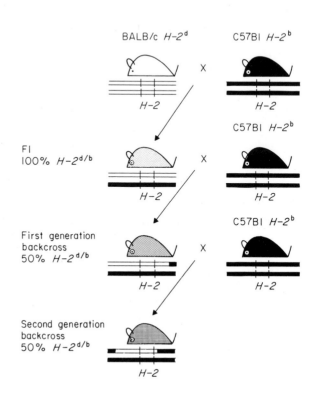

haplotypes are designated by small letters and numbers as superscripts, e.g. *H-2^a*, *H-2^b*, *H-2^{i3}*. *H-2* is not the only genetic region involved in histocompatibility and there is a large number of minor histocompatibility loci called *H-1*, *H-3*, *H-4* and so on. Their rôle in tissue compatibility will be discussed in Chapter 19.

6.3.1 H-2 *serology*

Much of our understanding of the *H-2* complex comes from the use of antisera to the products of the genes in this region. Although alloantisera were originally noticed in the serum of mice which had rejected tumour or skin grafts, it is now more common to raise anti-H-2 sera by a combination of skin grafting and immunization with lymphoid cells between congeneic strains. The antisera are tested for their ability to cause complement-mediated lysis of lymphocytes.

An H-2 antigenic specificity is defined by the pattern of reactivity of a given antiserum on a standard panel of different mouse strains. Most sera contain antibodies which react with cells belonging to haplotypes other than those used for immunization. Each separate antigenic determinant (or specificity) is assigned an arabic number. The correlation between serologically defined antigenic specificities and differences in amino acid sequences is not yet known.

6.3.2 The H-2 map

The H-2 complex can be divided into different regions. In most cases the boundaries of the regions are defined by recombinant strains of mice. It is currently accepted that each H-2 haplotype consists of at least six regions (K, I, S, G, D and L) with the I region being further divided into subregions I-A. I-B, I-J, I-E and I-C. A gene map of chromosome 17 and a detailed map of H-2 are shown in Fig. 6.2.

With H-2 recombinant mice it is important to designate the haplotype origin of the various H-2 regions. Table 6.1 shows that when intra-H-2 recombination occurs the recombinant chromosomes carry parts of each parental H-2 haplotype. These differences are similarly expressed at an antigenic and functional level.

6.4 The regions of H-2

It is important to remember that although each region is associated with a particular locus (or gene) there may be more than one locus per region. A recombination distance of 0.5 centimorgans represents enough DNA to code for 1,000 proteins. However, the organization of the eukaryotic genome makes it very unlikely that the

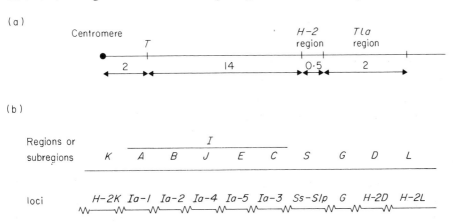

Fig. 6.2. (a) A simplified gene map of chromosome 17. The numbers represent approximate map distances in centimorgans. (b) A detailed map of H-2. The overall recombination frequency from H-2K to H-2D is about 0.5 centimorgans. The order of H-2D and H-2L is not known as so far no recombinants between H-2D and H-2L have been found. The nomenclature for the I-region loci must not be confused with the numbered Ia specificities (see Table 6.3).

Table 6.1. Various commonly used *H-2* recombinant mouse strains

Strain	*H-2* haplotype	Parental haplotype	Origin of *H-2* regions K A B J E C S G D
A/J	*a*	*k/d*	*k* *k* *k* *k* *k* | *d* *d* *d* *d*
B10.A(2R)	*h2*	*a/b*	*k* *k* *k* *k* *k* *d* *d* | . | *b*
B10.A(3R)	*i3*	*b/a*	*b* *b* *b* *b* | *k* *d* *d* *d* *d*
B10.A(4R)	*h4*	*a/b*	*k* *k* | *b* *b* *b* *b* *b* *b* *b*
B10.A(5R)	*i5*	*b/a*	*b* *b* *b* | *k* *k* *d* *d* *d* *d*
A.AL	*a1*	*k/d*	*k* *k* *k* *k* *k* *k* *k* *k* | *d*
A.TL	*t1*	*s/al*	*s* | *k* *k* *k* *k* *k* *k* *k* *d*
A.TH	*t2*	*s/a*	*s* *s* *s* *s* *s* *s* *s* *s* | *d*

The vertical bars represent the position where the crossover occurred. '.' indicates that the origin of the region is not known. Adapted from Klein *et al.* (1978).

MHS codes for such a large number of proteins but there are certainly more than the ten regions in Fig. 6.2.

6.4.1 K *and* D *regions*

The products of the *K* and *D* regions are detected serologically and found on most cell types including lymphocytes, although the number of molecules per cell varies (e.g. red blood cells have less *H-2* antigen than lymphocytes). Table 6.2 shows the distribution of the antigenic determinants found on the K and D products of

Table 6.2. Public and private antigenic specificities of *K* and *D* region alleles

H-2 haplo-type	K-region Private	Public	Found in D	D region Private	Public	Found in K
b	33	39	5, 28, 35, 36	2	6	28
d	31	8, 34	3, 28	4	6, 13, 41, 42, 43, 49	3, 28, 35, 36
f	26	8, 37, 39		9	6	
k	23	8, 11, 25, 45	1, 3, 5	32	49	1, 3, 5
p	16	8, 34, 37, 38	1, 3, 5, 28, 35	22	6, 41, 49	1, 3, 5, 28, 35
q	17	11, 34, 45	1, 3, 5	30	6, 13, 49	3, 28
r	18	8, 11, 25, 45	1, 3, 5, 28	?	6, 49	1, 3, 5, 28
s	19	45	1, 3, 5	12	6, 42, 49	28, 36

Adapted from Festenstein and Demant (1978).

commonly used *H-2* haplotypes of independent origin. They can be grouped into private specificities which are unique to K or D of a particular haplotype and public specificities which are shared between haplotypes and are either restricted to K or D or present on both. All three classes of antigenic determinant occur on the same molecule. Some molecules carrying the public specificity 28, lack the private antigenic determinants associated with K or D and are the products of another gene *H-2L*, closely associated with *H-2D* (Demant & Neauport-Santes, 1978). So far no recombinant has occurred to separate *H-2L* from *H-2D* and the private specificities of *H-2L* have not yet been identified.

6.4.2 The I region

The antigenic determinants coded for by genes in the *I* region are known as the *I* region associated or Ia antigens. These are expressed predominantly on B lymphocytes, macrophages, Langerhans cells, thymus epithelial cells but not detected on red cells, platelets and resting T lymphocytes. Table 6.3 shows the distribution of the first reported Ia specificities amongst different mouse strains and the different *I* subregions. Of the *I* subregions, *I-A* is best characterized and the majority of the Ia specificities are found in this region. *I-B* is least well characterized, containing no Ia specificities and is defined by the immune response pattern of one recombinant strain. *I-B* may not exist, as the pattern of immune response defining the region can be explained by complementation of immune response genes (see Chapter 12). The *I-J* subregion codes for molecules found on the surface of suppressor T cells or their soluble suppressor factors (see Chapter 10).

Table 6.3. Ia specificities in independent haplotypes

Strain	*H-2* haplotype	*I-A*	*I-E/I-C*	Unassigned
B10	*b*	3, 8, 9, 15, 20	—	—
B10.D2	*d*	8, 11,* 15, 16	6, 7, 23	—
A.CA	*f*	1, 5, 17, 18	—	14
B10.K	*k*	1, 2, 3, 15, 17, 18, 19	7, 22	—
B10.P	*p*	5, 13	6, 7, 21*	—
C3H.Q	*q*	3, 5, 9, 13, 16	—	10
B10.RIII	*r*	1, 3, 5, 12, 17, 19	7	—
B10.S	*s*	4, 5, 9, 12, 17, 18	—	—

The specificities marked with an asterisk have been assigned by co-precipitation. Adapted from Klein *et al.* (1978).

6.4.3 Ss, Slp and G

Ss and Slp are antigenic determinants on a serum protein of 200,000 M.W. This protein is C4, a component of the classical complement pathway, consisting of three covalently-linked polypeptide chains all derived from a common precursor. It is possible that there are two copies of the gene for this precursor and Ss and Slp represent pseudo-alleles (Roos *et al.*, 1978).

The G locus codes for a red cell antigen, now shown to be C4 absorbed to the red cell surface.

6.5. The *Tla* region

To the right hand of *H-2D* there are several loci which code for lymphocyte membrane proteins. The relationship of these genes to *H-2* is not clear but the products of some share structural features with the products of *H-2* (see § 6.13.2). A map of the *Tla* region is shown in Fig. 6.3.

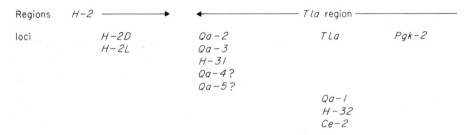

Fig. 6.3. Map of the *Tla* region. Where the order of the loci is not known they have been placed in vertical columns. See § 6.5 for description of the loci. (Adapted from Flaherty, 1978.)

The products of the *Tla* locus, the TL antigens, are found on thymocytes and certain mouse leukaemias. The different alleles of *Tla* are distinguished by six different antigenic determinants (TL1–TL6) present on the same molecule but in different combinations (Table 6.4). There are two puzzling features about the expression of TL; leukaemic T cells in TL⁻ mice express TL antigens and the amount of H-2D expressed on thymocytes varies inversely with the expression of TL.

The *Tla* region has at least five further loci (*Qa 1–5*) which code for membrane molecules. Qa-1, Qa-2 and Qa-3 have been identified by alloantisera and Qa-4 and Qa-5 by monoclonal antibodies. The distribution of these products on lymphocyte subpopulations is discussed in Chapter 9. Unlike many of the other loci in the *Tla* and *H-2* regions there are only two alleles at each *Qa* locus, one of which appears to be a null allele since no antisera have been found which detect its products.

Other loci in the *Tla* region include two histocompatibility loci, *H-31* and *H-32* which determine skin and tumour graft rejection. Finally there are genes which

Table 6.4. *Tla* alleles and TL
specificities

| Prototype strain | Allele | TL phenotype on | |
		Thymus	Leukaemic thymus cells
A	*a*	1, 2, 3, 5, 6	1, 2, 3, 5, 6 or -ve
C57Bl/6	*b*	-ve	1, 2, 4 or -ve
BALB/c	*c*	2	1, 2 or -ve
A.CA	*d*	1, 2, 3, 6	nt
P	*e*	1, 2, 3, 5	nt

nt=not tested. Adapted from Flaherty (1978).

control isoenzyme variation of the two enzymes, kidney catalase (*Ce-2*) and phosphoglycerate kinase (*Pgk-2*).

6.6 The *T-t* complex

This complex is involved in the control of differentiation and lies some 14 recombination units to the left of *H-2*. For a detailed discussion of the *T-t* complex see Klein and Hammerberg (1977) and Bennett (1975). Certain mutants in this region influence the genetics of the *H-2* complex and will be discussed again later. In brief, recessive lethal mutants (*t*) when combined with the recessive lethal (*T*) produce tail-less fertile mice. By using *T* as a marker strain it is possible to isolate different lethal *t* mutants which fall into six complementation groups.

6.7 The HLA system

The major histocompatibility system in man (HLA) is coded by a genetic region located on the short arm of chromosome 6. Siblings identical for this region can exchange and accept grafts much more readily than non-identical siblings.

6.7.1 HLA *serology*

When anti-HLA antisera were first grouped according to their reaction patterns, it was found that certain groups seemed to detect alleles and the HLA antigens which they defined were given numbers. At first, only two segregant series of antigens were discovered, HLA-A and HLA-B, but the discovery of antisera with discordant reaction patterns showed the existence of a further locus, *HLA-C*. As all three loci are closely linked, alleles are usually inherited *en bloc* as haplotypes. In family studies, rare recombinants between the loci have been observed.

6.7.2 HLA *map*

Fig. 6.4 shows a map of the short arm of chromosome 6 and a detailed map of the *HLA* region. *HLA-A*, *-B*, and *-C* correspond to *H-2K* and *D* while *HLA-DR* (which in all probability is the product of several different loci) corresponds to *H-2I*. It will be seen from Figs 6.4 and 6.2 that the order of corresponding loci is different in mouse and man. In mice the *I* region lies inside *H-2K* and *D* while in man *DR* lies outside the *HLA-A*, *-B*, and *-C* loci. A comparison with other species shows that the mouse is the exception so far.

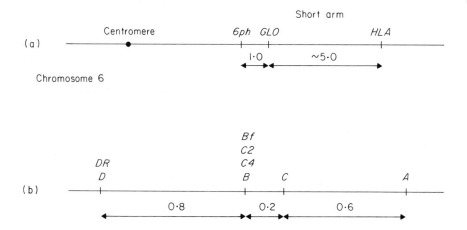

Fig. 6.4. (a) A genetic map of the short arm of chromosome 6 and (b) the *HLA* complex. *GLO* codes for glyoxalase I and *6ph* is a heterochromatic region in band ph. The order of genes coding for C2, C4, Factor B (Bf) and HLA-B is not known. The numbers represent approximate map distances in centimorgans.

6.8 *HLA* loci

6.8.1 *HLA-A*, *-B*, *and -C*

HLA-A, -B and -C determinants are found on most cells and a list of currently recognized antigens together with their frequency in European Caucasoids is shown in Table 6.5. New antigens are still being described.

It should be emphasized that many antisera do not precisely define an allele. These extra reactions represent either a mixture of specificities in the antiserum or cross-reaction of a particular antibody with the products of more than one allele. Some cross-reacting groups are shown in Fig. 6.5 and these suggest that alleles of HLA-A and HLA-B have many common determinants analogous to the public specificities of H-2K and D. Another example of cross-reaction amongst HLA-B

Table 6.5. *HLA-A, -B* and *-C* locus gene frequencies

Allele	Frequency (%)	Allele	Frequency (%)	Allele	Frequency (%)
A1	15.8	*B5*	5.9	*Cw1*	4.8
A2	27.0	*B7*	10.4	*Cw2*	5.4
A3	12.6	*B8*	9.2	*Cw3*	9.4
Aw23 } *A9*	2.4	*B12*	16.6	*Cw4*	12.6
Aw24	8.8	*B13*	3.2	*Cw5*	8.4
A25 } *A10*	2.0	*B14*	2.4	*Cw6*	12.6
A26	3.9	*B18*	6.2	Blank	46.7
A11	5.1	*B27*	4.6		
A28	4.4	*B15*	4.8		
A29	5.8	*Bw38* } *Bw16*	2.0		
Aw30	3.9	*Bw39*	3.5		
Aw31	2.3	*B17*	5.7		
Aw32	2.9	*Bw21*	2.2		
Aw33	0·7	*Bw22*	3.6		
Blank	2.2	*Bw35*	9.9		
		B37	1.1		
		B40	8.1		
		Bw41	1.2		
		Blank	2.4		

The allele frequencies are for European Caucasoids. For further information see Joysey and Wolf (1978) (see p.90). Adapted from Bodmer and
Bodmer (1978).

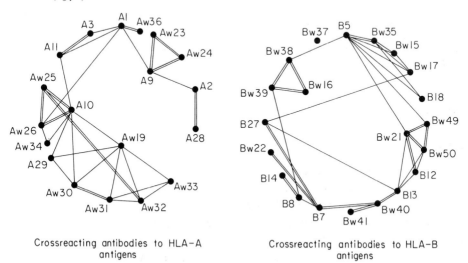

Crossreacting antibodies to HLA—A antigens

Crossreacting antibodies to HLA—B antigens

Fig. 6.5. Cross-reacting antibodies to HLA-A and HLA-B antigens. Double rules signify a
greater extent of cross-reactivity than single rules. Taken from van Rood (1980) and Albert *et
al.* (1980).

molecules is the allelic system BW4 and BW6 found on all HLA-B molecules. As more specificities of this type are recognized it would be better to describe HLA-A and B as a series of numbered determinants rather than as one-name alleles.

6.8.2 HLA-D and HLA-DR

HLA-D is defined by a mixed lymphocyte reaction and differences in HLA-D will lead to cell proliferation. On the other hand HLA-DR is defined by a serological reaction using antisera that have been absorbed with platelets to remove antibodies to HLA-A, B and C. These sera detect determinants on B lymphocytes and macrophages which are analogous to the Ia determinants in mice. There is a good but not complete correlation between HLA-D and determinants defined by selected anti-HLA-DR antisera. There are at least two and possibly more *HLA-DR* loci and it is too soon to know the numbers of alleles at the different loci (Lampson and Levy 1980).

6.8.3 Complement components

The genes for Factor B, C2 and C4 lie in the *HLA* region close to *HLA-B*. Polymorphism of C4 is responsible for the Rodgers and Chido red blood cell antigens through the absorption of C4 to the surface of the cell (see § 5.5.2).

6.9 Special features of the genetics of the MHS

6.9.1 Extent of polymorphism

A feature of some loci in the MHS is that in an outbred population there is a very large number of different alleles. Finding a large number of different alleles at one locus is not in itself unusual (for example the β chain of haemoglobin) but normally two or three alleles will account for more than 95 per cent of the gene pool. This is not the case with the MHS loci as can be seen from Table 6.5. In mice a total of 56 alleles at *H-2K* and 45 at *H-2D* have been described. The *HLA-D* and *H-2I* region loci show similar but less extensive polymorphism. A consequence of this polymorphism is that individuals in a random breeding population are very unlikely to be homozygous in all the loci at the MHS. It has been argued frequently that the maintenance of this form of polymorphism requires some selection, possibly against homozygosity at these loci. We will discuss in Chapters 11 and 12 the relationship between the products of the MHS and the range of diversity of the immune response of T cells. This relationship may provide a selective advantage to individuals carrying certain alleles by conferring resistance to particular diseases and in this way favour the spread of new genes through the population (Bodmer, 1972).

6.9.2 Linkage disequilibrium

In a random breeding population which has reached equilibrium, the frequency with which a particular pair of alleles at different loci occur on the same chromosome will be the product of the frequencies of the two alleles. If an allele p of one locus has a frequency of 0.05, and q the allele of a second locus has a frequency of 0.2, then p and q should occur together on the same chromosome with a frequency of $(0.05 \times 0.2) = 0.01$. This holds true for the population irrespective of whether p and q are unlinked or linked. In a population which has reached true equilibrium, linked alleles will be randomly distributed throughout the population as a result of past recombinations. When the actual frequency of a pair of alleles occurring together is significantly larger or smaller than the product of the frequencies of the two individual alleles, then the alleles are said to be in linkage disequilibrium. This may reflect a system in which natural selection acts in favour of or against particular combinations of alleles, or a system in which insufficient time has elapsed since the origin of the alleles to ensure random mixing of linked genes. The closer genes are together, the more generations are required to spread the alleles throughout a population. The difference between the observed and the expected haplotype frequency is a measure of linkage disequilibrium. In man several pairs of HLA alleles show linkage disequilibrium. For example, in Caucasoids, the combinations A1 with B8, A3 with B7, and B8 with DRW3 occur more frequently as a haplotype than would be expected from the frequency of the individual alleles (Fig. 6.6). In these cases sufficient time has elapsed since the appearance of the alleles to provide for their random mixing. Therefore this linkage disequilibrium is due to selection. On the other hand the linkage disequilibrium between alleles at HLA-B and HLA-C is probably due to the close linkage of these two loci. The existence of linkage disequilibrium is important in understanding the association of HLA antigens and disease and will be discussed further in Chapter 18.

6.9.3 Mutants of H-2

All genes are liable to spontaneous mutation and those coding for histocompatibility antigens are no exception. Skin grafts exchanged within a given inbred strain are normally accepted, but rejected when a mutant in histocompatibility genes is used. Being a rare event this requires a mammoth skin grafting programme and so far over 200,000 exchange skin grafts have revealed about 60 mutants, half of which occur within H-2. Inbred strains are derived from the mutants and then used in complementation tests to determine the position of the mutant within H-2 (Klein, 1978). Most of the mutations reported so far map within K, D or L regions of H-2, possibly reflecting the importance of these regions to skin-graft rejection (see Chapter 19).

The mutation rate is different for different alleles, with the highest mutation rate

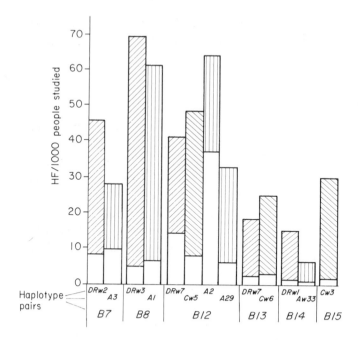

Fig. 6.6. Examples of linkage disequilibrium in *HLA*. The histogram shows the haplotype frequency (HF) and the proportion of that frequency attributable to linkage disequilibrium. ▨ HLA-B, DR; ▨ HLA-B, C; ▥ HLA-B, A. (Taken from Bodmer & Bodmer, 1978).

of about 2×10^{-4} mutants per locus per gamete occurring in K^b. The other alleles of *H-2K* and alleles of other loci in *H-2* have mutation rates of about 4×10^{-5}. These mutation rates are about one to two orders of magnitude higher than those for other genes not associated with *H-2*. The two possible reasons for this are that graft rejection is a very sensitive assay for mutants and/or the DNA sequences for these regions have above average mutation rates. If the latter were true then it would help to explain the extensive polymorphism associated with *H-2* genes. *H-2* mutants are useful for understanding the biology and biochemistry of the products of *H-2*.

6.9.4 *The* T-t *complex and* H-2

In mice the *T-t* complex can have a marked effect on *H-2* through two unusual properties of certain *t* alleles. First, they can suppress recombination between *t* and *H-2*. Second, with heterozygous *t/+* male mice the frequency of transmission to their offspring of the mutant *t* allele, rather than the wild type, is much higher than the expected 1:1 ratio, indeed it can be as high as 20:1. Surprisingly *t* alleles with these two properties occur with an average frequency of 20 per cent in wild mouse populations. Bearing in mind that *t/t* homozygotes are lethal and that *t* alleles suppress recombination between themselves and *H-2*, the effect of this high frequency of *t* will be to further reduce the number of homozygotes at *H-2* in a breeding deme of mice.

6.10 Biochemistry of membrane proteins

Many of the products of the MHS occur as cell surface proteins. Cell membrane proteins are usually free floating in the two-dimensional plane of the membrane and occur either as integral or peripheral membrane proteins (see Fig 6.7). Integral membrane proteins interact with the lipid bilayer, require detergent for their removal from the membrane and are often transmembrane proteins. Peripheral membrane proteins are more loosely attached and freed by milder treatments such as low pH or high ionic strength. Many transmembrane proteins are asymmetrical with their N-terminal regions on the outside of the cell and their C-terminal ends available

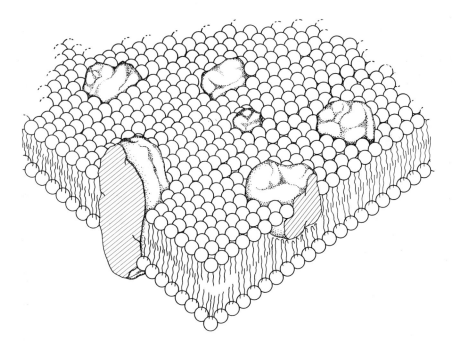

Fig. 6.7. The fluid mosaic model of membrane structure. The spheres represent the hydrophilic heads of the lipid molecules; the hydrophobic side chains are represented by the thin wavy lines. The bulky objects represent the integral membrane proteins 'floating' in the lipid bilayer with hydrophobic regions in contact with the lipid side chains and their hydrophilic regions exposed to the aqueous phase on the outside or the inside of the cell. (Taken from Singer & Nicholson, 1972.)

to the cytoplasm. There are other asymmetrical features of membranes, for example, all the membrane carbohydrate, whether attached to protein or lipid, is on the outside surface of the membrane.

Most cell membrane proteins are present in small amounts, usually about 10^4–10^5 molecules per cell. A common approach to their isolation for biochemical analysis is to radiolabel the cell-surface molecules, detergent-lyse the cell and precipitate the labelled membrane proteins with antibody. The isolated proteins can be further purified and characterized by SDS polyacrylamide gel electrophoresis. It is even possible to determine the amino acid sequence of the purified membrane proteins by using radioactive techniques or conventional sequencing procedures on material isolated from kilograms of cells. It is now easier to clone and sequence the genes of the MHS rather than to sequence their products.

With integral membrane proteins it is important to know if they traverse the membrane. If fragments of membranes are allowed to reseal some vesicles reform the wrong way round with their inner surface now exposed to the outside. These can be separated from the vesicles which form the correct way round by using affinity chromatography on lectin columns taking advantage of the ability of lectins to bind to carbohydrates (Fig. 6.8). Both types of vesicles are then separately labelled by procedures which only label the proteins on the outer surface and the labelled proteins isolated. If the same protein is found labelled in both types of vesicle then it clearly must span the membrane.

Fig. 6.8. Preparation of inside out vesicles. (Adapted from Walsh & Crumpton, 1977.)

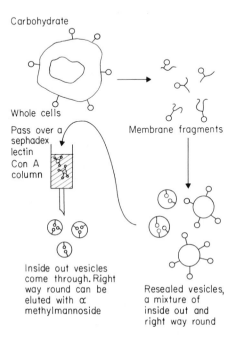

Carbohydrate

Whole cells

Pass over a sephadex lectin Con A column

Membrane fragments

Inside out vesicles come through. Right way round can be eluted with α methylmannoside

Resealed vesicles, a mixture of inside out and right way round

6.11 Biochemistry of the HLA-, B or C and H-2K and D

The alloantigenic determinants coded for by the *HLA-A, B* or *C* loci in man or *H-2K* and D in the mouse are carried on integral membrane proteins of about 44,000 M.W. (p44). These occur as transmembrane proteins associated at the cell surface with a 12,000 M.W. light chain called β_2 microglobulin. The latter is not an integral protein and is required for the stable expression of p44 molecules at the cell surface since cell lines which synthesize p44 but not β_2 microglobulin fail to express HLA-A and B. The gene for β_2 microglobulin does not lie on chromosome 6, the chromosome carrying the HLA system.

The complete amino acid sequence of one p44 molecule (HLA-B7) and substantial parts of others from mouse and man have been determined (Cooligan *et al.*, 1978; Orr *et al.*, 1979a,b). Sequence comparisons show that there is greater homology between the products of different MHS loci within a species than there is between the comparable regions of different species. This suggests that gene duplication to create the two or more loci for the classical transplantation antigens has occurred relatively recently during speciation.

Unfortunately there are insufficient data to define accurately the sites of the allotypic determinants but a comparison of mouse and human sequence shows that the differences tend to be clustered, for example, in the first 100 residues, there seems to be a region of high variability around positions 60–80. These clusters may be the sites of the alloantigenic specificities. Figure 6.9 shows the general features of the p44 and β_2 microglobulin molecules. The portion of p44 crossing the membrane lipid bilayer contains 26 hydrophobic residues with a C-terminal region of some 32 amino acids on the inside of the cell. This latter region is rich in serines, many of which are phosphorylated and may interact with the actin of the cytoskeleton.

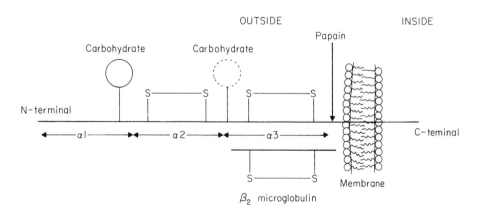

Fig. 6.9. A diagram of the p44 molecule of the MHS from mouse and man, attached to the cell membrane and associated with β_2 microglobulin. For mice the molecules have an additional carbohydrate groups — ⊙. (Adapted from Orr *et al.*, 1979a; Nathenson *et al.*, 1980.)

The sequence studies have also shown interesting similarities between the p44 molecule and immunoglobulins. The α3 but not α1 or α2 regions of HLA-B7 has a striking homology with an immunoglobulin domain and conserves the hydrophobic residues involved in the formation of the two anti-parallel β-pleated sheets (Table 6.6). This implies that the α3 region of HLA is folded like an immunoglobulin domain and that HLA and immunoglobulin share a common ancestral gene. Lack of homology between the whole of HLA and immunoglobulin may be a further example of evolution of proteins in pieces.

A comparison of the sequence of β_2 microglobulin with immunoglobulin shows similar conserved features (Table 6.6) and β_2 microglobulin will likewise be folded into the shape of an immunoglobulin domain. It seems probable that β_2 microglobulin and p44 will interact in a manner analogous to domain–domain interaction in immunoglobulins.

Comparison of tryptic peptides of certain H-2 mutants with the wild type products show amino acid substitutions in the p44 molecules. Knowledge of the structural changes in these mutants will be important in understanding the evolution of the MHS and the relationship of structure with function. Already we know that mutant bm1 which has a profound influence on the activity of cytotoxic T cells (see Chapter 11) involves the substitution of a single amino acid, Arg at position 155. Mutant bm3 on the other hand has marginal influence on T cells and involves two amino acid substitutions in a different part of the molecule (Table 6.7).

6.12 Biochemistry of *DR* and *I* region antigens

The DR and Ia determinants are carried on a molecule consisting of two separate-chains of glycoprotein with molecular weights of approximately 34,000 and 28,000. In mice these subunits have been called α and β respectively while in man they are referred to as p34 and p29. Both chains are integral membrane proteins that transverse the lipid bilayer. In mice different structures are isolated using alloantisera specific for differences in *I-A* or *I-E/C*. This implies that there are at least four polypeptide chains (but certainly more) that can be precipitated with anti-*I* region antisera, the four being, I-A$_\alpha$ and I-A$_\beta$; and I-E/C$_\alpha$ and I-E/C $_\beta$. These four chains need not necessarily be coded for by their respective subregions as it is possible that the alloantisera only react with one chain and precipitate the other by association. In man there are at least two separate loci coding for DR specificities.

6.12.1 *Amino acid sequence data of* DR *and* Ia

There is less sequence information for these proteins than there is for the classical transplantation antigens. However, the available sequences show that p34 and p29 proteins of man are homologous to I-E/C$_\alpha$ and I-E/C$_\beta$ respectively. There are no sequence homologies so far with other MHS products, immunoglobulins or other

Table 6.6. Sequences of human C$_\lambda$, β_2 microglobulin and part of HLA-B7. The features of the folded immunoglobulin C$_\lambda$ domain seen in crystallographic models are indicated above the sequence for C$_\lambda$. 4.1–4.4 and 3.1–3.3 refer to the segments of the four and three chain surfaces of the domain (see Fig. 2.5). The side chains pointing to the interior of C$_\lambda$ are underlined as are the corresponding residues in the other two sequences. For key to amino acid one letter code see the Glossary

```
                 4.1                                          4.2

C λ    Q P K A A P S V T L F P P S S E E L Q A N K A T L V C L I S D F Y P G A V T V A W K A D S S - P V K A -
β₂M  - I Q R T P K I Q V Y S R H P A E N - G K S N F L N C Y V S G F H P S D I E V D L L K D G - - E R I - -
HLA      D P P K T H V T H H P I S - - - D H E A T L R C W A L G F Y P A E I T L T W Q R D G E D T Q D T

                                    200                                        220


                 4.3              4.4                   3.1          3.2          3.3

C λ   - G V E T T T P S K Q S N N - K Y A A S S Y L S L T P E Q W K S H K S Y S C Q V T H E G S T V E K T V A P T E C S
β₂M   E K V E H S D L S F - S K N W S F Y L L Y S Y T E F T P T - E K - D E Y A C R V N H V T L S Q P K I V K W D R D M
HLA   E L V E T R P A G D R T F E - K W A A V V V - - - P S G - - - E E Q R Y T C H V Q H E G L P K P L T L R W E P S S

                                    240                                        260
```

Table 6.7. Five commonly used *H-2* mutant mouse strains

Haplotype	Synonyms	Location	Amino acid substitution
bm1	*H-2*^{ba}, *Hz1*	*H-2K*	Arg 155 → ?
bm2	*H-2*^{bb}, *Hz49*	*H-2K*	Not known
bm3	*H-2*^{bd}, *M505*	*H-2K*	Asx 77 → ? Lys 89 → ?
dm1	*H-2*^{da}, *M504*	*H-2D* or *H-2L*	Multiple changes
dm2	*H-2*^{db}	*H-2L*	Not known

A mutation in an *H-2* haplotype is designated by the addition of the letter *m* to the haplotype symbol, followed by an arabic numeral assigned according to the order in which the mutants are discovered. Data from Nathenson *et al.* (1980) and Kohn *et al.* (1978).

proteins. The sequence data also show that the four *I*-region polypeptide chains are probably all coded for by the *I* region. In *H-2* congeneic mice, amino acid sequence and tryptic peptide analyses for I-A$_\alpha$, I-A$_\beta$ and I-E/C$_\beta$ show marked differences though the difference in the alleles of I-E/C$_\alpha$ are much less. In man p29 shows greater variability than p34 (Kaufman *et al.*, 1980).

Studies on the *I* region proteins in mice have shown that I-E/C$_\beta$ is in fact coded by the I-A region (Jones *et al.*, 1978). It interacts with the I-E/C$_\alpha$ coded by the I-E/C region and hence is indirectly precipitated with antisera to I-E/C. The interaction between these two proteins of quite different genetic regions is independent of whether the genes are on the same or different chromosomes (i.e. it can be *cis* or *trans*). Consequently in an F$_1$ mouse there are *I*-region coded surface structures that are not present in either parent. For example, in an F$_1$ (*H-2*^{d} × *H-2*^{k}) mouse there will be the following four complexes {E/C$_\alpha^d$+ E/C$_\beta^d$}, {E/C$_\alpha^k$+ E/C$_\beta^k$}, {E/C$_\alpha^d$+ E/C$_\beta^k$} and {E/C$_\alpha^k$+ E/C$_\beta^d$}. Only the first two will be in the parental strains.

One feels this observation is very important as it may well be the molecular reason for *Ir* gene complementation (see Chapter 12).

6.13 The products of other genes in or near the MHS

6.13.1 *Complement components*

Although several genes for complement components are found in the MHS the biochemistry of these is discussed with the other complement factors in Chapter 3 and their genetics in Chapter 5.

6.13.2 Qa *and* Tla

The products of *Qa2* and of *Tla* are 44,000 M.W. proteins and are both associated with β_2 microglobulin. If the binding of β_2 microglobulin to these proteins is by the same mechanism as its association with p44 in the classical transplantation antigens then all three classes of these 44,000 M.W. molecule will be evolutionarily related. It is tempting to speculate that products of *H-2* and *Tla* regions form a family of molecules with similar functions which have all evolved from a common origin. It may well be correct to consider the *Tla* region as part of the MHS.

6.13.3 T-t *complex*

There is a protein F9 on teratocarcinoma cells that is thought to be coded for by the *T-t* complex. This is a protein with one chain of 44,000 and other chains of lower molecular weight including one of 12,000. It was originally suggested that this pattern mimicked the classical transplantation antigens and the 12,000 M.W. protein was β_2 microglobulin. However, this is not the case, and there is even some doubt about which locus codes for the 44,000 M.W. protein. At present it is probably wiser not to include the *T-t* complex within the MHS.

References

ALBERT *et al.* (1980) Nomenclature for factors of the HLA system. *Tissue Antigens* **16**, 113.

BENNETT D. (1975) The *T*-locus of the mouse. *Cell* **6**, 441.

BODMER W.F. (1972) Evolutionary significance of the HLA system. *Nature* **237**, 139.

BODMER W.F. & BODMER J.G. (1978) Evolution and function of the HLA system. *Brit. Med. Bull.* **34**, 309.

COLIGAN J.E., KINDT T.J., EWENSTEIN B.M., VEHARA H., NISIZAWA T. & NATHENSON S.G. (1978) Primary structure of murine MHS alloantigens. *Proc. Nat. Acad. Sci. U.S.A.* **75**, 3390.

DEMANT P. & NEAUPORT-SANTES C. (1978) The *H-2 L* locus and the system of *H-2* specificities. *Immunogenetics* **7**, 295.

FESTENSTEIN H. & DEMANT P. (1978) HLA and *H-2*. *Current Topics in Immunology* Series No. 9. Edward Arnold, London.

FLAHERTY L. (1978) Genes of the *Tla* region: the new Qa system of antigens. In *Origins of Inbred Mice*, ed. H. C. Morse, Academic Press, London.

JONES P.P., MURPHY D.B. & McDEVITT H.O. (1978) Two genes control the expression of murine *Ia* antigen. *J. exp. Med.* **148**, 925.

JOYSEY V.C. & WOLF E. (1978) HLA-A, -B and -C antigens, their serology and cross-reaction. *Brit. Med. Bull.* **34**, 217.

KAUFMAN J.F., ANDERSEN, R.L. & STROMINGER J.L. (1980) HLA-DR antigens have polymorphic light chains. *J. exp. Med.* **152**, 375–535.

KLEIN J. (1977) Evolution and Function of the Major Histocompatibility System: Facts and Speculations. In GOTZE D. (ed.), *The Major Histocompatibility System in Man and Animals*, p. 339. Springer-Verlag, Berlin.

KLEIN J. (1978) *H-2* mutations: their genetics and effect on immune functions. *Adv. Immunol.* **26**, 56.

KLEIN J., FLAHERTY L., VAN DE BERG J.L. & SCHREFFLER D.C. (1978) *H-2* haplotypes, genes, regions and antigens: first listing. *Immunogenetics* **6**, 489.

KLEIN J. & HAMMERBERG C. (1977) The control of differentiation by the *T* complex. *Immunol. Rev.* **33**, 70.

KOHN H.I., KLEIN J., MELVOLD R.W., NATHENSON S.G., PIOUS D. & SHREFFLER D.C. (1978) The first *H-2* mutant workshop. *Immunogenetics* **7**, 279.

LAMPSON L.A. & LEVY R. (1980) Two populations of Ia like molecules on human B cell lines. *J. Immunol.* **125**, 293.

NATHENSON S.G., EWENSTEIN B.M., VEHARA H., MARTINKO J.M., COLIGAN J.E. & KINDT T.J. (1980) Structure of *H-2* major histocompatibility complex products: recent studies on the *H-2 K^b* glycoproteins and on *H-2 K^b* MHS mutants. In Reisfeld R.A. and Ferrore S.O. (eds) *Trends in histocompatibility.*

ORR H.T., LANCET D., ROBB R.J., LOPEZ DE CASTRO J.A. & STROMINGER J.L. (1979b) The heavy chain of human histocompatibility antigen contains an immunoglobulin-like region. *Nature.* **282**, 266.

ORR H.T., LOPEZ DE CASTRO J.A., PARHAM P., PLOEGH H.L. & STROMINGER J.L. (1979a) Comparison of amino acid sequences of two human histocompatibility antigens HLA-A2 and HLA-B7. *Biochemistry.* **18**, 5711.

PLOEGH H.L., CANNON E.L. & STROMINGER J.L. (1979) Cell-free translation of the mRNAs for the heavy and light chains of HLA-A and HLA-B antigens. *Proc. Nat. Acad. Sci. U.S.A.* **76**, 2273.

ROOS M.H., ATKINSON J.P. & SHREFFLER D.C. (1978) Molecular characterization of the Ss and Slp (C4) proteins of the mouse *H-2* complex. *J. Immunol.* **128**, 1106.

SINGER S.J. & NICHOLSON G.L. (1972) The fluid mosaic model for the structure of cell membranes. *Science* **175**, 720.

VAN ROOD, J.J., DE VRIES R.R.P. & BRADLEY, B.A. (1980) Genetics and biology of the HLA system. In DORF M. & BENACERRAF B. (eds), *The Rôle of the Major Histocompatibility Complex in Immunobiology*, Garland Press Publishing Inc., U.S.A.

WALSH F.S. & CRUMPTON M.J. (1977) Orientation of cell-surface antigens in the lipid bilayer of lymphocyte plasma membrane. *Nature* **269**, 307.

Further reading

BODMER W.F. (ed.) (1978) The HLA system *Brit. Med. Bull.* **34**.

DORF M. & BENACERRAF B. (eds) (1980) *The Rôle of the Major Histocompatibility Complex in Immunobiology.* Garland Press Publishing Inc., U.S.A.

KLEIN J. (1975) *The Biology of the Mouse Histocompatibility-2 Complex.* Springer-Verlag, New York.

KLEIN J. (1979) The major histocompatibility complex of the mouse. *Science* **203**, 516.

Section II
Cellular Immunology

II.1 Introduction

This section is concerned with the cellular basis of the immune response: the cells of the lymphoid system, their interactions, responses to antigenic stimulation, development and physiological environment. This preamble attempts to cover some of the general groundwork of this field and describes in a didactic way the nature of antigens and the consequences of exposure to them.

II.2 Antigens

In so far as antigens were discussed in Section I, they were considered as structures which could fit into an antibody combining site. In this section we are concerned with the properties of an antigen which permit it to evoke an immune response.

II.2.1 Rigidity

An antigenic determinant (or epitope) requires to be of consistent shape and charge pattern if it is to be recognized by a specific combining structure (e.g. antibody). Antigens range from proteins, polysaccharides, glycolipids, synthetic polypeptides and chemically modified proteins to synthetic substances such as polyvinyl-pyrrolidone.

II.2.2 Valency

Most biological molecules carry many epitopes. Monomeric proteins, like serum albumin, carry 10 or more, while polymers of one or more kind of subunit present the same few epitopes in a large array. Examples of the latter antigens are *Escherichia coli* endotoxin (LPS), capsular polysaccharides from *streptococci* and *pneumococci*, polymerized flagellin and polyvinylpyrrolidone. Some of these polymeric antigens have been found to be thymus-independent antigens since they evoke an antibody response without involving T cells. Their contribution to the analysis of B lymphocyte activation by antigen is discussed in Chapter 8.

Haptens are small molecules which on their own cannot induce an antibody response. They only become immunogenic when coupled to a larger molecule (carrier), usually heterologous proteins. The most commonly used haptens are benzene derivatives like 2,4,Dinitrophenyl (DNP). Hapten-carrier systems have been exploited to show that the antibody response to a hapten involves T cells which recognize the carrier and help B cells to respond to the hapten. This is the phenomenon of T–B cell cooperation which is discussed briefly below and in detail in Chapter 10.

II.2.3 The antigenic universe

One of the most remarkable features of the immune system is its capacity to recognize a seemingly limitless array of antigens. This raises several questions. Is there an equal universe of antibody-combining sites (the antibody repertoire)? What is the size of the repertoire in different species/individuals? Has the genetic information for the repertoire (i.e. V-region DNA) arisen during the evolution of the species and is it now maintained in germ cell DNA (the germ line argument)? Is the repertoire unique to each individual and generated during one's lifetime by somatic mutation of a few inherited V-region sequences (the somatic mutation theory)? If so how does the full repertoire develop before birth in the apparent absence of external antigen? Jerne has proposed that antibody combining sites are able to react with self structures, particularly the idiotypes on other V regions. Thus for all external antigens, such as a flu virus, there would be internal images. These ideas, for which there is some experimental support, are laid out in more detail in Chapter 7 but are germane to many aspects of immunology.

II.3 Lymphocytes

Much of cellular immunology is concerned with lymphocytes. These small round cells, without much cytoplasm, are functionally heterogeneous and express an array of cell surface molecules which define two major populations, T and B cells, and their subsets.

The analysis of lymphocyte populations has been facilitated by the detection of a large number of distinctive markers. These range from biochemically-defined molecules, including those associated with the MHS, to membrane 'receptors' for a variety of biological structures such as lectins, heterologous erythrocytes, viruses and complement components. Human T cells, for example, have a 'receptor' for sheep erythrocytes and most species' B cells express 'receptors' for bound C3b. Although these markers have undoubtedly served their purpose as simple means to identify lymphocyte populations there seems little doubt that future classification and isolation of distinct cell populations will rely on monoclonal antibodies and cell-sorting techniques.

II.3.1 Monoclonal antibodies

Monoclonal antibodies are of uniform specificity, chemically homogenous and ideal for analysing complex biological systems. They have great potential for use in many fields of biology and have far reaching diagnostic and therapeutic applications.

Immunization with complex antigens induces a very heterogenous antibody response, but single clones of antibody-forming cells can be immortalized by fusing them *in vitro* to permanently established myeloma cell lines (Fig. II.1). The cell lines of desired specificity are cloned and propagated *in vitro* or *in vivo*. Kohler and Milstein were the first to make monoclonal antibodies by this technique which has now been adopted by people working on diverse biological problems.

There is an ever-growing number of monoclonal antibodies which react with sub-populations of the lympho-myeloid system of several species including man. These antibodies are helping to define stem cells of the lymphocyte and myeloid lineages, mature T and B cells and their subsets, and also stages of differentiation within each subset. Although at present there is a considerable amount of stamp collecting going on, in time there will be monoclonal antibodies which can detect most of the molecules expressed on lymphocyte surfaces. The problem will then be to determine the function of these molecules.

There is no question that the monoclonal antibody technique is a revolutionary step forward in biological research with far-reaching implications (Milstein *et al.*, 1979; Milstein & Lennox, 1979).

II.3.2 B lymphocytes

B lymphocytes are defined as cells which are synthesizing immunoglobulin (see Chapter 8). The end cell of the B cell lineage is a plasma cell which secretes antibody homogeneous with respect to specificity, idiotype, allotype and class (i.e. mono-clonal). Individual plasma cells do not simultaneously synthesize antibodies of different specificities or class. Since there are different immunoglobulin classes, there are therefore different subsets of plasma cells for each class. (Chapter 14 describes how the proportion and tissue distribution of these subsets may vary.)

For B lymphocytes the story is slightly different. Within a given clone the specificity of the immunoglobulin synthesized is maintained throughout the different stages of B-cell differentiation (pre-B cells, mature B cells, memory cells and plasma cells) but the class of the immunoglobulin varies. B lymphocytes can simultaneously synthesize antigen receptors belonging to three different immunoglobulin classes (IgM, IgD, IgG) each with the same combining site and idiotype.

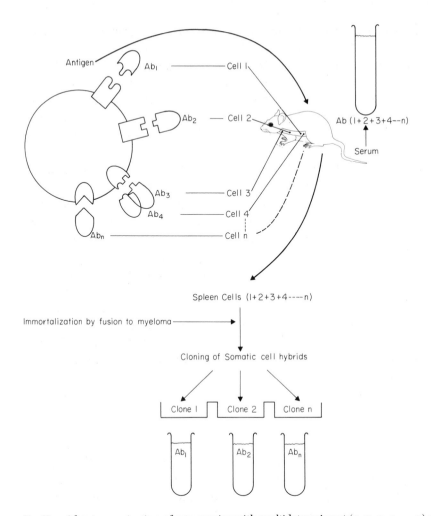

Fig. II.1. After immunization of rats or mice with multideterminant (1, 2, 3, 4 . . . n) antigens the spleen contains large numbers of cells each making antibodies to particular specificities (Ab_1, Ab_2, Ab_3, Ab_4 . . . . Ab_n). Some of the cells of these clones can be immortalized by fusing them to myeloma cells, culturing the hybrid cells and eventually isolating these hybrids as single clones. (See also Fig. I.2).

Switching of heavy-chain class expression during clonal expansion raises formidable problems with respect to the arrangement and transcription of immunoglobulin genes (see Chapter 4). This and the sequence of changes associated with B-cell differentiation are described in Chapter 8.

II.3.3 T lymphocytes

The thymus is a primary lymphoid organ wherein stem cells from the bone marrow differentiate into T cells which migrate to the peripheral or secondary lymphoid organs (Chapters 9, 14). The T cells which emerge from the thymus are hetero-geneous and comprise functionally distinct subsets which in mice can be dis-tinguished through the Lyt differentiation antigens, Lyt 1, Lyt 2 and Lyt 3 (so called because they are associated with T lymphocytes). For example, helper T cells (necessary for certain antibody responses) express Lyt 1 but not Lyt 2 and Lyt 3 while cytotoxic T cells (which kill virus-infected target cells) or suppressor T cells (which regulate immune responses) express Lyt 2 and Lyt 3. A similar dissection of func-tionally distinct T cell subsets in man has been achieved with xenoantisera and now more recently with a series of monoclonal antibodies (Chapter 9).

The mechanisms whereby T cells recognize antigen has perplexed immuno-logists for nearly a decade. T cells have a recognition repertoire equal to that of B lymphocytes yet they do not possess readily detectable surface immunoglobulin. This has led to the speculation that the antigen receptors on T-cells are not immunoglobulins. However, antigen recognition by T cells is more complex than first thought and involves recognition of the products of the MHS. Current evidence shows that antigen receptors from T cells express the same idiotype as serum antibody and that the genes coding for these T-cell idiotypes are genetically linked to the genes for the immunoglobulin H chains. This is compelling evidence that T cells use V-region structures to recognize antigen although the structure of the rest of the molecule remains a mystery (Chapter 9).

II.3.4 Arrangement of cell-surface molecules in the lymphocyte membrane

Although individual cell-surface molecules have a particular orientation in the cell membrane with respect to the inner and outer faces of the lipid bilayer, they are free to float or move within the plane of the membrane. This can be elegantly demon-strated using fluoresceinated or radiolabelled antibody to cell-membrane com-ponents such as surface immunoglobulin (Fig. II.2). If B lymphocytes are treated with labelled anti-immunoglobulin antibody at low temperatures ($<4°C$) the labelled antibody is uniformly distributed over the cell surface. At temperatures above $15°C$ the antibody begins to show a patchy distribution due to the cross-linking (lattice formation) of the individual receptor molecules on the cell surface. This process requires divalent antibody and does not occur with univalent Fab′ fragments. Patch formation eventually gives way to the formation of a cap of label over one pole of the cell. Cap formation is an energy-dependent process related to the normal active movement of the cell membrane. The cap may be internalized and the cell surface remain denuded of surface immunoglobulin until more is synthesized within about 12–24 hours. Redistribution of other molecules not recognized by the antibody does not occur. This phenomenon, known as capping, is useful in the analysis of the spatial arrangement of molecules within the plane of the membrane.

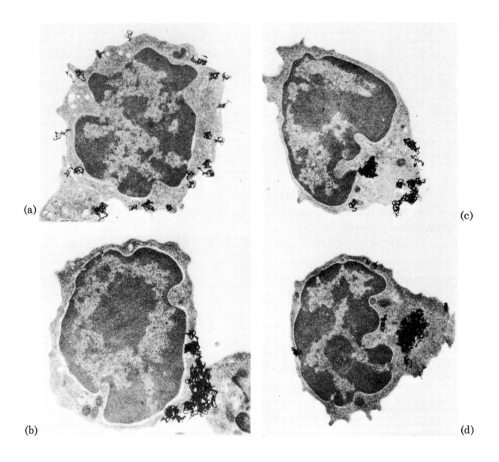

Fig. II.2. Electron microscope radioautograph of mouse lymphocytes reacted with ^{125}I-labelled anti-immunoglobulin at 4°C and then incubated:

(a) at 4°C. Magnification ×9,450;

(b) at 37°C for 1 minute. Note polar distribution of anti-immunoglobulin. Magnification ×12,250;

(c) at 37°C for 10 minutes. Magnification ×7,350;

(d) at 37°C for 10 minutes. Label now becoming internalized. Magnification ×12,250. (Unanue *et al.*, 1972.)

For example, the membrane molecules of the *K*, *D* or *I* region of the mouse *H-2* complex occur as individual molecules on the cell surface since they are independently redistributed by antibody. By contrast *β*2 microglobulin (the non-covalently associated light chain of certain membrane proteins) co-caps when the *H-2 K* or *D* region molecules are rearranged.

II.4. Antigen recognition and the immune response

When antigen is first injected into a normal, unprimed animal there is a short lag phase of about 12 days before antibodies, usually of the IgM class, appear in the serum. If the same antigen is reinjected the lag phase is very much shorter and IgG, the predominant antibody produced, persists in the serum for weeks or months (Fig. II.3). The first antigenic experience has primed the animal so that it can make a secondary response differing both quantitatively and qualitatively from the primary response. This is an example of the phenomenon of immunological memory.

The important point to recognize is that this serum response is based on the selective, clonal expansion and clonal suppression of different clones of antigen-specific T and B lymphocytes. Heterogeneity in the specificity of the antibody (and T cell) response is essential to immunity.

The immune response can be thought of as occurring in three phases, termed initial, central and effector (Fig. II.4).

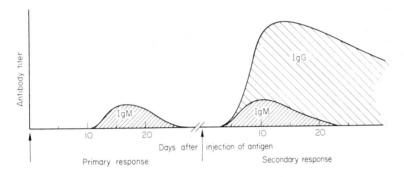

Fig. II.3. Primary and secondary antibody responses.

II.4.1 Initial phase

The initial phase of the immune response comprises the events between the entry of antigen and its presentation to antigen receptors on lymphocytes. Although phagocytic cells play an important rôle in the degradation and elimination of antigen, the processes whereby antigenic material becomes associated with the surfaces of antigen-presenting cells is a complex one (Chapters 10–12). A variety of macrophage-like cells are involved, some of which are non-phagocytic and ferry surface-associated antigen to appropriate parts of the secondary lymphoid tissue. Recognition of antigen within secondary lymphoid tissue depends on lymphocyte recirculation, and if this ceased, or was in any way abnormal, then the immune response would

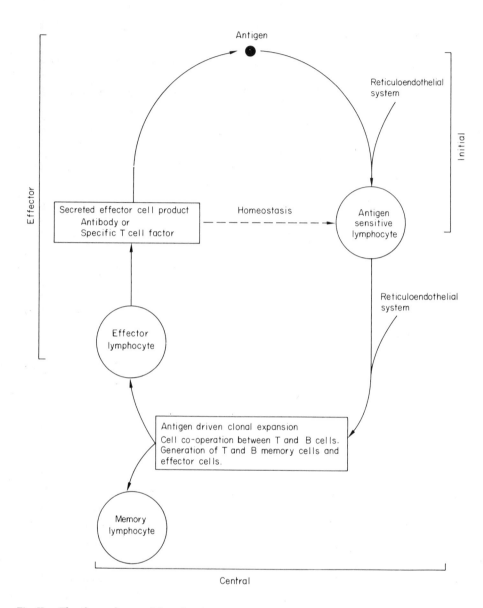

Fig. II.4. The three phases of the allergic response.

function poorly. The nature of the response may depend on that part of the secondary lymphoid tissue initially involved; antigens entering via mucosal surfaces (e.g. the gut) stimulate predominantly an IgA response (Chapter 14).

II.4.2 Central phase

The central phase of the immune response is to a large extent concerned with interactions between different subpopulations of lymphocytes and is the most complex (Chapter 10). It involves interactions between subpopulations of T cells, B cells and antigen-presenting cells. In many cases these interactions involve specific recognition of antigen but they may also involve recognition of the idiotypes on the lymphocyte receptors. The net effect is to produce selective clonal expansion or suppression. In addition to the specific regulation of clonal expansion there are a widespread number of non-specific growth factors, now tentatively designated as interleukins, which control the growth and differentiation of activated lymphocytes. Certain categories of growth factors have been used to produce cloned lines of antigen-specific T cells *in vitro*—the T-cell counterparts of monoclonal antibodies.

The first type of cell interaction to be recognized was that of T–B cell cooperation in the antibody response. It was shown by several groups that the secondary antibody response to many antigens was dependent on T cells. The classic example of this is seen in the secondary anti-hapten response—antigen-specific T cells recognize the carrier and help the hapten-specific B cells to respond.

This positive type of response is not the only possible consequence of antigenic stimulation. Sometimes the exposure to antigen results in the specific failure to respond to re-exposure to the same antigen. This is known as immunological tolerance (Chapter 13).

II.4.3. Effector phase

Antigen plays no rôle in this phase except as a target for destruction. Some of the clonally expanded B cells differentiate into plasma cells, short-lived end cells, which make antibody irrespective of the presence of antigen. Although some classes of effector T cells can act alone (e.g. cytotoxic T cells) their principal rôle in T cell immunity is mediated via the release of lymphokines and other growth factors. These amplify cell-mediated reactions through the recruitment of other cell types such as macrophages and eosinophils. The latter recruitment is especially important in parasitic infections (see section III).

II.4.4 Homeostatic control of the immune response

Most complex biological pathways are under exquisite homeostatic control to prevent untoward activation. The immune system is no exception. The main effect is to produce diversification of the specific response and to promote a response to antigens not adequately recognized in the initial phase. Both antibody and T cells play a major rôle in this process; antibody either by eliminating antigen or by competing with the lymphocyte receptor for a particular antigenic determinant, and T cells via suppression mechanisms. In fact in some systems, there is evidence that certain epitopes on a molecule preferentially stimulate suppressor cells, thus leading to a reduced immune response. If these suppressor determinants are removed then an antibody response occurs. The exact mechanisms are unknown but these observations are of practical significance with respect to manipulation of the immune response.

II.5 The biology of the MHS

The common thread running through much of cellular immunology is the MHS. The main impetus to the study of the MHS arose from its rôle as a system of antigens involved in allogeneic cell interactions (e.g. graft rejection and their *in vitro* correlates such as the mixed lymphocyte culture). It has gradually been recognized that the cell surface molecules coded by the MHS are not just involved in allogeneic interactions (an unnatural situation). They play a major rôle in cell interactions in the syngeneic environment.

The two areas of research which have led to this realization are MHS-associated immune response genes (MHS *Ir* genes) and MHS restriction. Both are complex areas of modern immunology and although MHS *Ir* genes and MHS restriction might strike the reader as separate areas of immunology it is our view that the experiments currently being described in each field are different ways of looking at the same phenomenon, namely the rôle of the MHS in lymphocyte activation.

II.5.1 MHS Immune response genes

The first indication of the involvement of the MHS in the immune response came from the discovery that defects in the immune response were linked to the MHS. That is, in inbred strains of mice responsiveness or non-responsiveness to certain antigens was determined by a particular *H-2* haplotype. Although there are many genes which control the response in a non-specific way the significance of MHS *Ir* genes is that they control the *specificity* of T-cell responses. This is a considerable puzzle for immunologists as the genes coding for immunoglobulin V regions are not linked to the MHS. MHS *Ir* genes, therefore, either code for a different T-cell recognition system which is not based on immunoglobulin V regions or alternatively the MHS directly influences the T-cell repertoire or T-cell activation. It is difficult to resolve this issue since we are ignorant of the molecular nature of the T-cell receptor.

II.5.2 MHS restriction

There is now a considerable literature to show that T-cell activation involves recognition not only of antigen but also of products of the MHS. This is known as MHS restriction. The particular regions which they recognize depend on the functional subclass of T cells—T cells involved in helper cell responses and in some delayed hypersensitivity reactions are governed by the *I* region of the MHS whereas cytotoxic cells seem to be governed by the *K* or *D* regions of the *H-2* complex.

A parallel situation exists in man, rats and many other species. Although at this stage it is difficult to make a clear-cut statement the overall impression is that the products of the MHS are somehow involved in the functional heterogeneity of T-cell responses.

Chapters 11 and 12 set out some of the experiments and arguments in this field. Not wishing to confuse the reader with data we have been selective rather than comprehensive since MHS restriction and MHS Ir genes are the current trends in immunology and like current economics suffer from a certain amount of hyper-inflation.

References

MILSTEIN C., GALFRE G., SECHER D.S. & SPRINGER T. (1979) Monoclonal antibodies and cell-surface antigens. In *CIBA Foundation Symposium 66, Human Genetics: Possibilities and Realities*, p. 251. Excerpta Medica, Elsevier, North-Holland, Amsterdam.

MILSTEIN C. & LENNOX E. (1980) The use of monoclonal antibody techniques in the study of developing cell surfaces. In FRIEDLANDER M. (ed.), *Current Topics in Developmental Biology*, Vol. II, p.1. *Developmental Immunology*. Academic Press, New York.

UNANUE E.K., PERKINS W.D. & KARNOVSKY M.V. (1972) Ligand-induced movement of lymphocyte membrane macromolecules. I. Analysis by immunofluorescence and ultrastructural radioautography. *J. exp. Med.* 136, 885.

Chapter 7
Theories of
Antibody Formation

7.1 Introduction

The ability of an animal to mount a specific immune response is such a remarkable phenomenon that theories about its mechanisms have been expressed since the turn of the century. This chapter will review these theories and discuss current views of how the immune system works.

7.2 Selective versus instructive theories

7.2.1 Ehrlich's selective hypothesis

In 1900 Ehrlich proposed the first selective theory of antibody formation. He suggested that toxin molecules (antigen) combined with pre-existing side chains on the surface of cells, thus stimulating them to generate additional side chains which appeared in the serum as antibody (Fig. 7.1). Apart from the terminology this is a very modern hypothesis. Later studies by Landsteiner (see Landsteiner, 1944), on antibody formation to non-biological antigens, appeared to create problems for Ehrlich's selective hypothesis since it seemed difficult to envisage that side chains could pre-exist for a vast number of synthetic haptens such as DNP or NIP. Unjustifiably the Ehrlich theory fell into disrepute.

7.2.2 Instructive or template hypothesis

From about 1935–55 instructive theories of antibody formation were in vogue (see Haurowitz, 1973). These proposed that antigen acted as a template for instructing the immune system to make specific molecules. It was suggested that there was a 'non-specific gamma globulin' that folded itself around antigen, possibly during protein synthesis which gave rise to the stable structure of a specific antibody. Difficulties for this hypothesis became overwhelming when specificity was shown to lie in the primary amino acid sequence of the antibody molecules. Haber (1964) found that if antibody molecules were completely unfolded in 6M urea and allowed to refold in the absence of antigen, then an appreciable amount of antibody activity was recovered.

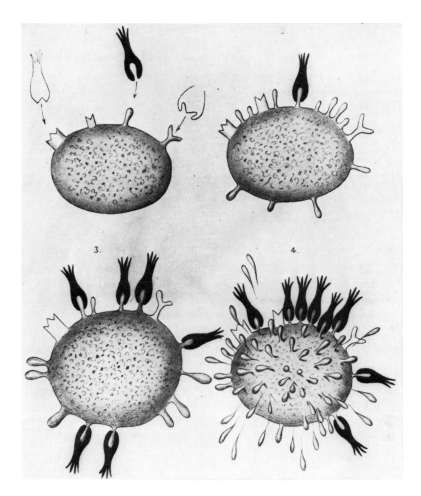

Fig. 7.1 Schematic representation of Ehrlich's 'side chain' theory of antibody formation. The antigen (black) combined with its corresponding 'side chain' or receptor, finally resulting in the excess regeneration of this receptor.

Indirect template hypotheses have been put forward but there is no evidence in their favour. It has been argued that the antigen specificity may be converted into a DNA sequence which then codes for the antibody. No evidence for such a process has ever been found.

7.3 The renaissance of the selective hypothesis

In 1955 Jerne proposed the first of the modern selective theories of antibody formation. The kernel of all these theories is that the diversity of receptors involved in the recognition of antigen arises spontaneously in the absence of antigen. The rôle of the antigen is to select these receptors, thereby initiating antibody formation. Burnet (1957) and Lederberg (1959) proposed that these pre-existing receptors were associated with cells which underwent specific clonal proliferation on meeting antigen. This became known as the clonal selection hypothesis. There is now overwhelming evidence for this hypothesis, the more important aspects of which will be discussed in relation to our current knowledge.

7.3.1. Specific receptors for antigen develop in the absence of antigen

The whole essence of the clonal selection hypothesis is that lymphocytes expressing surface receptors for antigen are present before antigen enters the system. The receptor for antigen on B lymphocytes is surface immunoglobulin. This appears on the surface of developing B cells during the early stages of ontogeny (see Chapter 8). The receptor for antigen on T cells has not been fully characterized (see §9.8) nor has the timing of its expression during T cell ontogeny been determined.

7.3.2 One cell and one receptor

The clonal selection theory implies that one cell will only express a limited range of receptor specificities, the response of the whole animal being equal to the sum of the responses of the individual cells. Numerous experiments have shown that B cells rarely bind two non-cross-reacting antigens to their surface. Evidence that all the immunoglobulin molecules on the surface of one cell have the same specificity is shown by the fact that when antigen-binding receptors are capped on the B cell surface by a multivalent antigen (polymerized flagellin) then all the surface immunoglobulin on that cell is also capped (Raff et al., 1973).

The situation for T cells is more complex. Activation of T cells involves specific recognition not only of antigen but also of the products of the MHS on antigen-presenting cells. At first sight this seems like dual specificity but there are other explanations (see Chapter 11).

The receptor for antigens on B cells is immunoglobulin. At the DNA level, single cells have half of their many V-region sequences on the maternal chromosome and half on the paternal chromosome. If sequences from both chromosomes were transcribed the cell would contain two different heavy chains and two different light chains. These could combine to give rise to four different antigen-combining sites and on antigen stimulation not one but four different types of combining sites would be made. This wasteful confusion is avoided by allelic exclusion (see Chapter 4). Although the molecular details are poorly understood, it is known that B cells only use the genetic information for an immunoglobulin chain from either the maternal or the paternal chromosome. This is clearly seen with the light- or heavy-chain allotypes, e.g. in a rabbit heterozygous for the *b* locus (light chain) allotypes (b4, b6) individual plasma cells and lymphocytes express either the b4 or the b6 allotype but never both simultaneously.

7.3.3 One clone—one antigen-combining site

All the antigen-specific molecules made by an expanded clone (both membrane receptors and secreted antibody molecules) will have antigen-combining sites identical to the surface receptors on the precursor cell of the clone. The selective event which initiates clonal expansion must involve recognition of the unique receptors on the surface of the precursor cell. This can occur in two ways; the first is through specific interaction with antigen and the second is via recognition of the unique structural features or idiotype of the receptor molecules (see Chapter 1). The importance of idiotype recognition for clonal selection was first recognized by Niels Jerne and led to his formulation of the network hypothesis which views the immune system as an interacting set of V-region domains (Jerne, 1974, 1975).

7.4 The network theory

Every antigen-combining site expresses its own particular set of idiotypic determinants (or idiotopes). If it is assumed that there are about 10^7 different combining sites per individual it follows that there are of the order of 10^7 different idiotopes per individual. It would be very surprising if amongst the 10^7 combining sites there were not some which could recognise idiotopes particularly as the interaction of antigen with antibody is degenerate; that is, one antibody-combining site will react with more than one different antigenic determinant (see §2.5.2). Jerne suggested that within an individual, the idiotopes expressed by a particular clone will inevitably be recognized by other combining sites. These, in turn, have their own idiotopes which will be recognized by a further set of combining sites and so on. In this way the entire immune system within an individual can be viewed as a closed network or 'web' of interacting molecules and cell receptors (Fig. 7.2). Since the combining sites which recognize idiotopes are the same as the combining sites which recognize external antigen then the idiotopes can be regarded as an internal image of a foreign antigen. In other words, all immunoglobulin molecules are anti-idiotypic and reactions of antibodies with foreign antigens represent useful cross-reactivity.

A further point of Jerne's network theory is that the idiotype–anti-idiotype interactions may lead to clonal selection through expansion or elimination of specific clones. Consequently, the elements of the network will be in dynamic equilibrium and the position of equilibrium is changed when antigen enters the system and induces clonal expansion of specific sets of cells. This in turn triggers clonal selection of the appropriate idiotype-bearing and idiotype-recognizing sets of

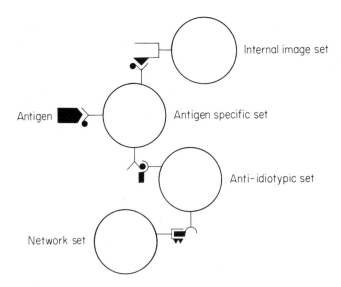

Fig. 7.2. The Jerne network hypothesis (description in text).

cells, sending a series of 'shock waves' through the network. This may explain why, during a specific antibody response, there is an increased synthesis of 'non-specific' immunoglobulin.

The network hypothesis has proved to be a focal point for a growing body of immunological research. Anti-idiotypic antibodies have been shown to arise during the course of a normal immune response and can induce or suppress the prolifer-ation of specific clones of both B and T lymphocytes. The same is also true for anti-idiotypic receptors on T cells and their regulatory effect on clonal expansion is discussed in Chapter 10.

7.5 The antibody response

To deal with the vast range of antigens present in the environment requires a large repertoire of specific antibodies. Before discussing the various ways for generating antibody diversity it is necessary to consider just how large the antibody repertoire has to be and to distinguish between the potential and the available repertoire. The potential repertoire represents the total number of V-region specificities which could arise in any one individual (a luxury), whereas the available repertoire is that which is actually present at any one instant to cope with environmental antigens.

7.5.1 The available repertoire

Since one cell expresses only one specificity the upper limit for the available repertoire will be the same as the total number of lymphocytes in an individual. This upper limit would only be achieved when all the clones consisted of one cell. In man there are about 10^{12} lymphocytes; in mice 5×10^8 and in tadpoles 10^6. However, since we do not know how many progenitor cells have remained as one-cell clones one cannot estimate the actual size of the available repertoire. It is also difficult to determine the average size of an expanded clone since this is likely to vary with species and antigenic exposure. What is clear is that the available repertoire will always be less than the total number of lymphocytes.

7.5.2 The required repertoire

Since tadpoles and mice survive, this would imply that a repertoire of less than 10^6 and less than 5×10^8 is adequate to cope with the normal environmental challenge to these two species. Tadpoles also respond to the immunologists' antigens like TNP and ovalbumin, but the antibody is of lower affinity than that in mice. Consequently, a repertoire of 10^6 may not be large enough to be able to make high affinity antibodies to these antigens.

The concept of a required repertoire depends on what the repertoire is required for. In evolutionary terms, this will be to enable the individual to survive long enough to reproduce efficiently and the size of the repertoire will be influenced by the pathogen load to the species and how long individuals have to survive before reaching sexual maturity. As we cannot precisely determine the available repertoire, it is impossible to define the required repertoire, but a concensus order of magnitude guess is of about 10^7 different antibodies, at least for mammals.

7.5.3 The potential repertoire

Antibody specificity is dictated by the amino acid sequence in the hypervariable regions of the light and heavy chains. If one assumes that there are only ten critical hypervariable residues in each chain and that only 10 of the possible 20 amino acids can be substituted at these positions, then there will be 10^{10} different V regions. Since heavy and light chains contribute equally to the combining site then 10^{20} different antibody specificities can be created. This is a very imprecise calculation but the potential repertoire is enormously large compared to the available repertoire.

There is evidence that the potential repertoire is much larger than the available repertoire. For example, Kreth and Williamson (1973) have shown that out of a total of 337 different clones of antibody raised to the hapten NIP in four identical mice, only five clones were common to any two of the mice. In man the frequency of a particular idiotype in the serum of normal individuals suggests that the repertoire is greater than 10^7, though by how much is unknown (Kunkel, 1970).

7.6 The generation of antibody diversity—somatic versus germ line

There are two theories on the origin of antibody diversity. The germ-line theory argues that all immunoglobulin genes are inherited and that antibody diversity has arisen by selection and mutation during the phylogenetic development of the species (Hood *et al.*, 1975). The somatic mutation theory on the other hand argues that the variants arise *de novo* in each individual from a small pool of inherited genes and that mutation and selection occur during the lifetime of the individual (Cohn *et al.*, 1974). Nobody doubts that inherited V-region genes exist and there is now very persuasive evidence that somatic mutation contributes to antibody diversity. The argument over the past 15 years has centred on the relative contribution made by each process to the total antibody repertoire. Not surprisingly the argument has been inconclusive since we do not know the size of the repertoire.

7.6.1 Germ-line theory

In time we will know from DNA-sequencing studies, the exact number of germ-line genes for antibody-variable regions. As discussed in Chapter 4, there are two ways of increasing the number of different antigen-combining sites from a set number of inherited genes. The first is intrachain rearrangement involving V regions and J-segment genes. The second, and probably much more important, is interchain combinatorial amplification between V_H and V_L gene products. In mice the estimated numbers of V-region genes for light and heavy chains could produce approximately 10^6 different antibodies. Before concluding that the entire repertoire in a mouse is carried in the germ line one should remember that we do not know the size of the required repertoire and that genetically identical mice normally produce different antibodies in response to the same antigen (see §7.5.3). With isogenic tadpoles this is not so and the antibodies to a particular antigen are very similar in different tadpoles. It would seem that in these tadpoles much of the repertoire comes directly from the germ line. In the adult frog the situation is very different since individual isogenic frogs, like mice, produce different antibodies to the same antigen (Du Pasquier & Wabl, 1978; see also Kobel & Du Pasquier, 1977).

7.6.2 Somatic mutation

The frequency of somatic mutation in eukaryotic cells is of the order of one mutation per gene per 10^6 cell divisions. Lymphocytes are rapidly proliferating cells during ontogeny (see Chapters 8 and 9) and in response to antigen. It is inevitable that somatic mutation will occur in V genes. It has been argued that the selective nature of the immune system (clonal expansion on successful encounter with antigen) will favour variants carrying mutations that affect the antigen-combining site of the molecules. The data on mouse λ-chain genes and amino acid sequences of different λ chains discussed in Chapter 4, illustrate this point (see Fig. 4.8) and provides good evidence that somatic mutation can occur for this chain. However, the extent to which λ chains contribute to the overall repertoire in the mouse is uncertain.

Recently two studies in mice, one on the sequential appearance of idiotypes during the course of any immune response and the other on the microheterogeneity of apparently homogenous antibodies, have provided evidence for somatic mutation in mouse κ and heavy chains. Capra and his colleagues (Capra & Nisonoff, 1979) have compared the amino acid sequence of antibodies raised in A/J mice to p-azo-phenylarsonate. This is an inheritable idiotype system and both idiotype positive and idiotype negative anti-arsonate antibodies are produced. The amino acid sequence of the heavy chains from the idiotype positive antibodies raised in eight different members of the same strain are identical, both in the framework and in the hypervariable residues. The idiotype negative anti-arsonate antibodies from the same eight mice have identical framework residues but show heterogeneity in the hypervariable region. The framework sequence of the anti-arsonate antibodies is not a common V_H sequence in mouse immunoglobulins, suggesting that the idiotype negative molecules have arisen by somatic mutation from a gene coding for the inherited idiotype.

In the above studies, serum antibodies were analysed and the sequencing techniques would not have detected a variant if it occurred in less than 5 per cent of the molecules. By using the hybridoma approach, it has been possible to sequence idiotype positive and idiotype negative antibodies which are truly monoclonal (Estess et al., 1979). Surprisingly, in the first two antibodies partially sequenced, amino acid substitutions were found at different places in the 30 N-terminal frame-work residues of the heavy chains of both the idiotype positive and idiotype negative monoclonal antibodies. This suggests that the apparently homogenous idiotype positive anti-arsonate antibodies from serum are, in fact, the product of a large number of separate clones differing from each other by a small number of unique amino acid replacements. Again, the simplest interpretation of this finding is that the variants have arisen through somatic mutation of the gene responsible for the inherited idiotypes. Obviously the weight of this argument will be increased as more sequence data becomes available.

A balanced view at the present time is that both germ line and somatic processes are involved in antibody diversity. The contribution of each will depend on the species involved and the immunoglobulin chain in question. Species with a short gestation period or a small number of lymphocytes (e.g. tadpoles) might have to rely more on inherent germ-line specificities, whereas species with more time and cells to generate their repertoire might rely more on somatic mutation.

7.7 Selection and somatic mutation

An immune system based on clonal expansion will favour cells that can successfully react with antigen. The network theory extends this selective stimulus to inter-actions with the idiotopes on receptor molecules. This point has not been overlooked by Jerne, nor has the notion that self molecules may act like antigens to drive clonal expansion during the development of the immune system. He has proposed two separate theories for selecting somatic mutants.

7.7.1 Idiotypes and diversity

Network interactions could aid the development of antibody diversity (Jerne, 1974). The argument goes as follows: during ontogeny the first receptors to appear are those encoded by the germ-line genes. Their germ-line idiotopes could act as 'internal antigens' to select mutant combining sites and these in turn would have different idiotopes which might select more combining sites and so on. Thus, the selection of mutants within the system is entirely self driven with external antigen playing no part (see Fig. 7.2).

7.7.2 Histocompatibility antigens and diversity

The second model is based on the observation that up to 10 per cent of T cells from one individual recognize the major histocompatability antigens of other members of the same species. Jerne (1971) proposed that the germ-line genes code for receptors specific for the MHS of the species. During lymphocyte ontogeny these auto-reactive clones would be driven into proliferation through recognition of the individual's own MHS and mutations would occur during this proliferative phase. Later in the development of the cells the non-mutated self-reactive clones would be eliminated and the mutant clones remain as the lymphocyte pool which reacts with all external antigens. The developing cells which did not react with self MHS would represent the large pool of cells reactive to the MHS of other members of the species. This implies two separate lymphocyte pools—one responsible for alloantigen recognition and the other for conventional antigens. There is no convincing evidence that two such pools exist and in this aspect the theory may be wrong.

Since the formulation of this theory it has become clear that T cell activation by antigen involves specific recognition of products of the major histocompatibility system expressed on the surface of the antigen-presenting cell. Furthermore, the specificity of MHS recognition is acquired during T cell development in the thymus (see Chapter 11). Jerne's concept of acquisition of receptor diversity in T cells driven by auto-reactivity may explain the many observed phenomena associating MHS and T cell responses to antigen and is discussed further in Chapters 11 and 12.

References

BURNET F.M. (1957) A modification of Jerne's theory of antibody production using the concept of clonal selection. *Aust. J. Sci.* **20**, 67.

CAPRA J.D. & NISONOFF A. (1979) The complete amino acid sequence of the heavy-chain variable region of anti-*p*-azophenylarsonate antibodies from A/J mice bearing a cross-reactive idiotype. *J. Immunol.* **123**, 279.

COHN M., BLOMBERG B., GECKLER W., RASCLEKE W., RIBLET R. & WEIGERT M. (1974) First-order Consideration in Analyzing the Generator of Diversity. In SERCARZ E.E., WILLIAMSON A.R. & FOX C.F. (eds), *The Immune System: Genes, Receptors, Signals*, p. 89. Academic Press, New York.

DU PASQUIER L. & WABL, M.R. (1978) Antibody diversity in amphibians: inheritance of isoelectric focussing antibody patterns in isogenic frogs. *Eur. J. Immunol.* **8**, 428.

EHRLICH P. (1900) On immunity with special reference to cell life. *Proc. Roy. Soc. Lond.* **66**, 424.

ESTESS P., NISONOFF A. & CAPRA J.D. (1979) NH_2-terminal amino acid sequence analysis of the heavy- and light-chain variable regions of monoclonal anti-*p*-azophenylarsonate antibodies. *Mol. Immunol.* **16**, 1111.

HABER E. (1964) Recovery of antigenic specificity after denaturation and complete reduction of disulphides in a papain fragment of antibody. *Proc. Nat. Acad. Sci. U.S.A.* **52**, 1099.

HAUROWITZ F. (1973) The problem of antibody diversity. Immunodifferentiation versus somatic mutation. *Immunochemistry* **10**, 775.

HOOD L., CAMPBELL J.H. & ELGIN S.C.R. (1975) The organization, expression and evolution of antibody genes and other multigene families. *Ann. Rev. Genet.* **9**, 305.

JERNE N.K. (1955) The natural selection theory of antibody formation. *Proc. Nat. Acad. Sci. U.S.A.* **41**, 849.

JERNE N.K. (1971) The somatic generation of immune recognition. *Europ. J. Immunol.* **1**, 1.

JERNE N.K. (1972) What precedes clonal selection? In *CIBA Foundation Symposium on Ontogeny of Acquired Immunity*, p. 1. Associated Scientific Publishers, Elsevier, Amsterdam.

JERNE N.K. (1974) Towards a network theory of the immune system. *Ann. Inst. Pasteur, Paris,* **125C**, 373.

JERNE N.K. (1975) The immune system: a web of V-domains. *Harvey Lecture*. Series 70, p. 93. Academic Press, New York.

KABEL H.R. & DU PASQUIER L. (1977) Strains and species of *Xenopus* for immunological research. In SOLOMON J.B. & HORTON J.D. (eds), *Developmental Immunobiology*, pp. 299–306. North-Holland, Amsterdam.

KRETH H.W. & WILLIAMSON A.R. (1973) The extent of diversity of anti-hapten antibodies in inbred mice. *Europ. J. Immunol.* **3**, 141.

KUNKEL H.G. (1970) Experimental approaches to homogeneous antibody populations. Individual antigenic specificity, cross-specificity and diversity of human antibodies. *Fed. Proc.* **29**, 55.

LANDSTEINER K. (1944) *The Specificity of Serological Reactions*. Dover Publications (rev. ed., 1962), London.

LEDERBERG J. (1959) Genes and antibodies. *Science* **129**, 1649.

RAFF M.C., FELDMANN M. & DE PETRIS S. Monospecificity of bone marrow-derived lymphocytes. *J. exp. Med.* **137**, 1024.

Chapter 8
B Lymphocytes

8.1 Introduction

The differentiation of haemopoietic stem cells into B lymphocytes and later fully mature plasma cells has two distinct stages. During the first stage (clonal development) pluripotential stem cells undergo programmed differentiation within the primary lymphoid organs giving rise to immunocompetent lymphocytes expressing surface immunoglobulin. This stage is dependent on the inductive microenvironment of the primary lymphoid organs, and independent of external antigen. The second stage (clonal selection by antigen) comprises the antigen-induced differentiation of virgin B lymphocytes into memory cells and plasma cells with T cells, macrophages and antibody all playing a regulatory rôle.

8.2 Clonal development

B cells are defined as cells expressing immunoglobulin either in the cytoplasm alone, or on the surface as surface immunoglobulin (sIg), or both.

8.2.1 B cell lymphopoiesis

B lymphocyte precursor cells originate in the blood islands of all embryonic tissues including the yolk sac. They seed via the circulation to the primary lymphoid organs where they differentiate into mature B lymphocytes. The primary lymphoid organ in birds which supports B cell maturation is a lymphoepithelial outgrowth of the hind gut known as the Bursa of Fabricius (Glick *et al.*, 1956). Mammalian species lack a bursa and its functions are carried out by placenta and fetal liver during early embryogenesis, and by bone marrow in neonatal and adult life.

The early stages of B cell development have been studied in both avian and mammalian species. Cytogenetic studies by Le Douarin *et al.* (1976) have shown that the Bursa of Fabricius, like the thymus (see Chapter 9.2) is particularly receptive to immigrant stem cells from the seventh to the eleventh day of embryonic life (Fig 8.1). In mice Owen *et al.* (1974) have demonstrated that precursor B cells are already present in the 11-day fetal liver and if organ cultures are established at this time lymphocytes bearing sIg appear 6 days later exactly as they would have done *in vivo*.

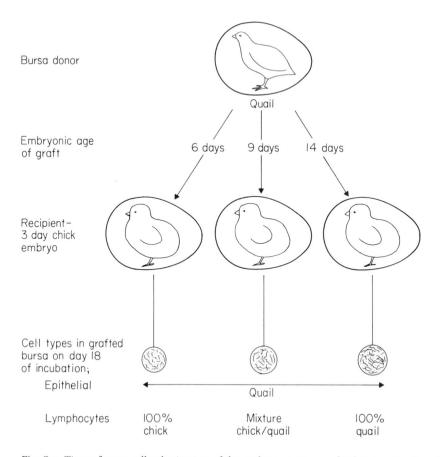

Bursa donor

Quail

Embryonic age
of graft

6 days   9 days   14 days

Recipient –
3 day chick
embryo

Cell types in grafted
bursa on day 18
of incubation;

Epithelial

Quail

Lymphocytes   100%   Mixture   100%
                 chick   chick/quail   quail

Fig. 8.1. Time of stem-cell colonization of the embryonic Bursa of Fabricius. Quail and chick tissue cells are cytogenetically distinct and by exchange grafting of embryonic tissue it is possible to determine whether the cells eventually found in the grafted tissue are derived from immigrant stem-cell precursors. In the above experiment bursae from embryonic quails were grafted into 3-day chick hosts. After 15 days the cell types present in the grafted tissue were determined. (Adapted from Le Douarin *et al.*, 1976.)

Distinct stages of B cell development can be recognized in humans and mice. Type I pre-B cells are the earliest detectable B cells in fetal liver and bone marrow. They are heterogeneous in size, rapidly dividing, appear 4 days before primary B cells and although they can synthesize IgM this only appears in the cytoplasm and not on the membrane. In adults these cells are exclusive to the bone marrow. Type II pre-B cells are homogeneous in size, with a thin rim of cytoplasm. They occur in fetal and adult bone marrow as well as peripheral lymphoid tissues. Pre-B cells show allelic exclusion (see Chapter 4) for IgM allotypes which strengthens the view that they are part of the normal B cell lineage and not an irrelevant cell type which has acquired immunoglobulin. It is unknown whether normal pre-B cells synthesize light chains.

Primary or immature B cells expressing sIgM first appear in the fetus at 16–17 days in mice or 9 weeks in man. They are presumed to be derived from pre-B cells. These cells are unlike mature B cells in three respects: (a) once their sIg is capped off by anti-immunoglobulin (see preamble II.3.4) it is not re-expressed; (b) low concentrations of antibody to IgM will inhibit mitogen induced proliferation; and (c) they are easily tolerized by exposure to low doses of antigen (Nossal & Pike, 1975; Metcalf & Klinman, 1976).

8.2.2 Immunoglobulin class expression during B cell ontogeny

There are several interesting features about immunoglobulin expression during B cell development (Fig. 8.2). Cells expressing IgM develop first and later generate cells committed to the expression of sIgM either alone or in conjunction with other sIg classes. IgD appears on the B cell surface after sIgM and often co-exists with this and other sIg classes. sIgD is lost as B lymphocytes differentiate into memory cells or IgM-, IgG- or IgA-secreting plasma cells. Once a cell expresses a particular class or subclass other than δ or μ on its surface then it remains committed to secrete that class or subclass when activated by antigen. The rôle of both sIgD and serum IgD is unknown. It is detected in serum at very low concentrations (in man less than 50 μg/ml) and IgD-secreting plasma cells can be found (albeit in low frequency) in lymphoid tissue.

All the immunoglobulin molecules on the surface of a single B cell expressing more than one immunoglobulin class have identical V-region sequences in both heavy and light chains and only differ in heavy-chain constant regions. If unprimed B cells specific for hapten are enriched and the receptors on the individual cells capped with antigen then both δ and μ chains simultaneously co-cap (Goding & Layton, 1976). Also malignant lymphocytes isolated from a patient with Waldenström's macroglobulinaemia have been shown to simultaneously express sIgM and sIgD of the same specificity (Fu et al., 1974). It is likely that B lymphocytes at this stage of their development may make a large heterogeneous nuclear RNA transcript of their heavy-chain genes which carries a single V region but multiple C-region sequences (Fig. 8.3; Liu et al., 1980; see also Chapter 4). Post-transcriptional modification of this heterogeneous nuclear RNA would yield smaller molecules of cytoplasmic mRNA all with the same V_H sequence but now contiguous to different C_H sequences. The amounts of different functional mRNA molecules made from the initial transcript will depend on the activities of the processing steps in post-transcriptional modification. It is unlikely that the same process applies to B cells which are irreversibly restricted to the synthesis of a single class of immunoglobulin.

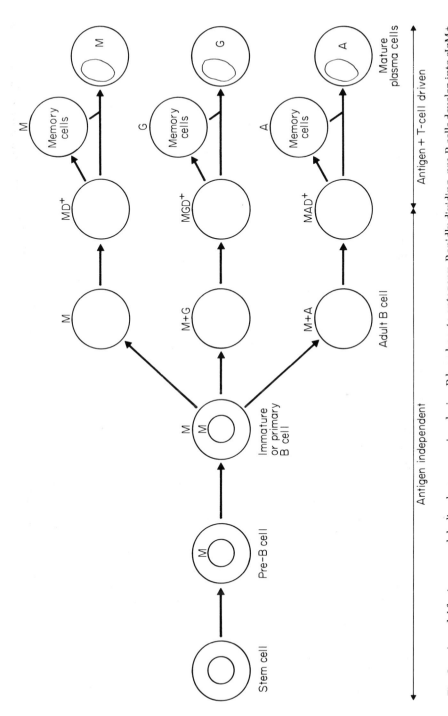

Fig. 8.2. A model for immunoglobulin class expression during B lymphocyte ontogeny. Rapidly dividing, pre-B cells develop into sIgM⁺ primary B cells. In the absence of antigen these cells give rise to lymphocytes expressing several different H-chain classes including IgD. This disappears, possibly after antigen stimulation as the cells develop into mature plasma cells. (Based on *Abney et al.*, 1977.)

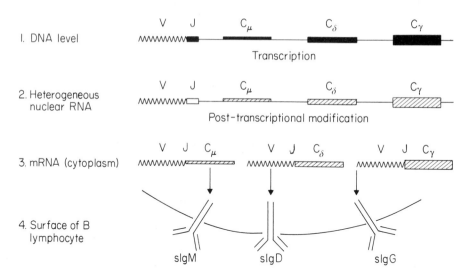

Fig. 8.3. Possible model to explain simultaneous synthesis by lymphocytes of different immunoglobulin classes each with the same V region (description in text). Intervening sequences in C regions are not shown.

Evidence suggests that at this stage of B cell maturation further gene rearrangement has occurred resulting in the loss of the unexpressed heavy chain constant regions (Rabbits *et al.*, 1980).

8.2.3 *V-region expression during B cell ontogeny*

The initial appearance of specific cells is antigen independent since antigen-binding cells can be detected in the bursa. Cells of the same specificity are adjacent within developing follicles suggesting that they originate from a single specific precursor (Fig. 8.4) (Lydyard *et al.*, 1976). There is also evidence to suggest that clones with different specificities develop at different times. In mice, clones of anti-DNP-specific B cells can be detected at birth whereas clones specific for other antigens such as fluorescein or phosphorylcholine appear about the seventh day of post-natal life (Fig. 8.5). This has also been demonstrated in chicks although in both cases one has to be careful that the apparent sequential apearance is not simply due to differences in the sensitivity of the various detection systems.

Although not formally proven it is reasonable to assume that the V- and C-region gene rearrangement necessary for making immunoglobulin in developing B cells is irreversible. Further, since synthesis of cytoplasmic IgM precedes the expression of IgM on the cell surface, antigen obviously plays no part in dictating which V gene is expressed. It is also unknown if the choice of V genes is random, or biased in favour of certain V genes.

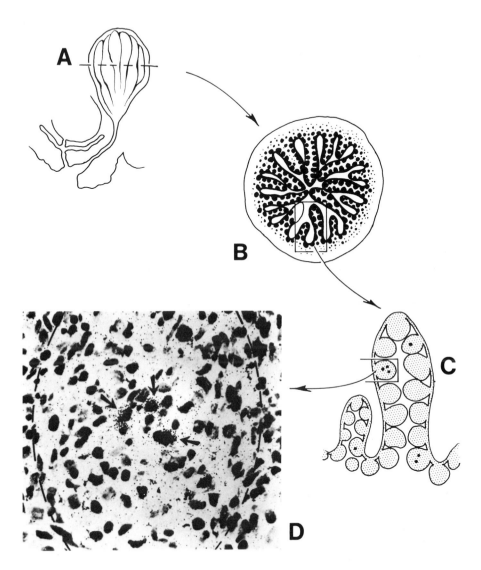

Fig. 8.4. Antigen-binding cells in the Bursa of Fabricius in a 16-day chick embryo. Transection of the bursa (A) reveals internal folds (B) each containing large numbers of lymphoid follicles (C). At this stage 60 per cent of the bursal cells are sIgM$^+$ and if the section is overlaid with ^{125}I-labelled (T, G)—A - - L then clusters of antigen-specific cells (arrowed) can be detected by radioautography. (From Lydyard *et al.*, 1976.)

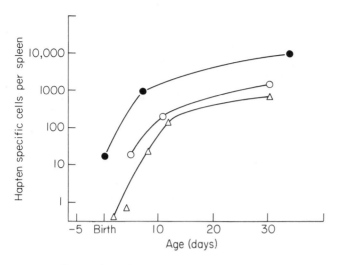

Fig. 8.5. The number of hapten-specific B cells present in the spleen of a BALB/c mouse at various ages from birth to adulthood (estimated from a functional assay). ●————● TNP-specific, o————o fluorescein-specific, ▵————▵ phosphorylcholine-specific. (Modified from Klinman *et al.*, 1977.)

8.3 Antigen-dependent phase of clonal development

The distinction between antigen-independent and antigen-dependent clonal expansion is very difficult to make since it depends on what is regarded as antigen. If the idiotypes of the inherited V regions act as the driving stimulus or 'internal antigen' in the development of the B cell repertoire (see Chapter 7.7.1) then 'antigen' exists from the moment the first primary B cell expresses surface immunoglobulin. The only cell which can really be said never to have recognized antigen is the pre-B cell.

Thus antigen-dependent clonal expansion only refers to the clonal expansion induced by giving external antigen. The two consequences of antigen-induced clonal expansion of B cells are the formation of memory cells and antibody-secreting cells. Little is known about the events which control the development of one or other of these phases of clonal development. In the response to some antigens, induction of memory appears less thymus-dependent than antibody formation (Roelants & Askonas, 1972) but in most cases memory is T dependent since athymic nude mice fail to develop memory to thymus-dependent antigens and lack germinal centres.

Germinal centre formation in lymph nodes or spleen (see Chapter 14) is a characteristic of memory cell development. This in turn requires localization of antigen or antigen–antibody complexes on the surface of the dendritic reticular cells in primary lymphoid follicles, a process which is dependent on C3 (the third component of complement). B mice (see glossary) fail to develop memory to KLH if they are chronically depleted of C3 (Klaus & Humphrey, 1977).

8.4 Thymus-independent antigens

Thymus-independent (TI) antigens have been extensively studied in the hope that they will provide clues to the signals involved in B cell activation by antigen. They have a number of similar characteristics, some of which may contribute to their ability to activate B cells (Table 8.1). Probably the most important is the ability of TI antigens, at high concentrations, to induce proliferation and immunoglobulin secretion in B cells, irrespective of the specificity of their antigen receptors and without involving T cells. This ability to induce polyclonal activation of B cells is an intrinsic property of TI antigens and not a peculiarity of the antibody repertoire. At low concentrations TI antigens stimulate many fewer B cells and only those that make specific antibody.

Of the other shared features, the most notable is that they are all large polymeric molecules of repeating identical determinants. Monomeric forms express the same determinants but are no longer thymus independent (e.g. flagellin). Many of them are highly resistant to degradation *in vivo* usually because the necessary degrading enzymes are absent. Most TI antigens elicit only IgM antibodies *in vivo* although the response can be manipulated to produce IgG. Pneumococcal polysaccharide (SIII) generates IgM antibody when given as SIII but if coupled to SRBC or in its natural state on a bacterium, the response becomes thymus dependent and IgG antibody is produced.

Table 8.1. Characteristics of thymus independent antigens. Haptens can be coupled to these antigens and the complex used to produce thymus independent responses to the hapten

Antigen	Resistance to degradation	Polymeric nature	Polyclonal activation	Other properties
LPS	+	+	+++	Active part of molecule is Lipid A which also activates the classical pathway of complement
Ficoll	+++	+++	−	
Polyacrylamide	+++	+++	−	
Dextran	++	++	+	
Levan	++	++	+	Activates alternative pathway of complement
Poly D-amino acids	+++	+++	−	The L forms are not TI antigens
SIII	+++	+++	+	
Polymeric flagellin	+	++	++	Monomeric flagellin is thymus-dependent

It has been argued that the capacity of TI antigens to activate B cells is related to their ability to activate complement via the classical or alternative pathway (see Chapter 3). The converse does not apply since many potent activators of complement, such as cobra venom factor (CVF) (see Chapter 3) are not thymus-independent antigens. Furthermore in C3-depleted mice many TI antigens will elicit a normal IgM response.

8.5 Nature of B lymphocytes responding to TI antigens

Polyclonal activators can activate B cells irrespective of the specificity of the antigen receptors on the cells. Information on the receptors for polyclonal activators can be obtained from a comparison of the response of inbred strains of mice to particular TI antigens (Watson & Riblett, 1974). B cells from C3H/HeJ mice are unresponsive to lipopolysaccharide (LPS) or haptens coupled to LPS (Coutinho et al., 1978). This defect in response is attributed to a mutation affecting the expression of a receptor on the B cell surface for the lipid A part of LPS. The mutant gene maps to chromosome 4 which also codes for two other B cell markers, the alloantigens Lyb 2 and Lyb 4 (see section 8.7). By immunizing the mutant strain with cells from normal C3H mice, an antibody can be raised which reacts with a membrane structure on normal B cells and this antisera will induce polyclonal activation. The antibody does not react with or activate B cells from the mutant strain. It is concluded that this antibody reacts with a lipid A sensitive mitogen site on B cells (Coutinho et al., 1978). Since the mutant strain can respond normally to other TI antigens, it has been suggested that there are multiple mitogen sites on B cells, each site sensitive to different TI antigens.

Another strain, CBA/N, responds well to certain TI antigens such as TNP–LPS but fails to respond to the same hapten on ficoll or dextran (Sher et al., 1975). This is due to an X-linked defect and the failure to respond is associated with the absence of a subpopulation of B cells bearing the Lyb 5 marker (see § 8.7). The response of the adult CBA/N mouse to TNP–ficoll and TNP–dextran is identical to the response of all neonatal mice to these two TI antigens. Neonatal mice also lack cells bearing the Lyb 5 marker and only respond to TNP–ficoll or TNP–dextran at about 2 weeks after birth when Lyb 5^+ cells appear.

8.6 Theories of B cell activation with TI antigens

There are two broad views as to how TI antigens activate B cells. Dintzis et al. (1976) have suggested that a critical degree of latticing of surface immunoglobulin is required. Polyacrylamide is not a polyclonal activator and a response to DNP on polyacrylamide only occurs with fragments of a certain size and carrying a certain number of DNP residues—usually at least 12–16 per polyacrylamide fragment (Fig. 8.6). In contrast Coutinho and Möller (1974) have argued that all TI antigens are mitogenic in their own right and that sIg on B cells is not directly involved in signalling to the cells. Instead sIg may play an indirect role through binding the antigen and concentrating the mitogenic signals in the vicinity of the specific B cell. This explains why with low doses of DNP–LPS only DNP-specific cells respond while with higher concentrations of DNP–LPS most B cells are activated (Figs 8.7 and 8.8). and 8.8).

The hypothesis of Coutinho and Möller can be extended to B cell activation by all antigens, with the B cell antigen receptor concentrating antigen on the surface of the antigen-specific cell. With T-dependent antigens the mitogenic signal would be generated through the interaction of T cells with the antigen held on the surface of the B cell (see Chapters 10 and 11).

8.7 Surface markers on B lymphocytes

A variety of marker systems based on the class of surface immunoglobulin, membrane alloantigens and receptors have been used to define the different stages of B cell development in mice (Fig. 8.9). During the first weeks of post-natal life B cells express a high density of sIg and a high ratio of sIgM/sIgD. Although they express Lyb 2, other markers of this series (Lyb 3 and Lyb 5), C3b receptors and Mls determinants are all absent and begin to appear between the first and second week of life depending on the strain. (Mls is a mixed lymphocyte stimulating determinant

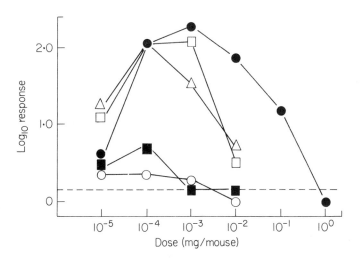

Fig. 8.6. The response (antibody-forming cells per 10^6 spleen cells) to different molecular weight polymers substituted to the level of approximately 1 DNP group per 40 acrylamide monomer units. Molecular weight: (o) 0.4×10^5; (■) 0.8×10^5; (▲) 1.4×10^5; (□) 1.8×10^5; (●) 5×10^6. The dashed line represents the response of unimmunized mice. (From Dintzis *et al.*, 1976.)

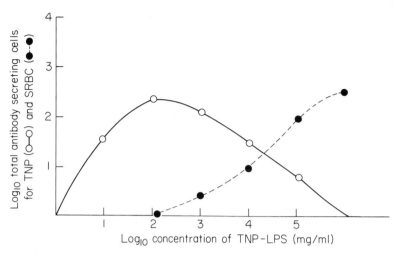

Fig. 8.7. B-cell activation by TI antigens. Normal mouse spleen cells were cultured with TNP–LPS for 2 days and the number of antibody-secreting cells to the specific (TNP) and an irrelevant (SRBC) antigen measured. Low concentrations of TNP–LPS only generate anti-TNP-specific cells whereas higher concentrations induce responses to antigens not present in the culture (i.e. a measure of polyclonal activation). (Adapted from Coutinho & Möller, 1974.)

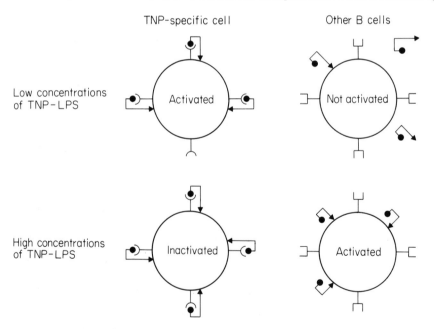

Fig. 8.8. The one non-specific signal hypothesis for B-cell activation. TI antigens have antigenic determinants (♦) and mitogen sites (ᵧ) and in low concentrations only bind in sufficient concentrations to the antigen-specific cells thereby producing activation. At higher concentrations TI antigens bind to the mitogen site on all B cells irrespective of specificity which in turn become activated and secrete antibody.

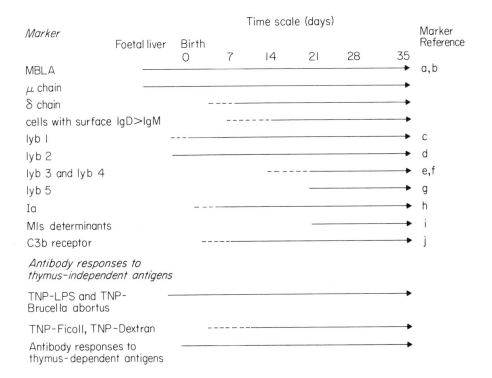

Fig. 8.9. Developmental sequence of B cell surface markers in the mouse. Antigenically the mouse B lymphocyte antigen (MBLA—defined by heteroantisera) can be detected very early in development together with μ-chain expression. The Lyb series of antigens also show differential expression. Functionally B cells of newborn mice can respond to certain TI antigens such as TNP (*Brucella abortus*) and TNP–LPS. Responses to TNP on different TI antigens (Ficoll, Dextran and Levan) can only be induced about 2 weeks after birth. Key to references:

(a) RAFF M.C., NASE S. & MITCHISON N.A. (1971) *Nature* **230**, 50.
(b) NIEDERHUBER J.E. & MÖLLER E. (1972) *Cell Immunol.* **3**, 599.
(c) SNELL G.D., CHERRY M., MCKENZIE I.F.G. & BAILEY D.W. (1973) *Proc. Nat. Acad. Sci. U.S.A.* **70**, 1108.
(d) SATO H. & BOYSE E.A. (1976) *Immunogenetics* **3**, 565.
(e) HUBER B., GERSHON R.K. & CANTOR H. (1977) *J. exp. Med.* **145**, 10.
(f) FREUND J.A., AHMED A., BUDD R.E., DORF M.E., SELL K.W., VANNIER W.E. & HUMPHREYS R.E. (1976) *J. Immunol.* **117**, 1903.
(g) AHMED A., SHER I., SHARROW S., SMITH A., PAUL W.E., SACHS D.H. & SELL K.W. (1977) *J. exp. Med.* **145**, 101.
(h) MCDEVITT H.O., DELOVITCH T.L., PRESS J.L. & MURPHY D.B. (1976) *Transplant. Rev.* **30**, 1977.
(i) AHMED A., SCHER I. & SELL K.W. (1976) In EIJSVOGEL V.P., ROOS D. & ZEYLEMAKER W.P. (eds), *Proc. 10th Leukocyte Culture Conference*, p. 703. Academic Press, New York.
(j) GELFAND M.C., ELFENBEIN G.J., FRANK M.M. & PAUL W.E. (1974) *J. exp. Med.* **139**, 1125.

coded by a non-*H-2* locus.) At later stages in their development B cells have a lower density of sIgM and increased amounts of sIgD. All B cells in CBA/N mice of any age express the neonatal marker phenotype. The only defining marker for memory cells is a reduced expression of sIgD and commitment to the expression of the class of immunoglobulin they will make as plasma cells. As B lymphocytes differentiate into plasma cells they begin to express Ala 1 and Pca 1 (alloantigens) and H9/25, an alloantigen defined by a monoclonal antibody. Although plasma cells have an increased amount of H-2 they do not express sIg or C3b receptors.

References

ABNEY E.R., COOPER M.D., KEARNEY J.F., LAWTON A.R. & PARKHOUSE R.M.E. (1977) A Model for the Development of Immunoglobulin Isotype Diversity. In SERCARZ E.E., HERZENBERG L.A. & FOX F. (eds), *Immune System, Genetics and Regulation*, p. 313. Academic Press, New York.

COUTINHO A. & MÖLLER G. (1974) Immune activation of B cells: evidence for 'one non-specific triggering signal' not delivered by the Ig receptors. *Scand. J. Immunol.* **3**, 133.

COUTINHO A., FORNI L. & WATANABE T. (1978) Genetic and functional characterization of an antiserum to the lipid A-specific triggering receptor on murine B lymphocytes. *Europ. J. Immunol.* **8**, 63.

DINTZIS H.M., DINTZIS R.Z. & VOGELSTEIN B. (1976) Molecular determinants of immuno-genicity: the immunon model of the immune response. *Proc. Nat. Acad. Sci. U.S.A.* **73**, 3671.

FU S.M., WINCHESTER R.J., FEIZI T., WALZER P.D. & KUNKEL H.G. (1974) Idiotypic specificity of surface immunoglobulin and the maturation of leukaemic bone-marrow derived lymphocytes. *Proc. Nat. Acad. Sci. U.S.A.* **71**, 4487.

GLICK B., CHANG T.S. & JAAP R.L. (1956) The Bursa of Fabricius and antibody production. *Poultry Sci.* **35**, 224.

GODING J.W. & LAYTON J.E. (1976) Antigen-induced co-capping of IgM- and IgD-like receptors on murine B cells. *J. exp. Med.* **144**, 82.

KLAUS G.G.B. & HUMPHREY J.H. (1977) The generation of memory cells. 1. The role of C3 in the generation of B memory cells. *Immunology* **33**, 31.

KLINMAN N.R., SIGAL N.H., METCALF E.S., PIERCE S.K. & GEARHART P.J. (1977) The interplay of evolution and environment in B cell diversification. *Cold Spr. Harb. Symp. Quant. Biol.* **41**, 165.

LE DOUARIN N.B., JOTEREAU F.V. & HOUSSAINT E. (1976) The lymphoid stem cells in the avian embryo. In WRIGHT R.K. & COOPER E.L. (eds), *Phylogeny of Thymus and Bone Marrow–Bursa Cells*. Elsevier, North-Holland, Amsterdam.

LIU C-P., TUCKER P.W., MUSHINSKI J.F. & BLATTNER F.R. (1980) Mapping of heavy chain genes for mouse immunoglobulin M and D. *Science* **209**, 1348.

LYDYARD P.M., GROSSI C.E. & COOPER M.D. (1976) Ontogeny of B cells in the chicken. 1. Sequential development of clonal diversity in the Bursa. *J. exp. Med.* **144**, 79.

METCALF E.S. & KLINMAN N.R. (1976) *In vitro* tolerance induction in neonatal murine B cells. *J. exp. Med.* **143**, 1327.

NOSSAL G.J.V. & PIKE B.L. (1975) Evidence for the clonal abortion theory of B-lymphocyte tolerance. *J. exp. Med.* **141**, 904.

OWEN J.J.T., COOPER M.D. & RAFF M.C. (1974) *In vitro* generation of B lymphocytes in mouse fetal liver, a mammalian 'Bursa' equivalent. *Nature* **249**, 361.

RABBITS T.H., FORSTER A., DUNNICK W. & BENTLEY D.L. (1980) The role of gene deletion in the immunoglobulin heavy chain switch. *Nature London* **283**, 351.

ROELANTS G.E. & ASKONAS B.A. (1972) Immunological memory in thymus-deprived mice. *Nature (New Biol.)* **239**, 63.

SHER I., AHMED A., STRONG D., STEINBERG A.D. & PAUL W.E. (1975) X-linked B lymphocyte immune defect in CBA/HM mice. 1. Studies of function and composition of spleen cells. *J. exp. Med.* **141**, 788.

WATSON J. & RIBLETT R. (1974) Genetic control of responses to bacterial lipopolysaccharides in mice. 1. Evidence for a single gene that influences mitogenic and immunogenic responses to lipopolysaccharides. *J. exp. Med.* **140**, 1147.

Chapter 9
T lymphocytes

9.1 Introduction

The thymus is central to immunological functions. This was first recognized by Miller and Good in the early 1960s who showed that neo-natal thymectomy or congenital absence of the thymus impaired T cell-mediated immune reactions. It is now clear that T cells have distinct developmental pathways, possess unique combinations of cell surface markers and within lymphoid tissue have characteristic homing potentials and anatomical locations.

9.2 Ontogeny of cells in the thymus

The fixed tissue framework of the thymus is predominantly derived from mesodermal and endodermal elements of the third and in some species the fourth pharyngeal pouches. Although the thymic epithelial cells and the connective tissue are derived from endoderm and mesoderm respectively, the bulk component of the thymus—the lymphocyte or thymocyte—is derived from immigrant stem cells originating in the bone marrow and fetal liver. The time of stem cell colonization of the developing thymus in birds has been accurately determined by embryonic tissue grafting between chicks and quails (Le Dourain et al., see Chapter 8). These studies (Fig. 9.1) have shown that in birds there is a short 'window' from about the fifth to sixth day of embryonic life when the thymus is receptive to colonization by immigrant stem cells. It was also found that a second wave of stem cells entered the thymus around birth, their progeny replacing the first set of lymphocytes. During the rest of the life of the bird it is presumed that small numbers of stem cells continuously enter the thymus.

In mice stem cell colonization of the thymus begins around the eleventh day of embryonic life. The entry of stem cells or their intrathymic proliferation is possibly restricted to very few stem cells. Wallis et al. (1975) showed that if lethally irradiated mice were repopulated with a 50:50 mix of normal and chromosomally marked bone-marrow cells then either one or other of the stem cell populations was found to predominate in the lobes of the repopulated thymus. It was calculated from these experiments that an irradiated thymus could be fully repopulated from as few as ten stem cells. Since T cells recognize more than ten specificities this result implies that

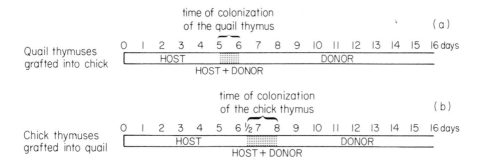

Fig. 9.1. Time of stem cell colonization of embryonic thymus in birds. (a) Quail thymuses were transplanted at different developmental stages into 3-day-old chick embryos. When the thymuses had reached the 14-day stage the origin of cell types present were determined cytogenetically. (b) Comparable studies in the reverse combination. For full details of experimental protocol see Chapter 8, Fig. 8.1. (From Le Douarin *et al.*, 1976.)

the development of the T cell repertoire occurs after the cells have either entered or left the thymus although in this experiment the ability of the mature T cells to respond to antigens was not tested.

9.2.1 Pre-T cells

It is unknown whether stem cells become committed to T cell differentiation before or after they have entered the thymus. The only evidence for pre-thymic commitment comes from studies on the 3.5 per cent of normal bone-marrow cells which express terminal deoxynucleotidyl transferase (TdT), an enzyme present in cortical thymocytes which sequentially adds mononucleotides to any 3'-OH end of DNA in a template independent reaction. Sixty per cent of the bone-marrow cells carrying TdT can be induced to express T cell markers following incubation *in vitro* with substances such as thymopoietin (see section 9.3) (Silverstone *et al.*, 1976).

9.3 Thymic 'hormones'

The possibility that the thymus is an endocrine organ which regulates T lymphocyte differentiation has been investigated by a number of laboratories. The impetus for this research lies in the hope that certain T cell immunodeficiencies might be due to an imbalance of thymic hormones and the possibility of correcting such deficiencies either with the isolated hormones or their synthetic analogues is attractive. There is no question that 'factors' can be isolated from the thymus of a wide variety of species (Table 9.1). The bioassays used to define the activities of these factors rely on the induction *in vitro* and *in vivo* of T cell characteristics or functions in immature

Table 9.1. Thymic hormones

Name	Original extract	Chemistry	Comments	Reference
Thymopoietin I and II	Bovine thymus	Sequenced; 49 amino acids, M.W. 5,562	Produced only within the thymus. Active peptide synthesized	(a), (b)
Ubiquitin	Bovine thymus	Sequenced; 74 amino acids, M.W. 8,451	Present in many tissues, bacteria, yeasts, and higher plants. Active peptide synthesized	(c), (d)
Facteur thymique serique (FTS)	Pig serum	9 amino acids	Present in serum; disappears after thymectomy. Recently extracted from thymus. Whole peptide synthesized	(e), (f)
Thymosin	Bovine thymus	Several poly-peptides; M.W. 2,000–5,000. Two (α_1 and α_2) are sequenced	Some are produced specifically by thymic epithelial cells. α_1 synthesized	(g)
Thymic humoral factor (THF)	Thymus of many species	M.W. 3,000	No sequence data yet available	(h)

References

(a) SCHLESINGER D.H. & GOLDSTEIN G. (1975) *Cell* **5**, 361.
(b) GOLDSTEIN G., SCHEID M.P., BOYSE E.A., BRAND A. & GILMOUR D.G. (1977) In *Cold Spr. Harb. Symp. Quant. Biol.* **41**, 5.
(c) SCHLESINGER D.H., GOLDSTEIN G. & NIALL H.D. (1975) *Biochemistry* **14**, 2214.
(d) SCHLESINGER D.H., GOLDSTEIN G., SCHEID M.P., BOYSE E.A. & TREGEAR G.W. (1975) *Fed. Proc.* **34**, 551.
(e) BACH J.-F., DARDENNE M., PLEAU J.-M. & ROSA J. (1977) *Nature* **266**, 55.
(f) BACH M.A., FOURNIER C. & BACH J.-F. (1979) In *Cell Biology and Immunology of Leukocyte Function. 12th International Leukocyte Culture Conference.* p. 177. Academic Press, New York.
(g) THURMAN G.B., MARSHALL G.D., LOW T.L.K. & GOLDSTEIN A.L. (1979) In *Cell Biology and Immunology of Leukocyte Function. 12th International Leukocyte Culture Conference.* p. 189. Academic Press, New York.
(h) TRAININ N., YAKIR J. & COOK A.I. (1979) In *Cell Biology and Immunology of Leukocyte Function. 12th International Leukocyte Culture Conference.* p. 201. Academic Press, New York.

populations. There are, however, a large number of pharmacologically active agents (epinephrine, ubiquitin and cyclic AMP) which have exactly the same effects and the physiological relevance of many of the assays for thymic factors remains to be established. Nonetheless, it is intriguing that certain synthetic analogues mimic the activity of the isolated 'hormones' (e.g. thymopoietin) and at least one has been found to restore immune functions *in vivo* in certain categories of immunodeficient animals (Bach *et al.*, 1979). So far none of the factors have been shown to fully substitute for the intact thymus and its rôle as an endocrine organ remains to be established.

9.4 T cell specific alloantisera

Thymocyte differentiation can be analysed by use of T cell specific alloantisera. Alloantisera which can define T cell alloantigens have been raised by cross-immunizing *H-2* identical mice with thymocytes (see Boyse & Old, 1978). The sera are tested for cytotoxic antibodies specific to T cells and suitable sera are used to determine the distribution of the allele in a variety of inbred strains. Success in this type of strategy depends entirely on the chance of cross-immunizing strains of mice which carry allelic variants of a T cell surface molecule.

Heteroantisera to T cells require extensive absorptions with non-T cells to obtain a T cell specific reagent and even then it is not clear whether they are specific for determinants on individual molecules or contain antibodies to a variety of T cell surface proteins. Monoclonal antibodies (Kohler & Milstein, 1975) produced through the technique of cell fusion are ideally suited for the characterization of molecules on cells since determinant specific antibody can be obtained without the need for first purifying the antigens. This approach is now being used extensively to detect cell surface differentiation antigens (see Williams *et al.*, 1977a; Milstein *et al.*, 1979).

9.4.1 *Membrane molecules characteristic of thymocytes and T cells*

Antigens associated with different populations of mouse thymocytes and T cells are shown in Table 9.2 and a gene map of those associated with chromosome 17 is shown in Fig. 6.3.

Table 9.2. Alloantigens on mouse thymocytes

Surface antigen	Alleles		Allelic antigens		Chromosome
Thy 1	*Thy 1ᵃ*	*Thy 1ᵇ*	Thy 1.1	Thy 1.2	9
Lyt 1	*Lyt 1ᵃ*	*Lyt 1ᵇ*	Lyt 1.1	Lyt 1.2	19
Lyt 2	*Lyt 2ᵃ*	*Lyt 2ᵇ*	Lyt 2.1	Lyt 2.2	6
Lyt 3	*Lyt 3ᵃ*	*Lyt 3ᵇ*	Lyt 3.1	Lyt 3.2	6
Qa1	*Qa1ᵃ*	*Qa1ᵇ*	Not designated		
Qa2	*Qa2ᵃ*	*Qa2ᵇ*	because products of		
Qa3	*Qa3ᵃ*	*Qa3ᵇ*	*Qa* of *b* type have not		17
Qa4	*Qa4ᵃ*	*Qa4ᵇ*	yet been detected and		
Qa5	*Qa5ᵃ*	*Qa5ᵇ*	indeed may not exist (e.g. null alleles)		
TL	See Chapter 6		TL 1, 2, 3, 4, 5 and 6		17
G IX	(Gross virus glycoprotein)				17 but 4 in AKR strain

(a) *Thy 1*. Thy 1 is the product of a single locus with two alleles *Thy 1ª* and *Thy 1ᵇ* which code for antigens designated Thy 1.1 and Thy 1.2 respectively. All mice express one or other of these two antigens. In rats a Thy 1-like molecule has been isolated from brain and thymus. It is a glycoprotein of 24,000 M.W. (Williams *et al.*, 1977b). In mice Thy 1 is of similar size and found on thymus cells, thymic epithelial cells, peripheral T cells, brain, epidermal cells and fibroblasts. Consequently the presence of Thy 1 on a cell does not imply T cell origin or involvement in immune functions.

(b) *Lyt antigens*. The Lyt series of alloantigens are unlike Thy 1 in being confined to T cells (Cantor & Boyse, 1975). There are three well characterized Lyt loci, *Lyt 1* on chromosome 19, *Lyt 2* and *Lyt 3* closely linked on chromosome 6. Each locus has two alleles (*a* and *b*) specifying alternative antigens denoted 1 and 2. Thus the alleles of *Lyt 1* specify antigens Lyt 1.1 and Lyt 1.2 and similarly for *Lyt 2* and *Lyt 3*. All inbred mice so far tested express one or other of these allelic forms which show differential expression on T cells and T cell subpopulations. Lyt 1 is carried on a polypeptide chain of 70,000 daltons. Early studies suggested that Lyt 2 and Lyt 3 were carried on the same 35,000 M.W. glycoprotein. Furthermore, no recombinants between *Lyt 2* and *Lyt 3* have yet been observed and it is claimed that antibodies to Lyt 2 and Lyt 3 weakly cross block on the cell surface. However, recent evidence that glycoproteins bearing the Lyt 2 and Lyt 3 antigens can be sequentially precipitated from soluble cell membrane preparations (Durda & Gottlieb, 1978) suggests that these determinants are in fact carried on distinct molecules.

(c) *TL antigens*. The determinants (TL 1–6) are coded by the *Tla* locus which lies to the right of the *H-2* region. They are all present on the same 44,000 M.W. glycoprotein (see Chapter 6.5) associated in the membrane with β_2 microglobulin.

(d) *Qa antigens*. These antigens are coded by five closely linked loci, *Qa1–Qa5*, which map between *H-2 D* and *Tla*. Qa1 and Qa2 are present on thymus cells as well as peripheral T cells defining in certain cases particular T cell subsets (see section 9.5.2) whereas Qa3, Qa4 and Qa5 are present on peripheral T cells only.

(e) *Virus-associated antigens*. Many strain specific murine leukaemia viruses are vertically transmitted and certain cell membrane associated viral glycoproteins on transformed or infected cells may masquerade as alloantigens. The most notable example is G IX, the 70,000 M.W. glycoprotein (gp 70) component of the Gross leukaemia virus whose distribution on T cells is similar to TL.

9.5 Organization and differentiation of cells within the thymus

Both the cortical and medullary regions of the thymus are interspersed with thymic epithelial cells. These cells have a stellate appearance in the cortex due to dense infiltration with thymocytes and their functions remain undetermined (Fig 9.2). The recent discovery that thymic epithelial cells express Ia antigens has implicated these cells in T cell development (see Chapter 11.6). The cortical–medullary distinction may have functional significance since peripheral T cells are largely derived from the cortical thymocytes whereas medullary thymocytes are predominantly a long-lived intrathymic population of unknown function. In addition, there are marked differences in the expression of alloantigens between cortical and medullary thymocytes (Fig. 9.3) the latter having surface markers similar to peripheral T cells (Mathieson *et al.*, 1979).

9.6 Distribution of markers on peripheral T cells

Both the Lyt and Qa alloantigenic systems have permitted the subdivision of peripheral T cells into functionally distinct T cell subsets (Fig. 9.4a). Most peripheral T cells are Lyt 1^+23^+, about 35 per cent are Lyt 1^+23^- and a minority (5–10 per cent) are Lyt 1^-23^+. As described below, the Qa system also permits further characterization of T cells and it seems inevitable that as more markers are described more subdivisions will be recognized.

9.6.1 *Lyt 1^+23^+ T cells*

These cells are derived from the Lyt 1^+23^+ cells in the thymic cortex. They are cortisone sensitive, relatively short lived, rapidly dividing and, although present in the peripheral lymphocyte pool, are predominantly found in peripheral blood and spleen. They are precursors of the more stable Lyt 1^-23^+ peripheral T cells (see section 9.6.3).

9.6.2 *Lyt 1^+23^- T cells*

Recent evidence suggests that these are derived directly from the Lyt 1^+23^- cortical thymocytes (Scollay & Weissman, 1979) and function as amplifier or helper T cells (see Chapter 10). They are relatively cortisone resistant and enhance the activity of other cells in the immune system including B cells, cytotoxic cells, macrophages in delayed hypersensitivity reactions and suppressor cells. The amplifying functions seem to be mediated by a subdivision of the Lyt 1^+23^- subset. For example, some of the cells which generate helper activity for B cells are Lyt 1^+23^-, Qa 1^- and are quite distinct from those amplifying suppressor cell functions (Lyt 1^+23^-, Qa 1^+). It is also quite possible that different T helper cells are involved in activation of B cells making different classes of antibody.

9.6.3 *Lyt 1^-23^+ T cells*

This subpopulation contains distinct cell types which are the effector cells in

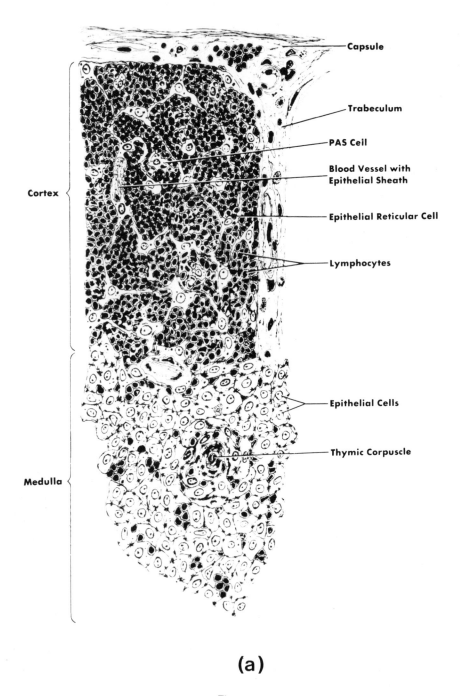

(a)

Fig. 9.2.

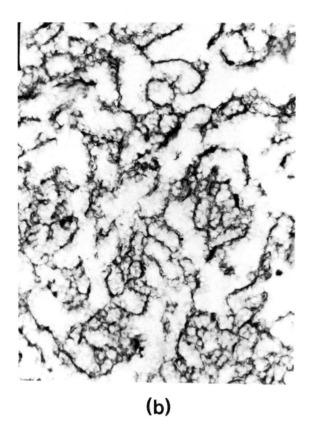

(b)

Fig. 9.2. (a) A portion of a thymic lobule. The thymic epithelial cells are spread throughout the thymus but in the cortex they are densely infiltrated with thymocytes. The epithelial cells have a stellate appearance (epithelial reticular cells) and their long dendritic processes are connected to each other. The medulla is closer to a pure epithelium with some infiltration by thymocytes (Weiss, 1972). (b) Frozen section of a thymic cortex stained indirectly with peroxidase labelled anti-mouse immunoglobulin to reveal thymic epithelial cells reacting with a monoclonal, mouse anti-Ia^k. The dendritic processes of the epithelial reticular cells are Ia^+ and are revealed as thick dark lines interwoven with Ia^- (unstained) thymocytes (by permission of Professor I. Weissman and Dr W. van Ewijk).

cell-mediated cytotoxicity and suppression. Many categories of suppressor cells express products of the I-J region of H-2, whereas cytotoxic cells do not. The latter, however, express a $145,000$ M.W. membrane glycoprotein (T145) which can bind a lectin from Vicia Villosa and this has been exploited in the isolation of activated cytotoxic cells (Kimura & Wigzell, 1978).

Lyt 1^+23^- and Lyt 1^-23^+ are stable T cell subsets and do not switch from one to the other cell type. If B mice (see glossary) are reconstituted with either subset of T

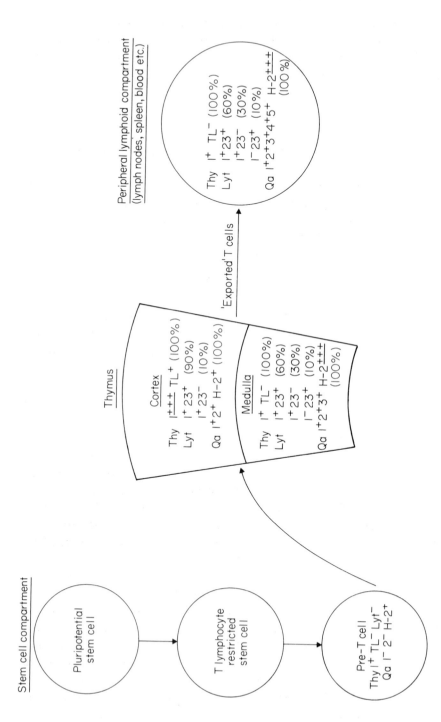

Fig. 9.3. Alloantigenic expression during T cell differentiation in mice. The relative amounts of many of the antigens vary at different stages ($- \rightarrow +++$). The approximate percentage of T cells expressing a particular phenotype is also shown. (Lyt $\text{I}^+ 23^+$ means presence of Lyt 1, Lyt 2 and Lyt 3. Since the expression of Lyt 2 and Lyt 3 always go together, T cells are designated as 23^+ or 23^-.)

cells, their T cell phenotype remains stable for up to 6 months (Huber *et al.*, 1976). Mice reconstituted with Lyt 1^+23^- cells have T helper cells for antibody formation, produce delayed hypersensitivity reactions to SRBC, but fail to generate cytotoxic cells. The Lyt 1^-23^+ mice are devoid of amplifier cells and only generate low levels of cytotoxic or suppressor cells.

9.7 T cell heterogeneity in man

As the human population is neither inbred nor experimentally immunized classification of T cells with alloantisera is less advanced than in mice. Nonetheless, certain allo- and heteroantisera have been used to define human T cells in addition to a variety of other idiosyncratic marker systems based on rosetting assays for membrane receptors and mitogen responsiveness. The peripheral T cell population in man also contains functionally distinct T cell subsets (Fig. 9.4).

9.7.1 *Heteroantisera*

Certain heteroantisera (rabbit or equine) have been described which after absorption with non-T cells detect antigens apparently restricted to thymocytes and peripheral T cell subsets. Schlossman and his colleagues (Chess & Schlossman, 1977; Reinherz *et al.*, 1979a) have described T cell specific antigens which they have designated as HTL (thymocyte only), TH_1 (thymocytes and 60 per cent of peripheral T cells) and TH_2 (thymocytes and 25 per cent of peripheral T cells). The TH_2^+ subset contains cytotoxic and suppressor T cells whereas the TH_2^- subset can provide T cell help for the generation of cytotoxic cells.

A number of monoclonal antibodies to human T cells have now been described. Reinherz and his colleagues have developed a panel of such antibodies which are believed to define distinct stages of T cell differentiation within the thymus and peripheral T cell pool. The antigens recognized by these antibodies have been designated T1, T2, T3, etc. (Reinherz *et al.*, 1979b; Reinherz & Schlossman, 1980). Their distribution on T cells and cell surface molecules precipitated by these reagents are shown in Fig. 9.4b,c and Table 9.3. The earliest stages of thymus cell differentiation are characterized by the expression of T9 and T10 only. These cells are believed to be the precursors of cells expressing T4, T5, T6 and T8. The T4 and T5 markers have proved the most useful since they define distinct T cell subsets within the thymus as well as in the peripheral T cell compartment where they appear to define both the helper ($T4^+$) and the suppressor/cytotoxic ($T5^+$) subsets. Another monoclonal antibody has been described which detects an antigen (HTA 1) with a similar distribution to TL in mice, in that it is present only on thymocytes and leukaemic T cells (McMichael *et al.*, 1979). The molecule detected by this monoclonal antibody is a 45,000 M.W. glycoprotein associated in the membrane with a 12,000 M.W. polypeptide which does not react with antisera to human β_2 microglobulin.

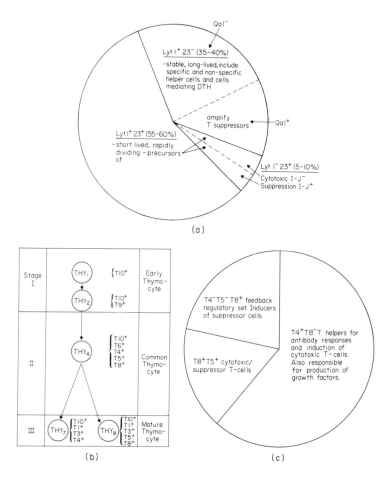

Fig. 9.4. Functional T cell sub-populations in mouse (a) and human (b) and (c). The divisions in mice are recognized by defined alloantisera and apply to T cells in the secondary lymphoid tissue. In man different T cell subsets are recognized monoclonal antibodies. The different stages of intrathymic T cell development are shown in (b) and the functions of the various peripheral T cell subsets is shown in (c) (b and c taken from Reinherz & Schlossman, 1980).

9.7.2 Alloantisera

Certain conventional tissue typing sera have been found to contain alloantibodies which react with the T_μ and T_γ populations (see section 9.6.3). Sera from patients with juvenile rheumatoid arthritis (JRA) have also been shown to contain an autoantibody which reacts with 30 per cent of TH_2 negative lymphocytes and these sera distinguish certain functionally different T cells in human peripheral blood.

Table 9.3. Monoclonal antibodies to human T cell surface antigens

| Monoclonal antibody | Molecular weight of antigen | | Cellular expression | | |
	Reduced	Unreduced	Thymus (%)	P.B. E+ (%)	E− (%)
Anti-T1 (Total)	65K	65K	10	100	0
Anti-T3 (Total)	19K	19K	10	100	0
Anti-T4 (Inducer)	62K	62K	75	60	0
Anti-T5 (Cytotoxic/Suppressor)	30K+32K	70K	80	20	0
Anti-T8 (Cytotoxic/Suppressor)	30K+32K	70K	80	30	0
Anti-T6	49K+12K	49K+12K	70	0	0
Anti-T9	100K	200K	10	0	0
Anti-T10	45K	45K	95 ,	<5	10

P.B. = Peripheral blood T cells.
E+ = E rosette positive T cells.
E− = E rosette negative cells.
(Data from Reinherz and Schlossman).

9.7.3 Receptors for the Fc part of IgM and IgG

In man T cells with different Fc receptors appear to have different functional properties (see Moretta *et al.*, 1979). Forty to fifty per cent of human peripheral blood T cells have membrane receptors for the Fc part of IgM (T_μ). These are distinct from those with membrane receptors for the Fc part of IgG (T_γ, 5–15 per cent). Claims have been made that the T_μ population contains helper cells and that the T_γ population contains suppressor cells.

9.8 The antigen receptor on T lymphocytes

The expectation that the T cell receptor for antigen is an immunoglobulin or at least uses immunoglobulin V regions has proved hard to demonstrate experimentally. The T cell receptor is still not fully characterized (see Lindahl and Rajewsky, 1979).

9.8.1 Attempts to detect surface immunoglobulin on T cells

Thymus and peripheral T cells do not express surface immunoglobulin at the concentration observed on B cells. Where claims have been made that trace amounts are detectable ($\sim 10^3$ molecules per cell) it is often difficult to determine whether the immunoglobulin detected is endogenous or passively acquired. In the latter case, the immunoglobulin could adhere either to Fc receptors on activated T cells or to antigen already bound to the true receptor. Equally forceful claims that not even trace amounts of immunoglobulin are present on T cells have made this a sterile argument.

A different approach to analysing the T cell receptor is to determine functionally

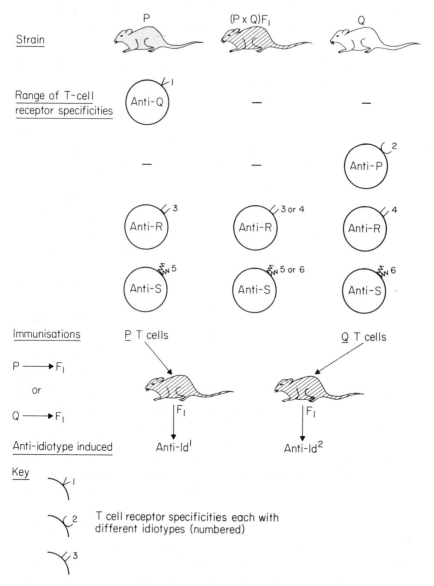

Fig. 9.5. Experimental procedure for raising antibodies to the idiotypes (anti-Id) on T cell receptors specific for MHS alloantigens (description in text).

whether T and B cells express the same idiotype (see Chapter 1) and, if so, whether the T cell idiotype is genetically linked to the immunoglobulin heavy chain genes.

9.8.2 Inheritable idiotypes on alloreactive T cells

Binz and Wigzell (1977) have shown that in certain strains of rat the specific T cell receptors for major histocompatibility antigens express the same idiotypes as serum antibodies of the same specificity. Their experimental system is outlined in Fig. 9.5. In principle F_1 animals derived from MHS different strains (say P and Q) inherit the capacity to recognize the alloantigens of both parents. This property is never expressed in the F_1 since T cells with these specificities will be clonally eliminated during ontogeny (see Chapter 13). The corollary to this is that the specific receptors on P (or Q) strain cells for Q (or P) strain alloantigens are foreign idiotypes to the F_1 and following immunization with cells bearing these idiotypes the F_1 will make anti-idiotypic antibodies to these receptors. (This would be expected from considerations of the network hypothesis although the original experiments by Ramseier and Lindemann (1972) were done before the network hypothesis was fully developed.) In practice, anti-idiotypic antibodies to P strain receptors for Q alloantigens are raised by injecting P strain T cells into the F_1. The P strain T cells proliferate to the Q strain alloantigens (i.e. a graft versus host reaction) and the F_1 in turn responds by making anti-idiotypic antibodies.

These antibodies have the following properties. They detect the idiotype on about 10 per cent of P strain T cells and these idiotype positive T cells are absent if the P strain rats have been rendered tolerant to Q or if a different strain (R) is used. (Strain R possesses T cells which recognize Q alloantigens but these cells express different idiotypes.) The anti-idiotypic antibodies can block the ability of P strain T cells to respond to Q alloantigens both *in vitro* (mixed lymphocyte reaction) or *in vivo* (graft rejection) and react with a proportion of the P strain alloantibodies to Q. This latter finding is important since it implies that T and B lymphocytes may express the same V regions. By immunoprecipitation of labelled T cell membrane proteins the idiotype was shown to be associated with a molecule of 150,000 M.W. comprising two chains each of 75,000 M.W. with no detectable light chains. Finally genetic analysis revealed that the T cell idiotype was linked to the immunoglobulin heavy-chain allotype (Binz et al., 1976). Antisera to immunoglobulin constant regions failed to react with the idiotype positive material, as did antisera to the rat MHS.

Similar findings have been reported in mice (Krammer & Eichmann, 1977). In these experiments genetic studies showed that the expression of the idiotype on T cells was dependent on the inheritance of genes linked to immunoglobulin heavy chain allotypes and the MHS. It is unknown in this case whether the MHS actually codes for part of the T cell receptor or indirectly influences the T cell repertoire (see Chapter 12).

9.8.3 Idiotypes on T cell receptors for haptens

Rajewsky and his colleagues (Krawinkel *et al.*, 1978) have characterized antigen-specific molecules made by T cells using an extremely sensitive phage neutralization assay. In their experiments antigen-specific T cells were first allowed to adsorb to insoluble hapten conjugated nylon fibres at 4°C. On raising the temperature to 37°C the cells became detached from the haptenated fibres leaving their 'receptors' still bound to the antigen. These were later recovered and tested for phage neutralization using hapten-coupled phages. The antigen-specific material isolated from T cells failed to react with anti-immunoglobulin antisera though material similarly isolated from B cells was found to be conventional immunoglobulin.

By exploiting an inheritable idiotypic system (see Chapter 1) the isolated T cell receptors were found to express the same idiotype as serum antibody to the hapten. The genes controlling the expression of the T cell idiotype were also shown to be linked to the genes for immunoglobulin heavy-chain allotype. Despite this genetic information the isolated T cell receptors were not associated with any known immunoglobulin constant region or with any of the products of the MHS (see Chapter 10.3.2).

The conclusion from these experiments is that the T cell repertoire is encoded at least in part by immunoglobulin V_H region genes but the nature of the rest of the molecule remains a mystery.

9.9 Antigen-specific T cell factors

A number of experimental systems have been described which claim to detect soluble antigen-specific T cell factors which can replace specific T cell functions. The relationship of these factors to cell interactions in the immune response is described in Chapter 10.3.2.

Antigen-specific T cell factors can be divided into two types depending on their biological activity (Table 9.3). Helper factors and suppressor factors substitute for helper and suppressor T cells in a variety of immune responses. They share certain properties with T cell receptors in that they show marked antigen specificity and in some cases express idiotypic determinants associated with the V_H region of immunoglobulin (Mozes and Haimovich, 1979; Germain *et al.*, 1979). Determinants associated with immunoglobulin constant regions have not been reproducibly found. These properties are similar to those of isolated T cell receptors, although in some cases their molecular weights (50,000–70,000) are in disagreement (see the Glossary for proper definition of molecular weight).

The fundamental differences between factors and isolated receptors is that the former express determinants coded for by the MHS, while the latter do not. Helper factors express *I-A* region determinants whereas suppressor factors react with

Table 9.4. Properties of isolated soluble antigen-specific T cell factors

Biological properties of factor	Cellular origin	Antigen specificity	Determinants			M.W. (approx.)	Reference
			V_H	C_H	MHS		
1. Helper	T—Lyt 1^+23^-	KLH		μ	?	150,000	(a)
	T—Lyt 1^+23^-	(T, G)-A--L		−	I-A	?	(b)
	T cells	SRBC		−	I-A	50,000	(c)
		(T, G)-A--L	+	−	I-A	50,000	(c), (j)
2. Suppressor	T—Lyt 1^-23^+	KLH+ various others		−	I	?	(d)
	T—Lyt 1^-23^+	KLH GAT	+	−	I-J	50,000	(e), (f), (k)
	T hybridoma	SRBC			+*	200,000	(g)
	T hybridoma	KLH			I-J	42,000–68,000	(h)
	T cells	Picrylchloride			+	50,000	(i)

+*=H-2 region undefined.

References

(a) FELDMANN M. (1972) *J. exp. Med.* **136**, 737.
(b) HOWIE S. & FELDMANN M. (1977) *Europ. J. Immunol.* **7**, 417.
(c) TAUSSIG M. & MUNRO A. (1974) *Nature* **251**, 63.
(d) KONTIAINEN S. & FELDMANN M. (1977) *Europ. J. Immunol.* **7**, 310.
(e) TADA T., TANIGUCHI M. & DAVID C.S. (1976) *J. exp. Med.* **144**, 713.
(f) THEZE J., KAPP J.A. & BENACERRAF B. (1977) *J. exp. Med.* **145**, 839.
(g) TAUSSIG M.J., CORVALAN J.R.F., BINNS R.M. & HOLLIMAN A. (1979) *Nature* **277**, 305.
(h) TANIGUCHI M., SAITO T. & TADA T. (1979) *Nature* **278**, 555.
(i) ZEMBALA M., ASHERSON G.L., MUNRO A.J. & TAGART V.B. (1977) *Int. Arch. Allergy. Appl. Immunol.* **54**, 183.
(j) MOZES E. & HAIMOVICH J. (1979) *Nature* **278**, 56.
(k) GERMAIN R.N., JU S.T., KIPPS T.J., BENACERRAF B. & DORF M.E. (1979) *J. exp. Med.* **149**, 613.

anti-I-J antisera. It is so far not known whether the MHS-associated products are an intrinsic part of the T cell molecule or become attached to the T cell receptor during the processes of release from the cell. In the latter case secondary association of MHS-coded products with secreted T cell receptors might direct their biological (i.e. secondary) functions; *I-A* region products determining help and *I-J* region products suppression.

It seems likely that the nature of T cell factors will remain unresolved until sufficient material becomes available for biochemical characterization. T-cell lines and T-cell hybridomas are being exploited to provide unlimited quantities of antigen-specific T cell factors for biochemical analysis.

References

BACH M.-A., FOURNIER C. & BACH J.-F. (1979) Biological Activities and Site of Action of the Circulating Thymic Factor. In QUASTEL M.R. (eds), *Cell Biology and Immunology of Leukocyte Function. 12th International Leukocyte Culture Conference*, p. 177. Academic Press, New York.

BINZ H., WIGZELL H. & BAZIN H. (1976) T cell idiotypes are linked to immunoglobulin heavy-chain genes. *Nature* **264**, 639.

BINZ H. & WIGZELL H. (1977) Antigen Binding, Idiotypic T Lymphocyte Receptors. In STUTMAN O. (ed.), *Contemporary Topics in Immunobiology* 7, 113. Plenum, New York.

BOYSE E.A. & OLD L.J. (1978) The Immunogenetics of Differentiation in the Mouse. In *Harvey Lectures Series 71*, p. 23. Academic Press, New York.

CANTOR H. & BOYSE E.A. (1975) Functional subclasses of T lymphocytes bearing different Ly antigens. 1. The generation of functionally distinct T cell subclasses is a differentiative process independent of antigen. *J. exp. Med.* **141**, 1389.

CHESS L. & SCHLOSSMAN S.F. (1977) Functional Analysis of Human T Cell Subsets Bearing Unique Differentiation Antigens. In STUTMAN O. (ed.), *Contemporary Topics in Immunobiology* 7, 363. Plenum, New York.

DURDA P.J. & GOTTLIEB P.D. (1978) Sequential precipitation of mouse thymocyte extracts with anti-Lyt 2 and anti-Lyt 3 sera. 1. Lyt 2.1 and Lyt 3.1 antigenic determinants reside on separate molecular species. *J. Immunol.* **121**, 983.

GERMAIN R.N., JU S.T., KIPPS T.J., BENACERRAF B. & DORF M.E. (1979) Shared idiotypic determinants on antibodies and T cell-derived suppressor factor specific for the random terpolymer L-glutamic acid L-alanine-L-tyrosine. *J. exp. Med.* **149**, 613.

HUBER B., CANTOR H., SHEN F.W. & BOYSE E.A. (1976) Independent differentiative pathways of Ly1 and Ly23 subclasses of T cells. Experimental production of mice deprived of selected T cell subclasses. *J. exp. Med.* **144**, 1128.

KIMURA A.K. & WIGZELL H. (1978) Cell surface glycoproteins of murine cytotoxic lymphocytes. 1. T145, a new cell surface glycoprotein selectively expressed on Ly1$^-$2$^+$ cytotoxic cells. *J. exp. Med.* **147**, 1418.

KOHLER G. & MILSTEIN C. (1975) Continuous culture of fused cells secreting antibody of predefined specificity. *Nature* **256**, 495.

KRAMMER P.H. & EICHMANN K. (1977) T cell receptor idiotypes are controlled by genes in the heavy-chain linkage group and the major histocompatibility complex. *Nature* **270**, 733.

KRAWINKEL V., CRAMER M., MELCHERS I., IMANISHI-KARI S. & RAJEWSKY K. (1978) Isolated hapten-binding receptor of sensitized lymphocytes. III. Evidence for idiotypic restriction of T cell receptors. *J. exp. Med.* **147**, 1341.

LINDAHL K.F. & RAJEWSKY K. (1979) T Cell Recognition: Genes, Molecules and Functions. In LENNOX E. (ed.), *Defense and Recognition*. Int. Rev. of Biochem. **22**, 97.

MCMICHAEL A.J., PILCH J.R., GALFRE G., MASON D.J., FABRE J.W. & MILSTEIN C. (1979) A human thymocyte antigen defined by a hybrid myeloma monoclonal antibody. *Eur. J. Immunol.* **9**, 205.

MATHIESON B.J., SHARON S.O., CAMPBELL P.S. & ASOFSKY R. (1979) A Lyt differentiated thymocyte subpopulation detected by flow microfluorimetry. *Nature* **277**, 478.

MILSTEIN C., GALFRE G., SECHER D.S. & SPRINGER T. (1979) Monoclonal antibodies and cell surface antigens. *CIBA Symposium No. 66*, p. 251. *Human Genetics: Possibilities and Realities*. Excerpta Medica, Amsterdam.

MORETTA L., FERRARINI M. & COOPER M.D. (1979) Characterization of human T cell subpopulations as defined by specific receptors for immunoglobulins. In STUTMAN O. (ed.), *Contemporary Topics in Immunobiology* 8, 19. Plenum, New York.

MOZES E. & HAIMOVICH J. (1979) Antigen-specific T cell factor cross-reacts idiotypically with antibodies of the same specificity. *Nature* **278**, 56.

RAMSEIER H. & LINDEMANN J. (1972) Similarity of cellular recognition structures for histocompatibility antigens and of combining sites of corresponding alloantibodies. *Eur. J. Immunol.* **2**, 109.

REINHERZ E.L., STRELKAUSKAS A.J., BRIEN C.O. & SCHLOSSMAN S.F. (1979a) Phenotypic and functional distinctions between TH$_2$+ and JRA+ T cell subsets in man. *J. Immunol.* **123**, 83.

REINHERZ E.L., KUNG P.C., GOLDSTEIN G. & SCHLOSSMAN S.F. (1979b) Separation of functional subsets of human T cells by a monoclonal antibody. *Proc. Nat. Acad. Sci. U.S.A.* **76**, 4061.

REINHERZ E.L. & SCHLOSSMAN S.F. (1980) The differentiation and function of human T lymphocytes. *Cell* **19**, 821.

SCOLLAY R. & WEISSMAN I. (1979) Lyt markers on thymus cell migrants. *Nature* **276**, 79.

SILVERSTONE A.L., CANTOR H., GOLDSTEIN F. & BALTIMORE D. (1976) Terminal deoxynucleotidyl transferase is found in prothymocyte. *J. exp. Med.* **144**, 543.

WALLIS V.J., LEUCHARS E., CHWALINSKI S. & DAVIES A.J.S. (1975) On the sparse seeding of bone marrow and thymus in radiation chimeras. *Transplantation* **19**, 1.

WEISS L. (1972) *The Cells and Tissues of the Immune System. Structure, Function and Interaction*, p. 81. Prentice-Hall, New York.

WILLIAMS A.F., BARCLAY A.N., LETARTE-MUIRHEAD M. & MORRIS R.J. (1977b) Rat Thy 1 antigens from thymus and brain: their tissue distribution, purification and chemical composition. *Cold Spr. Harb. Symp. Quant. Biol.* **41**, 51.

WILLIAMS A.F., GALFRE C. & MILSTEIN C. (1977a) Analysis of cell surfaces by xenogeneic myeloma-hybrid antibodies: differentiation antigens of rat lymphocytes. *Cell* **12**, 663.

Chapter 10
Cell Interactions in the
Immune Response

10.1 Introduction

About 10 years ago it was recognized through the discovery of T–B cell cooperation in the antibody response that lymphocyte interactions are an essential feature of the immune system. This is a central area of immunology and both this and the next two chapters will attempt to bring together the major principles. The reader is fore-warned that this is a rapidly moving field. Although the broad outlines are unlikely to change the fine details almost certainly will and you would be excused for thinking that one man's hypothesis is another man's nightmare. We hope we have spared you some of the nightmares.

10.2 Types of cell interactions

Cell interactions in the immune response allow selective expansion or suppression of specific clones of lymphocytes. The antigen receptor is the only clonally distributed structure on lymphocytes and must be involved in selective cell interactions either through interaction with antigen or through idiotype anti-idiotype recognition. The latter, somewhat surprisingly, can lead to lymphocyte activation or suppression in the *absence* of antigen.

The phenomenon of T–B cell cooperation in the antibody response was the first type of cell interaction to be studied and it remains the most widely used model system. The mechanisms for T–B cooperation are in principle the same as for other cell interactions. Direct contact of specific cells can occur either through an antigen bridge (linked recognition) or through idiotype recognition. Interactions not involving direct contact are mediated largely by non-specific factors released by one of the cell types which influence the response of the other cell (Fig. 10.1).

10.3 T cell help in the immune response

Helper T cells belong to the Lyt 1^+23^- subset. They can provide both specific and non-specific help for B cells or for the subsets of T cells involved in cytotoxic or suppressor reactions. The Lyt 1^+23^- subset can be subdivided (see Chapter 9) and it is likely that several functionally distinct categories of helper cells will eventually be recognized.

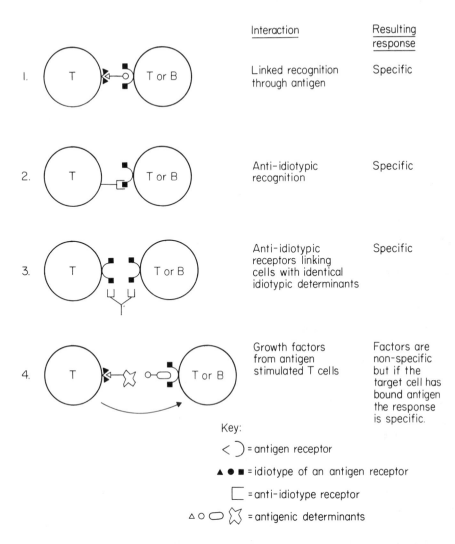

	Interaction	Resulting response
1.	Linked recognition through antigen	Specific
2.	Anti-idiotypic recognition	Specific
3.	Anti-idiotypic receptors linking cells with identical idiotypic determinants	Specific
4.	Growth factors from antigen stimulated T cells	Factors are non-specific but if the target cell has bound antigen the response is specific.

Key:

$<\,)$ = antigen receptor

▲ ● ■ = idiotype of an antigen receptor

$\llcorner\,$ = anti-idiotype receptor

△ ○ ⊂⊃ ⟨⟩ = antigenic determinants

Fig. 10.1. Various types of lymphocyte interaction. Antigen-specific lymphocytes may be linked either by antigen or through their idiotypes via anti-idiotype recognition by cells or antibody.

10.3.1 T cell help in the antibody response

The failure of irradiated adult mice to make an antibody response can be corrected by reconstitution with thymus and bone-marrow cells (Claman *et al.*, 1966; and see preamble II.4.2). The two populations act synergistically since if either is omitted no response occurs (Table 10.1). The thymus provides T cells which specifically respond to antigen, but do not make antibody. Neonatally thymectomised mice lack this population of cells and the response of such animals can be restored with T cells alone. The precursors of the antibody-secreting cells come from the bone marrow (Davies *et al.*, 1966; Miller & Mitchell, 1968; Nossal *et al.*, 1968). If bone-marrow cells with a known chromosomal or surface marker are used for reconstitution then this marker is found in all the antibody-forming cells. The essential points arising from these studies are listed in Table 10.1.

It was also shown by Mitchison and his colleagues that two cell populations were required in the secondary (IgG) anti-hapten response to hapten-carrier conjugates (Fig. 10.2). When irradiated mice were reconstituted with syngeneic spleen cells from donor cells primed to NIP (4-hydroxy-3-iodo-5-nitrophenacetyl) coupled to ovalbumin (OVA) as carrier (i.e. NIP–OVA) then a secondary anti-NIP response only occurred following challenge with NIP on the same but not different carriers (e.g. NIP–BSA). If the irradiated mice were reconstituted with a mixture of spleen cells primed separately to the carrier (BSA) or to the hapten (NIP as NIP–OVA), then high titres of anti-NIP were produced on challenge with NIP–BSA. The significance of these experiments is that a secondary anti-hapten response involves two separate

Table 10.1. Reconstitution of immune responsiveness to SRBC in immunologically unresponsive mice

Pretreatment[2] (CBA strain)	Reconstitution with	PFC response[1] of CBA recipients after *in vivo* challenge with SRBC
Lethal irradiation	No cells	−
	CBA thymus cells	−
	CBA bone-marrow cells	−
	Thymus cells and bone-marrow cells	+
Neonatal thymectomy	No cells	−
	CBA thymus cells	+
	CBA thoracic duct lymphocytes	+
	CBA thoracic duct lymphocytes from SRBC tolerant mice	−
	Bone-marrow cells	−
	(CBA × C57Bl) F_1 thymus cells	+ (all PFC have CBA alloantigens *only*)

Summary of data from Claman *et al.* (1966) and Miller and Mitchell (1968).

Notes

(1) Response: + = 20,000 PFC/spleen, − = 2,000 PFC/spleen.
(2) Lethal irradiation results in death in 14–21 days and all experiments are carried out within the first 7 days, thus avoid the effects of T cell precursors maturing in the thymus. PFC = plaque forming or antibody secreting cell.

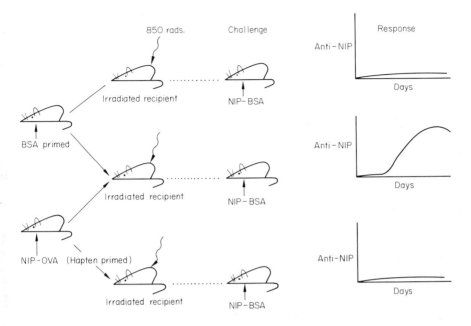

Fig. 10.2. Reconstitution of a secondary anti-hapten response in irradiated recipients with separate populations of hapten and carrier-primed spleen cells. (Adapted from Mitchison, 1971.)

cells—one hapten specific and the other carrier specific. Further experiments showed that carrier specificity was expressed in T cells and hapten specificity in B cells. For unknown reasons efficient cooperation between helper T cells and B cells requires that each cell type recognizes different determinants. When these occur on the same molecule it is known as intramolecular help. When the two determinants are present on the same cell or particle but associated with different molecules it is known as intermolecular help. This form of help operates in the antibody response to weakly immunogenic cell surface antigens such as Thy 1, where help is provided by other alloantigenic determinants on the same cell (Lake & Mitchison 1977). Intermolecular help is a mechanism for enhancing the response to weakly immunogenic cell surface antigens and may be exploited in promoting responses to weakly immunogenic tumour antigens.

10.3.2 Possible mechanisms involved in T–B cooperation

T–B cooperation may require direct cell contact or be mediated by soluble factors released by T cells. Although there is evidence for both processes, the failure to detect antigen-specific T cell helper factors in most experimental systems suggests that specific factors are not the main pathway for T–B cell cooperation.

(a) *Direct cell contact*. There is evidence that interaction between helper T cells and B cells is a localized phenomenon involving direct cell contact (Phillips and Waldmann, 1977). This was shown using the microculture system of Lefkovits in which low numbers of KLH-specific helper T cells are randomly distributed amongst a large number of microcultures, each containing excess B cells primed to TNP. Some wells contain no helper T cell and fail to produce antibody to TNP when challenged with TNP–KLH. In those wells containing KLH specific helper T cells, the number of clones of B cells induced to make antibody to TNP–KLH can be determined from the isoelectric focusing pattern of the anti-TNP antibody produced (Fig. 10.3). From the number of negative cultures it is possible to calculate (using the Poisson formula) how many wells would be expected to contain 0, 1, 2 or more KLH-specific helper T cells. The observed distribution of TNP clones compares well with the estimated distribution of KLH-specific T cells and implies that a single helper T cell can help only one TNP-specific B cell. If freely diffusible T cell factors were involved then several B cell clones would have been activated by a single helper cell.

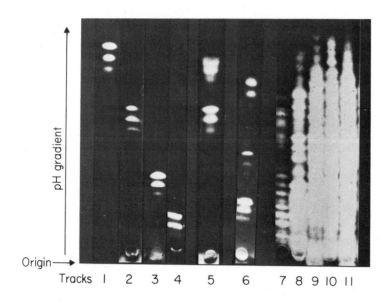

Fig. 10.3. Antibodies produced by different clones of cells have different iso-electric points and can be separated by the technique of iso-electric focusing (see glossary). In the above figure supernatant from microcultures of anti-TNP antibody is applied to one side of a gel (origin) and after electrophoresis in a pH gradient the gel is overlaid with TNP-coupled erythrocytes and complement. Focused spots of antibody produce zones of lysis in the gel. The product of a single clone usually appears as two to four separate bands (its spectrotype) due to minor post-synthetic modification of the antibody. Tracks 1–4, single clones; 5, two clones; 6, three clones; 7, several clones; 8–11, polyclonal responses.

(b) *Antigen-specific T cell factors*. In a few cell cooperation systems it is possible to demonstrate helper effects mediated by antigen-specific T cell factors (see Chapter 9).

It has been shown that the IgM response of DNP-primed B cells to DNP–KLH was the same irrespective of whether the helper T cells were together with, or separated from, the B cells by a cell impermeable membrane (Table 10.2). From this it was argued that the T cells released a specific soluble helper factor which diffused into the B cell compartment. Furthermore, the specific T cell factor either alone or complexed with antigen could bind to the surface of macrophages and could then cooperate with the hapten-primed B cells. A comparable and possibly identical factor(s) with activity *in vivo* has also been described (Taussig, 1974). If T cells primed to SRBC were challenged *in vitro* with antigen then the supernatant culture medium could substitute for T cells in the response of unprimed B cells to SRBC in irradiated recipients.

Specific helper factors have only been detected in a limited number of systems and the helper effects are not widely reproducible. Our own view is that there is insufficient evidence for specific helper factors being a major pathway for T–B cell interaction.

(c) *Non-specific helper T cell factors*. There are a variety of different non-specific factors collectively known as lymphokines. They mediate a diverse number of effects on lymphoid and haemopoietic cells and are released on T cell stimulation with antigens or mitogens such as Concanavalin A. Although it is generally assumed that lymphokines are T cell derived, this is not necessarily correct since the induction of

Table 10.2 Demonstration of cell cooperation via specific soluble T cell factors (from Feldmann & Basten, 1972)

Membrane		DNP response of spleen cells in lower chamber to DNP–KLH
Upper chamber	Lower chamber	
None	T_{KLH}+ DNP-primed spleen	+
T_{KLH}	DNP-primed spleen	+
T_{KLH}	DNP-primed spleen (anti-Thy1 and complement treated), i.e. B cells only	+
$T_{(not\ primed)}$	DNP-primed spleen	−
None	DNP-primed spleen	−
T_{FGG}	DNP-primed spleen	−

T_{KLH}, T_{FGG} = T cells primed to KLH or fowl gamma globulin.

The chambers are separated by a nucleopore membrane which permits the passage of soluble factors but not cells.

most T cell responses is macrophage dependent and macrophages could be a source of lymphokines.

One of the first lymphokine activities to be defined was macrophage migration inhibition factor (MIF). The spontaneous migration *in vitro* of macrophages from donors sensitized to an antigen such as tuberculin (PPD), was found to be inhibited

Table 10.3. The three categories of non-specific factors acting on lymphocyte differentiation (see Watson *et al.*, 1979; Hoffman & Watson, 1979)

Factor (and acronym)	M.W.	Iso-electric point	Sensitivity to		Cells required for production	Target
			Acid pH	Reducing agents		
Category I T cell replacing factor III (TRF-III) Macrophage-derived T cell replacing factor (TRF-M) B cell activating factor B cell differentiating factor Lymphocyte activating factor (LAF) Mitogenic protein	12,000–18,000	4.5–5.5 (Mouse) 6.5–7.5 (Man)	−	?	Macrophage	T and B cells. Does not promote prolonged culture of T cells
Category II Thymocyte-stimulating factor (TFS) Thymocyte mitogenic factor (TMF) T cell growth factor (TCGF) Costimulator (of thymocytes) Killer cell helper factor (KHF)	30,000–50,000	3.5–5.5	−	−	T (Lyt 1^+23^-) + Macrophage	Maintains long-term culture of activated T cells
Category III T cell replacing factor (TRF) Non-specific factor (NSF) Non-specific mediator (NSM)	30,000–50,000	3.0–4.2	+	+	T (Lyt 1^+23^-) + Macrophage	Synergizes with Category I factors and antigen in B cell activation

Interleukin I and II have been suggested as alternative names for factors in Category I and II (see *Immunol. Rev.* **51**).

in the presence of PPD, which induced the release of MIF from contaminating PPD-specific T cells in the macrophage preparation. Since then a number of lymphokines have been reported all masquerading under a variety of acronyms which reflect the assays used for their detection. At present their characterization is limited and the 'true' number is not known. There are three categories of lymphokines, all glycoproteins, which affect lymphocyte growth and differentiation (Table 10.3). Category I factors act during antigen triggering of lymphocytes; category II factors are growth factors for activated T cells including helper and cytotoxic cells; whilst category III factors enhance B cell differentiation into antibody-secreting cells.

The importance of these factors in T–B cell cooperation is not understood. One view is that they are obligatory for lymphocyte growth and differentiation (see *Immunol. Rev.*, **51**).

10.3.3 *T cell help in T cell responses*

Cytotoxic T cells kill allogeneic or virus-infected syngeneic cells. The former can be conveniently detected in a mixed lymphocyte reaction (MLR) *in vitro*. This reaction is characterized by an initial phase of T cell proliferation and subsequent generation of alloreactive cytotoxic T cells. Two sets of cells are involved in this response—one reacting to differences in the classical transplantation antigens coded by the *K* or *D* region (mice) and *HLA-A -B -C* (man); the other to the *I* region or to its equivalent in other species (Table 10.4). In mice, the cells responding to the *I* region differences are Lyt 1^+23^- and they are distinct from cells responding to *K* or *D* region differences, which are Lyt 1^-23^+, or Lyt 1^+23^+ precursors which later develop into Lyt 1^-23^+ cytotoxic cells. Optimal generation of cytotoxic cells requires help from the Lyt

Table 10.4. Requirement for helper T cells responding to *HLA-D* region differences in the generation of cytotoxic T cells specific for HLA-A, B and C antigens in man

Responder	Stimulator	MHS difference	MLC	Cytotoxicity on P	Q	R
P	Q_m	HLA-A, -B, -C	—	—	—	—
P	R_m	HLA-D	+++	—	—	—
P	$Q_m + R_m$	Complete	+++	—	+++	—

To generate cytotoxic cells in an allogeneic reaction with human lymphocytes the responder cells (P) must be stimulated by stimulator cells (mitomycin treated Q and R; Q_m and R_m respectively) which differ at HLA-D and HLA-A, -B or -C. The cytotoxic cells are specific for the differences in HLA-A, -B or -C while the initiation of proliferation requires a difference in HLA-D. This experiment shows that the different stimulator cells can separately provide these two antigenic requirements. Adapted from Eijsvoogel *et al.* (1973).

1^+23^- subset and failure to detect cytotoxic T cells can occur either because there are no *I* region differences in the MLR under study (only *K* and *D* region differences) or because the Lyt 1^+23^- helpers have been eliminated. The exact nature of the interaction between these cells is unclear but may involve direct cell contact and/or non-specific factors.

10.4 T cell suppression in the immune response

Clonal expansion is under homeostatic control. For example secreted antibody successfully competes with lymphocyte receptors for antigen and limits antigen-driven clonal expansion. It is now apparent that in addition to this there is a further level of control mediated by antigen-specific suppressor T cells.

Certain regimes of immunization result in specific unresponsiveness. This unresponsiveness can be transferred to normal recipients by T cells (Fig. 10.4a). The T cells involved are distinct from helper T cells and express Lyt 1^-23^+ and *I-J* region determinants.

T cell suppression is complex and analysis of the mechanisms involved is less

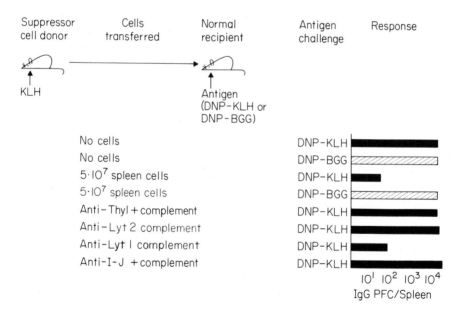

Fig. 10.4a. Ability of suppressor T cells to inhibit the primary IgG anti-DNP response to DNP–KLH. Spleen cells from mice primed to KLH which contain KLH-specific suppressor cells were transferred to normal mice which were then challenged with either DNP–KLH or DNP–BGG as control. IgG anti-DNP plaque-forming cells (PFC) were detected in the spleen 9 days later. By treating the spleen cell inoculum with alloantisera and complement to eliminate cells bearing the particular alloantigen, the cells mediating the suppression were identified as being Thy 1^+, Lyt 1^-23^+, I–J$^+$. (Adapted from Tada & Takemori, 1974.)

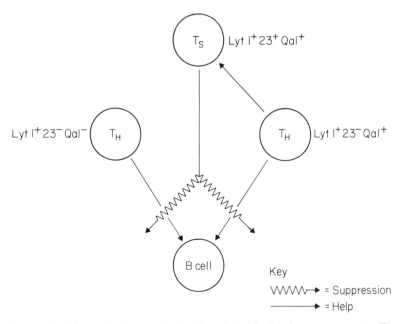

Fig. 10.4b. Schematic diagram for T-cell mediated feedback suppression. B cells can be helped by two types of Lyt 1^+23^- helper T cells, one of which expresses the Qa1$^+$ marker. The Lyt 1^+23^- Qa1$^+$ cells also initiate a feedback suppression via activation of Lyt 1^+23^+ Qa1$^+$ cells which in turn suppress T–B cell cooperation. (Adapted from Cantor *et al.*, 1978.)

advanced than that for T cell help. There are two reasons for this. First, suppression is only observed through the reduction of a positive response and hence suppression is always measured indirectly. Second, the generation of suppressor cells is a complex process involving cell interactions. This is well illustrated by experiments which indicate that Lyt 1^+23^-, Qa1$^+$ helper T cells can activate both B cells as well as a distinct T cell subset (Lyt 1^+23^+, Qa1$^+$) which then produces feed-back suppression of the specific helper response (Fig. 10.4b).

10.5 The balance between help and suppression

It seems likely that both helper and suppressor T cells are activated in the normal course of the response to a multideterminant antigen. The level of the antibody response reflects the net balance between these two T cell subsets. This would predict that any imbalance in the ratio of these subsets might lead to excess antibody formation or suppression. For example, NZB mice have a deficiency of Lyt 1^+23^+ cells and also make excess autoantibodies. Also in man there is evidence that certain forms of acquired immunodeficiency are mediated by increased levels of suppressor T cells.

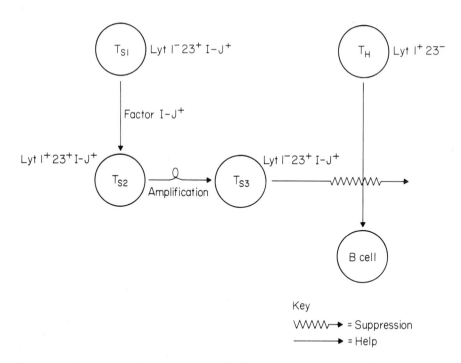

Fig. 10.4c. Antigen-specific T suppressor cells (Ts 1) contain an extractable suppressor factor which acts on Lyt 1+23+ T cells (Ts 2). These in turn generate Lyt 1-23+ (Ts 3) suppressor T cells which interfere with T–B cell cooperation. All T suppressor cells involved in this process express I–J determinants on their surface. (Adapted from Takemori & Tada, 1975.)

10.5.1 Helper and suppressor determinants

The balance between helper and suppressor T cells is also influenced by the combinations of determinants on the antigen. Sercarz and his colleagues (Sercarz et al., 1978) have used hen egg white lysozyme (HEL) to study the contribution of different determinants to help and suppression. Lysozyme is a globular protein (14,000 M.W.) with a known amino acid sequence and conformation (Fig. 10.5). By mild acid hydrolysis it is possible to cleave a 27 amino acid fragment (the N-C peptide) from the native molecule. Cyanogen bromide cleavage yields a larger fragment (LII) comprising amino acids 13–105.

The response of mice to avian lysozymes is thymus-dependent and in certain strains is under H-2 linked Ir gene control (see Chapter 12). H-2^b and H-2^s strains fail to make antibody to HEL (non-responders) whereas other strains do (Table 10.5). In the responder strains the LII fragment of HEL is preferentially recognized as a helper determinant for an antibody response to the N-C peptide.

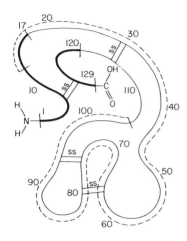

Fig. 10.5. Structure of the HEL moelcule. Amino acid residues included in solid lines represent the N–C peptide (a.a. 1–17 : Cys 6-Cys 127 : 120–129). Amino acid residues included in dotted line represent the LII peptide (aa. 13–105). (Adapted from Adorini *et al.*, 1979.)

H-2^b and H-2^s mice fail to make antibody to HEL because they produce high levels of suppressor cells that are specific for the N-C peptide. Following immunization of non-responders with HEL the suppressor cells inhibit the development of the LII specific helpers and no antibody response occurs. If non-responders are immunized with HEL from which the N-C peptide has been removed, then LII specific helper T cells are generated to levels similar to that seen in responder strains. Thus the unresponsiveness of the H-2^b and H-2^s strains is due to an imbalance in the ratio of T suppressors to T helpers in responding to different determinants on the same molecule.

Table 10.5. The ability of hen egg lysozyme (HEL) and its fragments to stimulate T helper cells, T suppressor cells and antibody in responder and non-responder strains of mice (based on Adorini *et al.*, 1979)

| Antigen or Fragment | Response to HEL | | | | | |
| | H-2^b (non-responder) | | | H-2^a (responder) | | |
	Suppressor cells	Helper cells	Antibody to N–C	Suppressor cells	Helper cells	Antibody
HEL	+++	+	+	+	+++	+++
N-C Peptide	+++	−	−	+	+	++
LII Fragment	−	+++	−	−	+++	−

+++ =Marked response.
  + =Weak response.
Helper cells are assayed through their ability to produce help for an antibody response to N–C using HEL as antigen.

10.5.2 Mechanisms of suppression

The mechanisms of suppression are mediated by both antigen-specific and non-specific interactions involving either cell contact or soluble suppressor factors. It is possible to extract by sonication an antigen-specific T cell factor from Lyt 1^-23^+ KLH-specific suppressor T cells which carries I-J subregion determinants (see Chapter 9). This factor does not appear to share any of the known properties of immunoglobulin molecules other than antigen specificity and acts on KLH-specific Lyt 1^+23^+ T cells to give rise to a specific Lyt 1^-23^+ suppressor T cell (Fig. 10.4c). In the presence of KLH these cells are then able to block T–B cell interactions in response to TNP–KLH and to other unrelated antigens. Comparable suppressor factors for the linear copolymers of GAT and GT have also been described (Germain *et al.*, 1978).

Non-specific suppressor factors are readily obtained from Lyt 1^-23^+ cells stimulated with high concentrations of antigen or mitogens such as the lectin, Concanavalin A. Suppressor T cells are not restricted to mice and in man can be isolated from human peripheral blood.

The analysis of T cell interactions will be improved once sufficient quantities of the specific and non-specific factors become available. It has been claimed that if KLH-specific suppressor T cells are fused with a murine T cell lymphoma, then hybrid cells secreting monoclonal suppressor factors can be isolated (Taniguchi *et al.*, 1979). This material is similar to that extracted from sonicated suppressor T cells.

10.6 Macrophage–T cell interactions

Interactions between macrophages and T cells are relevant to our understanding of the immune response since the induction of T cells is often macrophage dependent. Both T and B lymphocytes have membrane attachment sites for macrophages and binding is enhanced by antigen (Fig. 10.6). Studies on the handling of antigen by macrophages have revealed that although a substantial part of phagocytosed antigen is catabolized within the phagolysosomes, small amounts of highly immunogenic antigen can be found associated with the macrophage surface. Removal of this surface-bound antigen either by trypsin or chelating agents reduces the immunogenicity of the macrophages. The failure of antigen to reappear at the surface, indicates there is no internal pool of antigen waiting to be incorporated into the membrane (Unanue & Cerrotini, 1970).

The state of degradation of the antigen on the macrophage surface is unknown. Benacerraf (1978) has argued that the antigen on the macrophage surface has been extensively degraded possibly to its primary amino acid sequence and is intimately associated with the products of the I region of the MHS. This view is based partly on the fact that the stimulatory capacity of antigen-presenting macrophages can be

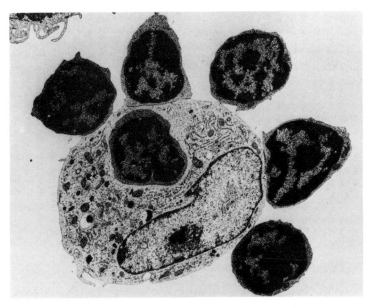

(a)

(b)

Fig. 10.6. (a) The clustering of guinea pig thymocytes around syngeneic glass adherent macrophages. Magnification ×4550. (Adapted from Lipsky & Rosenthal, 1973.) (b) Scanning electron micrograph of lymphocytes adhering to macrophages. (Taken from Rosenthal et al., 1976.)

blocked by anti-Ia sera but not by antibodies to the undegraded antigen, and partly on the isolation of a soluble macrophage product which appears to be a 30,000 M.W. complex of an Ia-bearing molecule and degraded antigen. This material is immuno-genic *in vitro* for T cells (Erb *et al.*, 1976). The recognition of antigen by T cells and the involvement of the MHS in this is discussed fully in Chapter 11.

These studies raise a number of questions regarding antigen processing by macrophages or other antigen-presenting cells: is it obligatory for antigen to be catabolized before presentation to T cells; how do macrophages partition antigen into a surface-bound fraction and a degraded fraction and how is antigen main-tained at the surface either as whole antigen or as fragments? In view of the involvement of Ia antigens in antigen recognition by T cells, it is interesting that many macrophages are Ia negative. Although these cells phagocytose antigen they probably play no rôle in presenting antigens to the immune system.

10.7 Idiotype recognition in cell interactions

So far clonal expansion has been considered in the context of selection by antigens. Selective clonal expansion can also be induced by the recognition of idiotypes on receptors and although the precise details are unclear the experiments nonetheless provide evidence for the network hypothesis (see Chapter 7).

10.7.1 Anti-idiotypic antibodies

Anti-idiotypic antibodies were first described independently by Oudin (1966), and by Gell and Kelus. (For a review of the early literature on anti-antibodies see Gell and Kelus (1967).) It is possible for individual animals to make auto-anti-idiotypic antibodies to their own idiotypes. For example if five different rabbits are each immunized with their own anti-hapten antibody then each rabbit makes auto-anti-idiotypic antibodies which react only with their own anti-hapten antibody and not with that of any of the other four rabbits (Table 10.6).

Auto-anti-idiotypic antibodies also arise spontaneously during a normal im-mune response. These are easily detected in responses involving the inheritable idiotypes. Five days after secondary immunization of BALB/c mice with phosphoryl choline (PC), auto-anti-idiotypic antibody secreting cells can be detected in the spleen (Fig. 10.7). Findings of this type led to the search for the involvement of idiotypes in cell interactions.

10.7.2 Idiotypic interactions in T–B cooperation

The antibody response in A/J mice to a carbohydrate determinant (ACHO) on Group A *streptococci* (Strep A) is associated with an inheritable idiotype (see Eichmann,

Table 10.6. Production of auto-anti-idiotypic antibody in rabbits. F(ab')$_2$ fragments of anti-body to the hapten (p-aminophenyl-N-trimethylammonium chloride) from five different rabbits were later injected back into the autologous rabbit. The percentage binding of iodinated ^{125}I labelled F(ab')$_2$ fragments of the anti-hapten antibody by the anti-idiotypic serum was then determined (adapted from Rodkey, 1974).

[125]I F(ab')$_2$ anti-hapten antibody from rabbit

Serum		I	2	3	4	5
Normal serum		1.1	1.5	2.0	2.3	1.2
Anti-Id serum	1.	<u>17.0</u>	2.3	0.6	2.3	2.7
	2.	0.9	<u>39.3</u>	1.6	2.0	2.4
	3.	0.6	<u>3.4</u>	<u>40.7</u>	1.3	2.3
	4.	0.1	0.7	0.3	<u>23.3</u>	0.7
	5.	0.2	1.6	0.1	0.3	<u>23.3</u>

1978). The antibody response is thymus-dependent and 50 per cent of the antibody to Strep A expresses the same idiotype (Id A5A). In the secondary response *in vitro* of T and B cells primed *in vivo* to Strep A, about 40 per cent of the antibody-secreting cells express Id A5A.

The cell interactions involved in this system are shown in Fig. 10.8. The response to Strep A involves antigen-specific T and B cells (1 and 2 respectively, Fig. 10.8) which recognize identical determinants on the antigen and express the same idiotype. This idiotype is in turn recognized by anti-idiotypic T and B cells (3 and 4 in

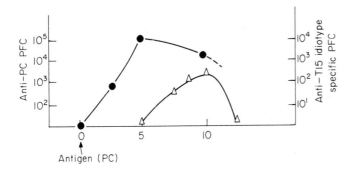

Fig. 10.7. The generation of auto-anti-idiotypic antibody during an immune response. BALB/c mice were injected with 10^8 organisms of rough strain *Pneumococci pneumoniae*, R36A bearing the phosphorylcholine (PC) epitope. Within 5 days plaque-forming cells (PFC) secreting anti-PC antibody were detected in the spleen (●———●). Some days later PFC making antibody to the PC idiotype (T 15) were also detected in the spleen (△———△). (Adapted from Cozenza, 1976.)

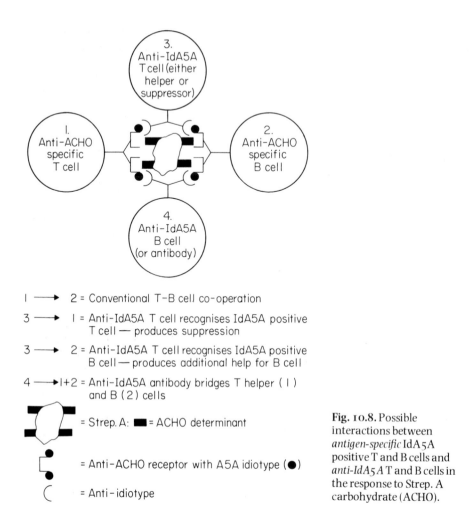

Fig. 10.8. Possible interactions between *antigen-specific* Id A5A positive T and B cells and *anti-IdA5A* T and B cells in the response to Strep. A carbohydrate (ACHO).

Fig. 10.8). This creates the opportunity for several combinations of antigen-specific and idiotype-specific interactions. Exactly which interactions result in help or suppression for the idiotype positive B cells will depend on which functional subset of T cells is expanded and the relative proportions of antigen-specific and idiotype-specific cells. In turn this depends on the methods of immunization, experimental protocol and so on.

   (a) *Anti-idiotypic antibody and T cell help.* The experimental protocol is shown in Fig. 10.9. Guinea pig anti-idiotypic antibodies to Id A5A are separated into the IgG1 and IgG2 subclasses. Treatment of unprimed mice with the IgG1 fraction produces a level of priming in both T helper and B cells equivalent to the priming obtained with

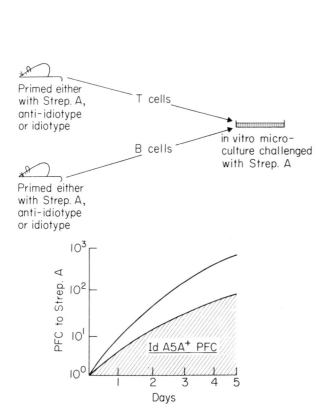

Primed either
with Strep. A,
anti-idiotype
or idiotype

T cells

B cells

in vitro micro-
culture challenged
with Strep. A

Primed either
with Strep. A,
anti-idiotype
or idiotype

PFC to Strep. A

10^3

10^2

10^1

10^0

Id A5A$^+$ PFC

1 2 3 4 5

Days

Fig. 10.9. Experimental protocol for demonstrating the involvement of idiotype and anti-idiotype interactions in the immune response to Group A carbohydrate in A/J strain mice. The results are shown in Tables 10.7 and 10.8. Spleen cells from A/J mice primed either with antigen (Strep. A), anti-idiotype (anti-IdA5A) or idiotype (IdA5A) were used as a source of primed T cells or B cells. These were then mixed together in microcultures of 1.10^6 cells/100 μl of medium in the presence of Strep. A as antigen. The number of plaque-forming cells (PFC) per culture secreting antibodies to Strep. A were assayed and the percentage of PFC expressing the idiotype (IdA5A) determined. In the example shown cells were primed to Strep. A and in the secondary response *in vitro* more than 50 per cent of the PFC express IdA5A. (Adapted from Eichmann, 1978.)

antigen (Strep. A). However, after anti-idiotype priming, the bulk of the antibody produced in the secondary response expresses Id A5A (Table 10.7). While this is to be expected with anti-idiotype primed B cells (i.e. only Id A5A positive B cells are expanded with anti-Id A5A antibodies), it is surprising that T cells primed with anti-Id A5A should cooperate with only Id A5A positive B cells. The simplest explanation (believe it or not) is that the Id A5A positive B cells are selectively helped both by antigen and by anti-Id A5A helper T cells. The latter have been generated by the IgG1 anti-Id A5A antibodies expanding the Id A5A positive cells (1 and 2 in Fig. 10.8) which in turn induce proliferation of anti-Id A5A T cells (3 in Fig. 10.8).

(b) *Anti-idiotypic antibody and suppression.* If a similar experiment is repeated using the IgG2 fraction of the anti-Id A5A then the mice still make specific antibody on challenge with Strep A but all the antibody is Id A5A negative. The suppression of

Table 10.7. Selective cooperation between T cells and B cells in the response to Strep. A carbohydrate (based on Hetzelberger & Eichmann, 1978)

In vivo priming		Possible cell interactions[1]	In vitro secondary antibody response to ACHO	
T cells	B cells		Total PFC	%IdA5A PFC
Unprimed	Unprimed	—	1	—
Unprimed	Strep A	—	5	—
Strep A	Strep A	1 → 2	84	39
Strep A	IgG1 anti-IdA5A	1 → 2	52	92
IgG1 anti-IdA5A	Strep A	1, 3 → 2	66	86
IgG1 anti-IdA5A	IgG1 anti-IdA5A	1, 3 → 2	67	92
IgG2 anti-IdA5A + Strep A	Strep A	3 ⤳ 1	140	13

(1) 1   2   3 refer to cells depicted in Fig. 10.8 involving idiotype-anti-idiotype interactions. → =help, ⤳ =suppression.

the ability to make Id A5A is mediated by anti-idiotypic T suppressor cells which are presumably generated as a result of the proliferation of Id A5A positive cells as in section 10.7.2(a). It is unclear why the subclasses of heterologous anti-idiotypic antibodies should generate functionally distinct anti-idiotypic T cells.

(c) *Antigen-independent antibody responses.* The generation of a specific antibody response in the complete absence of antigen is not as paradoxical as it sounds. T cell help for Id A5A positive B cells can be delivered by anti-Id A5A helper T cells on their own in the *complete absence* of both Strep A-specific T cells and antigen (Table 10.8). The anti-Id A5A helper T cells can be expanded either by priming with immunoglobulin expressing Id A5A or indirectly as described in section 10.7.2(a).

Antigen-independent cooperation can also be mediated by anti-idiotypic antibody. In this case the anti-idiotypic antibody brings together the Id A5A positive helper T cells and Id A5A positive B cells (cells 1 and 2 in Fig. 10.8) in exactly the same way as antigen would have done and the B cells become activated (see Fig. 10.1).

Although we have chosen to concentrate on one idiotypic system it must be stressed that similar types of idiotype directed cell interactions are now being detected in the response to other antigens (Harvey *et al.*, 1979; Woodland & Cantor, 1978).

The overall conclusion is that during clonal expansion of lymphocytes, helper or suppressor signals can be directed via the idiotype. It is not surprising that idiotypic

Table 10.8. Antigen-independent T–B cooperation resulting in the production of IdA5A positive antibody (based on Eichmann *et al.*, 1978)

In vivo priming		Possible cell interactions[1]	*In vitro* secondary antibody response[2] to ACHO	
T cells	B cells		Total PFC	% IdA5A PFC
Unprimed	Unprimed	—	1	—
IdA5A	Unprimed	—	3	—
IdA5A	IgG1 anti-IdA5A	3 → 2	59	93
IdA5A	Strep. A	3 → 2	47	85

(1) 1 2 3 refer to cells depicted in Fig. 10.8.
(2) No antigen is added to the culture of primed cells.

interactions can only be revealed in responses of limited heterogeneity involving restricted sets of interacting cells—a 'mini-network'. The normal polyclonal response to a multideterminant antigen will contain a large number of mini-networks making any one difficult to detect. Consequently it may be impossible to obtain formal proof of idiotype control in immune responses to conventional antigens.

10.8 The significance of cell interactions

In their broadest sense cell interactions are necessary for the activation and regulation of clonal expansion during an immune response. Although the events which occur at the cell surface during lymphocyte activation are not biochemically characterized, there is now evidence to suggest that lymphocyte activation involves more than just antigen binding to the specific membrane receptors.

Most information is available for B cell activation for which there are at least two pathways. Thymus-independent antigens bypass the requirement for T cell help and alone can deliver the necessary signal for activation. Their ability to do so may in part be related to epitope density or in some cases to their intrinsic property of producing polyclonal activation through some as yet ill-defined mitogen site on the B cell surface (see Chapter 8.6). In contrast the response to thymus-dependent antigens involves antigen-specific and idiotype-specific helper T cells as well as a variety of non-specific lymphokines or growth factors. To what extent these act independently or together is unknown and almost certainly depends on the nature of the antigen as well as the stage of development of the B cells. The requirement for B cell activation may vary depending on whether the cells are virgin B cells or memory cells committed to the expression of a particular class of immunoglobulin.

Specific clonal suppression is as essential as specific clonal expansion. Although clonal 'suppression' is largely mediated through the competing effects of antibodies and cell receptors for the antigenic determinants it is also clear that specific homeo-static control or 'fine tuning' can be mediated by suppressor cells via mechanisms which are at present obscure.

References

ADORINI L., HARVEY M.A., MILLER A. & SERCARZ E.E. (1979) Fine specificity of regulatory T cells. II. Suppressor and helper T cells are inducing different regions of hen egg white lysozyme in a genetically non-responder mouse strain. *J. exp. Med.* **150**, 293.

BENACERRAF B. (1978) An hypothesis to relate the specificity of T lymphocytes and the activity of *I*-region-specific *Ir* genes in macrophages and B lymphocytes. *J. Immunol.* **120**, 1809.

CANTOR H., HUGENBERGER J., McVAY-BONDREAU L., EARDLEY D.D., KEMP J., SHEN F.W. & GERSHON R.K. (1978) Immunoregulatory circuits among T cell sets. Identification of a subpopulation of T cells that induce feedback inhibitor. *J. exp. Med.* **148**, 871.

CLAMAN H.N., CHAPERON E.A. & TRIPLETT R.F. (1966) Immunocompetence of transferred thymus–marrow combinations. *J. Immunol.* **97**, 928.

COSENZA H. (1976) Detection of anti-idiotype reactive cells in the response to phosphoryl-choline. *Eur. J. Immunol.* **6**, 114.

DAVIES A.J.S., LEUCHARS E., WALLIS V. & KÖLLER P.C. (1966) The mitotic response of thymus-derived cells to antigenic stimulus. *Transplantation* **4**, 438.

EICHMANN K. (1978) Expression and function of idiotypes on lymphocytes. *Adv. Immunol.* **26**, 195.

EICHMANN K., FALK I. & RAJEWSKY K. (1978) Recognition of idiotypes in lymphocyte inter-actions. II. Antigen-independent cooperation between T and B lymphocytes that possess similar and complementary idiotypes. *Eur. J. Immunol.* **8**, 853.

EIJSVOOGEL V.P., RIA DU BOIS J.P., MELIEF C.J.M., ZEYLEMAKER W.P., RAAT KONING L. & DE GROOT-HOOY L. (1973) Lymphocyte activation and destruction *in vitro* in relation to MLC and HLA. *Transplantation Proc.* **5**, 415.

ERB P., FELDMANN M. & HOGG N. (1976) The role of macrophages in the generation of T helper cells. IV. Nature of genetically related factor derived from macrophages incubated with soluble antigens. *Eur. J. Immunol.* **6**, 365.

FELDMANN M. & BASTEN A. (1972) Cell interactions in the immune response *in vitro*. III. Specific collaborations across a cell-impermeable membrane. *J. exp. Med.* **136**, 49.

GELL P.G.H. & KELUS A.S. (1967) Anti-antibodies. *Adv. Immunol.* **6**, 467.

GERMAIN R.N., THEZE J., WALTENBAUGH C., DORF M.E. & BENACERRAF B. (1978) Antigen-specific T cell-mediated suppression. II. *In vitro* induction by I-J coded GT-specific T cell suppressive factor of suppressor T cells bearing I-J determinants. *J. Immunol.* **121**, 602.

HARVEY M.A., ADORINI L., BENJAMIN C.D., MILLER A. & SERCARZ E.E. (1979) Idiotypy and antigen specificity of Th, Ts and B cells induced by hen egg white lysozyme. *J. Supramol. Structure* **9**, Suppl. 3, 769.

HETZELBERGER D. & EICHMANN K. (1978) Recognition of idiotypes in lymphocyte interactions. I. Idiotypic selectivity in the cooperation between T- and B-lymphocytes. *Eur. J. Immunol.* **8**, 846.

HOFFMANN P. & WATSON J. (1979) Helper T cell replacing factors secreted by thymus-derived cells and macrophages: cellular requirement for B cell activation and synergistic properties. *J. Immunol.* **122**, 1371.

LAKE P. & MITCHISON N.A. (1977) Regulatory mechanisms in the immune response to cell surface antigens. *Cold Spr. Harb. Symp. Quant. Biol.* **41**, 389.

LIPSKY P.E. & ROSENTHAL A.S. (1973) Characteristics of the antigen-independent binding of guinea-pig thymocytes and lymphocytes to syngeneic macrophages. *J. exp. Med.* **138**, 900.

MILLER J.F.A.P. & MITCHELL G.F. (1968) Cell to cell interaction in the immune response. I. Haemolysin-forming cells in neonatally thymectomized mice reconstituted with thymus or thoracic duct lymphocytes. *J. exp. Med.* **128**, 801.

MITCHISON N.A. (1971) Carrier effects in secondary response to hapten protein conjugates. I. Measurement of the effect with transferred cells and objection to the local environment hypothesis. *Eur. J. Immunol.* **1**, 10.

NOSSAL G.J.V., CUNNINGHAM A., MITCHELL G.F. & MILLER J.F.A.P. (1968) Cell to cell interaction in the immune response. III. Chromosomal marker analysis of single antibody-forming cells in reconstituted, irradiated or thymectomized mice. *J. exp. Med.* **128**, 839.

OUDIN J. (1966) Genetic control of immunoglobulin synthesis. *Proc. Roy. Soc. Lond. B* **106**, 207.

PHILLIPS J. & WALDMANN H. (1977) Monogamous T helper cell. *Nature* **268**, 641.

RODKEY L.S. (1974) Studies of idiotypic antibodies. Production and characterization of auto-anti-idiotypic antisera. *J. exp. Med.* **139**, 712.

ROSENTHAL A.S., BLAKE J.J., ELLNER J.J., GREINEDER D.K. & LIPSKY P.E. (1976) Macrophage function in antigen recognition by T lymphocytes. In NELSON D.S. (ed.), p. 131. *Immunobiology of the Macrophage*. Academic Press, New York.

SERCARZ E.E., YOWELL R.L., TURKIN D., MILLER A., ARANEO B.A. & ADORINI L. (1978) Different functional specificity repertoires for suppression and helper T cells. *Immunol. Rev.* **39**, 108.

TADA T. & TAKEMORI T. (1974) Selective roles of thymus-derived lymphocytes in the antibody response. I. Differential suppressive effect of carrier primed T cells on hapten-specific IgM and IgG antibody responses. *J. exp. Med.* **140**, 239.

TAKEMORI T. & TADA T. (1975) Properties of antigen-suppressive T cell factor in regulation of antibody response of the mouse. I. *In vitro* activity and immunochemical characterizations. *J. exp. Med.* **142**, 1241.

TANIGUCHI M., SAITO T. & TADA T. (1979) Antigen-specific suppressive factor produced by a transplantable *I-J*-bearing T cell hybridoma. *Nature* **278**, 555.

TAUSSIG M.J. (1974) T cell factor which can replace T cells *in vivo*. *Nature* **248**, 236.

UNANUE E.R. & CERROTINI J.C. (1970) The immunogenicity of antigen bound to the plasma membrane of macrophages. *J. exp. Med.* **131**, 711.

WATSON J., GILLIS S., MARBROKE J., MOCHIZUKI D. & SMITH K.A. (1979) Biochemical and biological characterization of lymphocyte regulatory molecules. I. Purification of a class of murine lymphokines. *J. exp. Med.* **150**, 849.

WOODLAND R. & CANTOR H. (1978) Idiotype-specific T helper cells are required to induce idiotype positive B memory cells to secrete antibody. *Eur. J. Immunol.* **8**, 600.

Further reading

See also *Immunol. Rev.* **51**, T cell stimulating growth factors (MÖLLER G. ed.). Munksgaard, Copenhagen.

Chapter 11
The Biology of the Major
Histocompatibility Complex—
MHS Restriction

11.1 Introduction

'Lymphocytes only recognize antigen when it is presented through the proper diplomatic channels.' Although this remark by a well known immunologist pre-dates much of modern cellular immunology it accurately sums up our current views of lymphocyte activation by antigen.

In general T lymphocytes respond to antigen only when it is presented on the surface of viable antigen-presenting cells and not to antigen in free solution. For example, T cell proliferation to soluble antigens *in vitro* has a strict requirement for macrophages or other antigen-presenting cells and little response occurs if these are absent. In addition to recognizing specific antigen the T cells must also interact with the MHS on the antigen-presenting cells. This requirement for MHS involvement in T cell activation has been mainly studied through the phenomenon of MHS restriction.

Evidence for involvement of the MHS in all T cell responses was first obtained in the early 1970s. At that time the experiments were difficult to interpret and it was not until the studies of Zinkernagel and Doherty (1974) with cytotoxic T cells that the fundamental importance of the MHS in the immune responses was appreciated.

This chapter will attempt to put into perspective the relationships between T cell development and MHS restriction. In view of the overwhelming literature in this field our synthesis will be selective rather than comprehensive. Although our discussion will be confined mainly to cytotoxic T cell reactions, the basic principles apply to a wide variety of T cell functions.

11.2 MHS restriction in effector T cell functions

The killing of virus-infected cells by cytotoxic T cells is a widely used assay in studying MHS restriction. Cells expressing viral antigens serve as targets for cyto-toxic T cells.

In 1974 Zinkernagel and Doherty showed that cytotoxic T cells from mice infected with lymphocytic choriomeningitis virus (LCM) could kill LCM-infected target cells only if the targets expressed the same *H-2* haplotype as the effector cells (Table 11.1). This is an example of MHS restriction. The requirements for MHS matching have been mapped to the *K* or *D* regions of *H-2* by the use of *H-2* recombinant mice (see Table 11.5). Since then, MHS restriction in cytotoxic T cell killing has been widely reported in other species including man (Goulmy *et al.*, 1977; McMichael, 1978).

MHS restriction is not unique to cytotoxic T cells. In mice T–B cell cooperation (Katz *et al.*, 1973) is optimal (Table 11.2) when the interacting cells are *I-A* subregion identical. Only weak interactions occur if they differ at *I-A* but are identical at other regions of *H-2*. Apart from the involvement of different *H-2* regions, MHS restriction in T–B cell cooperation has many features in common with MHS restriction associated with cytotoxic T cells.

Table 11.1 MHS restriction in cytotoxic T cells

H-2 of effector T cells	*H-2* of target T cells	T cell cytotoxicity for targets infected with		
		LCM	Ectromelia	None
k	k	+++	−	−
	d	−	−	−
d	k	−	−	−
	d	+++	−	−

+++ =target cell lysis, − =no lysis.
Mice of different *H-2* haplotype were infected with lymphocytic choriomeningitis virus (LCM) and 7 days later their T cells were tested for cytotoxicity on virus-infected target cells of the same or different *H-2* haplotype. Adapted from Zinkernagel and Doherty (1974).

Of the other specific T cell responses both the proliferative response to antigens and delayed hypersensitivity reactions show MHS restriction. So far it is unknown whether MHS restriction applies to cell interactions involving suppressor T cells or T cell-mediated anti-idiotype recognition (see Chapter 10).

There are no trivial explanations for MHS restriction. It is neither due to interference by alloreactive cells since their removal makes no difference to the MHS restriction of the effector population. Nor is it due to 'like–like' recognition. In a normal animal all tissues have the potential to express the same MHS products and consequently cell interactions between T cells and their targets might involve some form of homologous interaction. This is formally excluded by experiments which will be described later in 11.4 (Fig. 11.4), which show that under appropriate circumstances completely histoincompatible cells can interact in the expression of normal T cell functions.

Table 11.2. Mapping of genes within the *H-2* complex which control optimal co-operation between T and B cells in the antibody response

H-2 regions and subregions

K	I-A	I-B	I-C	S	G	D	Cooperative response
●	●	●	●	●	●	●	+
○	○	○	○	○	○	○	−
●/○	●/○	●/○	●/○	●/○	●/○	●/○	+
●	●	●	●	●	●	○	+
●	●	●	●	○	○	○	+
●	●	●	○	○	○	○	+
●	●	●	○	○	○	●	+
○	●	●	○	○	○	●	+
○	●	●	●	●	●	●	+
○	○	○	○	○	○	●	−
○	○	○	●	●	●	●	−
●	○	○	○	○	○	●	−
●	○	○	○	○	○	○	−

T and B cells from various inbred and recombinant strains of mice were assayed for their ability to cooperate in the antibody response in a conventional T–B cell cooperation system *in vivo* involving adoptive transfer of cells into irradiated recipients. Adapted from Katz *et al.* (1973).
● Gene identities.
○ Gene differences.

11.3 Explanations for MHS restriction

MHS restriction implies that T cells have an apparent dual specificity since they seem to specifically recognize antigen as well as a product of the MHS. For cytotoxic T cells the critical products are the serologically defined alloantigens of the *K* and *D* regions. Pretreatment of F_1 (H-$2^{d/k}$) target cells with anti-H-2^d sera blocks the cytotoxic effect of H-2^d T cells but not H-2^k T cells (Table 11.3). (For comparable experiments see Blanden *et al.*, 1977.) This inhibition acts on target cells since pretreatment of effector cells does not inhibit their cytotoxicity. Monoclonal antibodies to the classical transplantation antigens behave similarly, formally proving that recognition of the classical transplantation antigens on the target cell are important to cytotoxic T cell function. Compatible with this is the observation that virus-infected cells which lack the classical transplantation antigens are not killed by virus-specific cytotoxic T cells.

Since we do not understand the molecular nature of the T cell receptor, it is difficult to provide an explanation for MHS restriction. A number of explanations have been proposed, the more extreme forms of which are 'dual recognition' and 'altered self'.

Table 11.3. Ability of alloantisera to block cytotoxicity of
virus-specific T cells

Pretreatment of F_1 ($H\text{-}2^{d/k}$) virus-infected target cells	Cytotoxicity of parental strain ($H\text{-}2^d$ or $H\text{-}2^k$) T cells for LCM-infected targets	
	$H\text{-}2^d$ cells	$H\text{-}2^k$ cells
Nil	+++	+++
Anti-H-2^d	−	+++
Anti-H-2^k	+++	−

The virus-infected target cells were treated with alloantisera, washed free of antibody and then tested in a cytotoxic T cell assay. Similar treatment of effector T cells did not inhibit cytotoxicity.

Dual recognition proposes that individual T cells have two distinct receptors, one for antigen and the other for the appropriate product of the MHS. T cell activation would require specific binding to both receptors (Fig. 11.1). Altered self suggests that antigen on the surface of the antigen-presenting cell interacts with the products of the MHS producing a conformational change in the MHS molecules which is then recognized by a single receptor on T cells.

There are a number of intermediate models which have some but not all of the features of the two extreme forms. For example, T cells may have a compound receptor with a combining site that reacts simultaneously with antigen and an MHS determinant (associative recognition). Alternatively, the T cell receptor for antigen may also have a weak affinity for MHS products and it is the latter recognition event which is important in activation (see 11.6).

Whichever explanation turns out to be correct MHS restriction raises a number of important questions. First, at what stage in T cell development do cells acquire the capacity to recognize the products of the MHS and is this expressed throughout their clonal development? Second, are the T cell receptors involved in MHS restriction clonally distributed. Finally, what determinants on the MHS molecules are recognized by T cells in MHS restriction?

11.4 MHS restriction and T cell development

The involvement of the MHS in effector T cell functions is only a part of the story. The MHS is now viewed as playing an important rôle during the intrathymic development of T cells as well as during the antigen-induced clonal expansion of T cells in peripheral lymphoid tissues. The involvement of the MHS during these two earlier stages of T cell development has been determined by different experimental protocols and these are described below.

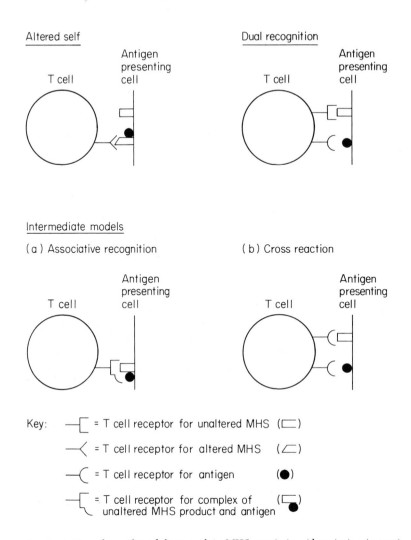

Fig. 11.1. Hypothetical models to explain MHS restriction (description in text).

11.4.1 *The rôle of the MHS in intrathymic T cell development*

The influence of the MHS on T cell development in the thymus can be studied by arranging for T cells of one genotype to mature in a thymus of a different genotype. This is achieved either by thymus grafting or by reconstituting irradiated mice with stem cells from donors of different genotypes. Both types of experiment (Figs 11.2 and 11.3) indicate that the *H-2* of the environment in which the T cells develop determines the haplotypes to which the T cells are subsequently restricted. The thymus-grafting experiments show that the thymus obviously plays an important

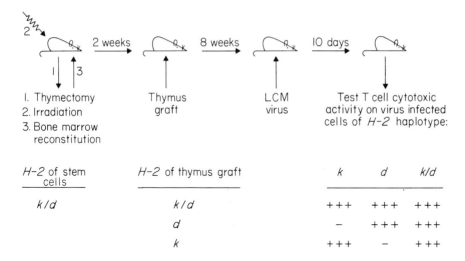

$H\text{-}2$ of stem cells	$H\text{-}2$ of thymus graft	k	d	k/d
k/d	k/d	+++	+++	+++
	d	−	+++	+++
	k	+++	−	+++

Fig. 11.2. The influence of the MHS of the thymus on the MHS preference of cytotoxic T cells. F_1 animals are first thymectomized, irradiated and reconstituted with F_1 bone marrow cells. They are then grafted with parental or F_1 thymus which is also previously irradiated to destroy any immunocompetent cells. The thymus graft is usually placed under the kidney capsule. After about 8 weeks the peripheral lymphoid tissue becomes repopulated with mature lymphocytes derived from the F_1 bone marrow. The F_1 T cells, however, will have developed in the grafted thymus. The animals are then challenged with virus and their spleens tested for virus-specific cytotoxic T cells as in Table 11.1. +++ =target cell lysis, − =no lysis. (Adapted from Zinkernagel *et al.*, 1978a.)

rôle in determining MHS restriction although with the bone-marrow chimeras it cannot be formally shown that the thymus is the critical factor. The result from experiment 2 in Fig. 11.3 appears inconsistent. $H\text{-}2^d$ cells that have matured in the F_1 ($H\text{-}2^{d/k}$) environment, fail to interact with targets expressing the $H\text{-}2^k$ haplotype. The reason for this anomaly is explained below.

11.4.2 *The rôle of the MHS in antigen priming*

In order to determine the rôle of the MHS in antigen priming it is necessary to use an adoptive transfer system. Virgin T cells which have developed in the first host are transferred to mice of a different $H\text{-}2$ haplotype prior to stimulation with antigen. Using this protocol (Fig. 11.4) it becomes apparent that the MHS of the antigen-presenting cells influences the population of virgin T cells which can be expanded. T cells which have developed in an $H\text{-}2^{d/k}$ thymus have the capacity to recognize antigen either in association with H-2^d or with H-2^k. If the antigen-presenting cell expresses only one of the parental haplotypes (say $H\text{-}2^d$) then T cells which recognize the other parental haplotype ($H\text{-}2^k$) are not expanded by antigen. The failure of the

H-2^d T cells that have developed in an H-$2^{d/k}$ thymus in experiment 2 (Fig. 11.3) to interact with H-2^k targets is probably due to the fact that the antigen-presenting cells in the chimera at the time of antigen challenge are predominantly derived from H-2^d stem cells (compare Fig. 11.3 with Fig. 11.4).

Three other important facts emerge from these experiments. First, the antigen-priming environment does not alter the pattern of restriction. H-$2^{d/k}$ T cells which have developed in an H-2^d thymus remain restricted to recognizing H-2^d in their

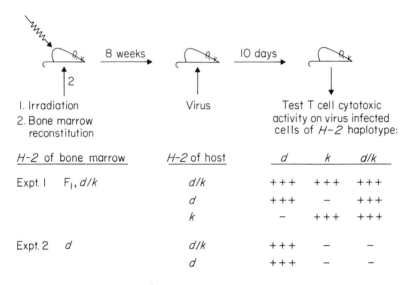

		Test T cell cytotoxic activity on virus infected cells of H–2 haplotype:		
H–2 of bone marrow	*H–2 of host*	*d*	*k*	*d/k*
Expt. 1 F₁, *d/k*	*d/k*	+++	+++	+++
	d	+++	–	+++
	k	–	+++	+++
Expt. 2 *d*	*d/k*	+++	–	–
	d	+++	–	–

Fig. 11.3. MHS restriction in stem cell chimeras. Mice of various haplotypes are irradiated and then reconstituted with bone marrow cells. The donor stem cells develop in the recipient's thymus and after about 8 weeks mature donor T cells appear in the peripheral lymphoid tissue. The mice are then challenged and tested as in Fig. 11.1. (Adapted from Zinkernagel *et al.*, 1978b; Bevan, 1977.)

effector phase even after they are primed to antigen in an F₁ H-$2^{d/k}$ environment (Fig. 11.4). Second, there appears to be no limit to the number of different H-2 haplotypes that T cells of one genotype can be selected to recognize. Figure 11.4 illustrates the ability of H-2^d stem cells to mature into effector T cells restricted to both H-2^d and H-2^k. In a similar experiment using the same source of stem cells but F₁ mice with different second H-2 haplotypes (H-$2^{d/f}$; H-$2^{d/s}$; H-$2^{d/etc.}$) the H-2^d stem cells seem to have an unlimited capacity to develop different restriction patterns. Third, as already mentioned this also shows that MHS restriction is not due to like–like recognition since cells of H-2^d genotype can, after appropriate manipulations, interact with H-2^k targets.

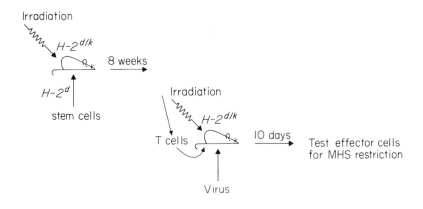

H-2 of stem cells	H-2 of thymic environment	H-2 of priming environment	T cell cytotoxic activity on virus infected cell of H-2 haplotype:		
			d	k	d/k
d	d/k	d/k	+++	+++	+++
		d	+++	−	+++
d/k	d	d/k	+++	−	+++
d/k	d/k	d/k	+++	+++	+++
		d	+++	−	+++
		k	−	+++	+++

Fig. 11.4. The influence of the MHS of the antigen-priming environment on the MHS preference of cytotoxic T cells. Stem cells are allowed to develop to mature T cells in a first host (exactly as in Fig. 11.3). To vary the H-2 haplotype of the antigen-priming environment, mature T cells from this animal are adoptively transferred to second irradiated recipients. These are then challenged and the level of cytotoxic T cell activity determined by the usual protocol. (Adapted from Zinkernagel *et al.*, 1978b.)

11.5 Clonal aspects of MHS restriction

The results of the experiments described above are most easily explained if the specificity of the receptors on T cells for MHS products is clonally distributed. This is well illustrated in the proliferative response of guinea-pig T cells to protein antigens on antigen pulsed macrophages. Using a protocol outlined in Table 11.4 it has been shown that if F_1 guinea pigs (strain 2 × strain 13) are primed *in vivo* with antigens, then the primed T cell population contains two sets of specific T cells—those which can respond to antigen presented only on strain 2 macrophages, and a second set

Table 11.4. Evidence for the clonal distribution of MHS restriction amongst T cells (adapted from Paul *et al.*, 1977). The ability of T cells from (strain 2 × strain 13) F_1 guinea pigs to respond *in vitro* to antigen associated with macrophages of either parental haplotype was tested in a two-stage assay. In the first stage F_1 T cells primed *in vivo* to PPD and ovalbumin were cultured with antigen-pulsed macrophages. Any proliferating cells were killed by bromodeoxyuridine and ultraviolet light. The remaining non-proliferated cells from this first culture were then similarly tested in a second culture using fresh antigen-pulsed macrophages

			Proliferative response in second culture		
Antigen-pulsed macrophages in first culture	BuDr+Light	Antigen	Macrophages from strain		
			2	13	F_1
PPD–strain 2		PPD	–	+++	+++
		OA	+++	+++	+++
PPD–strain 13		PPD	+++	–	+++
		OA	+++	+++	+++
PPD-F_1 (strain 2 × strain 13)		PPD	–	–	–
		OA	+++	+++	+++

PPD=tuberculin antigen.
OA=ovalbumin.

which can respond to the same antigen presented only on strain 13 macrophages (Paul *et al.*, 1977).

Where there is more than one locus in the MHS controlling the restriction of a particular functional class of T cells (e.g. the K or D region with cytotoxic cells) then different T cells respond to the same antigen associated with the products of either region. In an F_1 (H-$2^{b/k}$) (Table 11.5) there can be at least four distinct sets of cytotoxic T cells recognizing antigen in association with K^b K^k D^b and D^k respectively (Fig. 11.5).

11.5.1 The fine specificity of MHS restriction

MHS restriction can apply to very fine differences within H-2. Strains of mice carrying mutations of H-2 were described in Chapter 6. One mutant ($bm1$) involves a single amino acid replacement in the K region of the H-2^b strain. Cytotoxic T cells restricted to the wild type (K^b) interact poorly with target cells carrying the mutant allele (K^{bm1}) and vice versa. Cytotoxic T cells from stem cell chimeras created with combinations of wild type cells and mutant mice have shown that the ability to discriminate between the wild type and the mutant is selected for during intrathymic

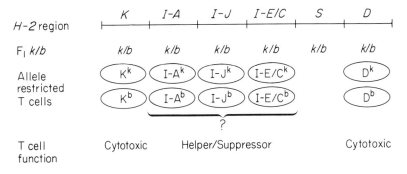

Fig. 11.5. Possible MHS restriction of functionally distinct T cells for different alleles within the MHS.

development of the T cells. On the other hand, studies with the K region mutant ($bm3$) show that there is considerable cross-reaction (i.e. no restriction) between the K^{bm3} and the K^b wild type in cytotoxic assays.

Failure to observe MHS restriction may mean that the critical parts of the molecule involved are present on all the targets tested. If the determinants involved in MHS restriction were the serologically defined public specificities (Chapter 6) or other invariant parts of H-2 products then MHS restriction would never have been observed. Consequently the parts of the H-2 molecules critical for MHS restriction

Table 11.5. Sets of cytotoxic T cells restricted to K or D region products in F_1 animals. Following challenge with virus four sets of cytotoxic cells can be detected. Each set can recognize virus in association with either the K or D end allelic products of both parental strains

LCM virus challenged mouse						Cytotoxic T cells assayed on virus-infected targets from H-2 recombinant mice					
	H-2						H-2				Cyto-toxicity
Strain	K	I-A	I-E	I-C	D	Strain	K	I-A	I-E	I-C	D	
F₁ (B10× B10.Br)	b/k	b/k	b/k	b/k	b/k	B10	$\underline{b}$	b	b	b	$\underline{b}$	+++
						B10.Br	$\underline{k}$	k	k	k	$\underline{k}$	+++
						B10.D2	d	d	d	d	d	−
						B10.A	$\underline{k}$	k	d	d	d	+++
						B10.A(5R)	$\underline{b}$	b	d	d	d	+++
						B10.OH	d	d	d	d	$\underline{k}$	+++
						B10.HTG	d	d	d	d	$\underline{b}$	+++
						B10.TL	s	$\underline{k}$	$\underline{k}$	$\underline{k}$	d	−

are either the private specificities or allelic determinants which have so far not been recognized by conventional alloantisera. An analysis of the *H-2* mutants may identify the parts of the *H-2* molecules important for T cell activation.

11.6 Significance of MHS restriction

MHS restriction occurs at three discrete stages during T cell development (Fig. 11.6). The first stage is in the thymus where stem cells are presumed to express a wide range of MHS restriction patterns. However, only those cells which recognize the MHS products within the thymus are preferentially expanded. When virgin T cells first meet antigen in the peripheral lymphoid tissue only those with the appropriate MHS restriction patterns are expanded (stage 2) and this pattern is maintained in the effector phase (stage 3).

The thymus is the site where MHS restriction patterns are first selected. Since MHS restriction patterns apply to all regions of the MHS then *K*, *I* or *D* region products must be present either together or separately on 'selector' cells within the thymus. Thymus-grafting experiments suggest that these selector cells cannot be thymocytes. Two possible candidates are the thymic epithelial cells which express *I* as well as *K* and *D* region products, or an immigrant cell type. It is widely assumed that only the former are important but there are recent experiments apparently incompatible with this view. When *H-2*[b] nude (athymic) mice were grafted with a

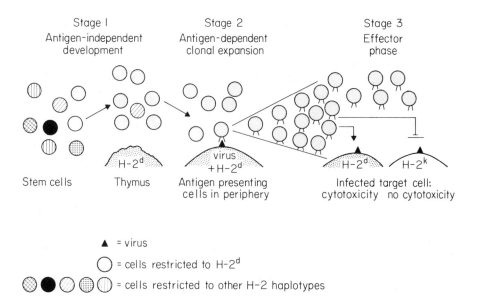

Fig. 11.6. Involvement of the MHS during the three stages of T cell development.

fully allogeneic *H-2^d* thymus then the mature *H-2^b* T cells which developed in the nude mice were found to be restricted for *H-2^b* and not *H-2^d* (Kindred, 1979). These experiments point to the fact that we are ignorant of the processes occurring in the thymus during T cell development.

The phenomenon of MHS restriction was the first indication that products of the MHS were involved in the T cell response to antigen. MHS restriction can obviously only be detected using histoincompatible cells but its significance is that MHS recognition is necessary for T cell responses to antigen in a syngeneic environment. The rôle of the MHS molecules in T cell activation is not at present known but these molecules may well form part of the signalling pathways for the interactions of T cells with their various targets. In this context it is of considerable interest that MHS products are transmembrane proteins and might transfer signals across cell membranes.

In conclusion, the MHS is almost certainly ambiguously named. The true significance of this system is in T cell activation and it should not be viewed simply as a system of histocompatability antigens frustrating the wishes of transplantation surgeons.

References

BEVAN M.J. (1977) In a radiation chimaera host *H-2* antigens determine the immune responsiveness of donor cytotoxic cells. *Nature* **269**, 417.

BLANDEN R.V., MCKENZIE I.F.C., KEES V., MELVOLD R.W. & KOHN H.I. (1977) Cytotoxic T cell response to *Ectromelia* virus-infected cells. Different *H-2* requirements for triggering precursor T cell induction or lysis by the effector T cells defined by the Balb/c–*H-2^{db}* mutation. *J. exp. Med.* **146**, 869.

GOULMY E., TERMIJTELEN A., BRADLEY B.A. & VAN ROOD J.J. (1977) H-Y antigen killing by T cells of women is restricted by HLA. *Nature* **266**, 544.

KATZ D.H., HAMOAKA T., DORF M.E. & BENACERRAF B. (1973) Failure of physiologic cooperative interactions between T and B lymphocytes from allogeneic donor strains in humoral responses to hapten protein conjugates. *J. exp. Med.* **137**, 1405.

KINDRED B. (1979) Functional activity of T cells which differentiate from nude mouse precursors in a congenic or allogeneic thymus graft. *Immunological Rev.* **42**, 60.

MCMICHAEL A. (1978) HLA restriction of human cytotoxic T lymphocytes specific for influenza virus. Poor recognition of virus associated with HLA-A2. *J. exp. Med.* **148**, 1458.

PAUL W.E., SHEVACH E.M., PICHERAL S.F., THOMAS D.W. & ROSENTHAL A.S. (1977) Independent populations of primed F$_1$ guinea-pig T lymphocytes respond to antigen-pulsed parental peritoneal exudate cells. *J. exp. Med.* **145**, 618.

ZINKERNAGEL R.M., CALLAHAN G.N., ALTHAGE A., COOPER S., KLEIN P.A. & KLEIN J. (1978a) On the thymus in the differentiation of '*H-2* self recognition' by T cells. Evidence for dual recognition. *J. exp. Med.* **147**, 882.

ZINKERNAGEL R.M., CALLAHAN G.N., ALTHAGE A., COOPER S., STREILEIN P.W. & KLEIN J. (1978b) The lymphoreticular system in triggering virus plus self on specific cytotoxic T cells. Evidence for T cell help. *J. exp. Med.* **147**, 897.

ZINKERNAGEL R.M. & DOHERTY P.C. (1974) Activity of sensitized thymus-derived lymphocytes in lymphocytic choriomeningitis reflects immunological surveillance against altered self components. *Nature* **257**, 547.

Further reading

MILLER J.F.A.P. (1978) Influence of genes of the major histocompatibility complex on the reactivity of thymus-derived lymphocytes. *Cont. Topics in Immunobiology* **8**, 1. Plenum, New York.
See also *Immunol. Rev.* (1978) **42**, Acquisition of the T cell repertoire (MÖLLER G. ed.). Munksgaard, Copenhagen.

Chapter 12
The Biology of the Major Histocompatibility System— MHS Immune Response Genes

12.1 Introduction

There are a large number of genes which control the level and/or specificity of the immune response. They are known as immune response or *Ir* genes and act in many ways. Some *Ir* genes act non-specifically by affecting antigen handling, degree of clonal expansion, catabolism of secreted immunoglobulin and so on (Biozzi *et al.*, 1975). Genes which influence the response to a specific antigen fall into two major categories: those linked to the Ig constant regions and those linked to the major histocompatibility system (MHS *Ir* genes). There are other apparently antigen-specific *Ir* genes which fall into neither of these two categories but so far they have not been extensively studied.

Immunoglobulin-linked *Ir* genes represent inherited V-region genes. MHS *Ir* genes cannot be coding for antibody molecules and either code for a non-immunoglobulin recognition system or alternatively code for cell surface structures which interfere with or interact with a recognition system based on immunoglobulins.

The MHS *Ir* genes control T cell responses to antigen. They were first discovered in guinea pigs and mice in the response to a variety of synthetic polypeptides (see section 12.2.1) and they have now been recognized in a wide variety of species including man. They are of considerable importance to our understanding of the function of the MHS in the immune response (Benacerraf & McDevitt 1972).

12.2 The detection of MHS *Ir* genes

12.2.1 Antigens used to reveal MHS Ir genes

MHS *Ir* genes have been defined by measuring the immune response to a restricted antigenic challenge. The antigens used included those of limited structural heterogeneity such as synthetic polypeptides of either linear or branched form (Table 12.1); alloantigens such as immunoglobulin allotypes; evolutionarily conserved proteins (e.g. insulin, myoglobin, lysozyme, cytochrome C) from other species and finally low doses of complex antigens such as ovalbumin. Although less than 100 antigenic systems have been described, it is likely that MHS *Ir* genes participate in responses to all thymus-dependent antigens. Failure to reveal a defect in response to a given

Table 12.1. Some synthetic polypeptides used for the detection of *Ir* genes

---

Random linear polymers
   GAT   (poly-L-glutamic acid; L-alanine; L-tyrosine)
   GA   (poly-L-glutamic acid; L-alanine)
   GT   (poly-L-glutamic acid; L-tyrosine)
   GLPhe (poly-L-glutamic acid; L-lysine; L-phenylalanine)
   PLL   (poly-L-lysine)

Random branched polymers
   (T,G)-A--L   (poly-L-lysine backbone, sidechains of poly-D, L-alanine, and 'tips' of
                 randomly arranged residues of tyrosine and glutamic acid)
   (Phe,G)-A--L (as (T,G)-A--L but with tips of phenylalanine and glutamic acid)
   (H,G)-A--L   (as (T,G)-A--L but with tips of histidine and glutamic acid)

Basic structure of branched polymer

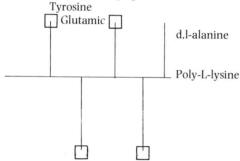

---

antigen could simply mean that insufficient strains had been screened or that the
antigenic challenge had been inappropriate.

12.2.2 Ir genes and T cell help

Many *Ir* gene defects are detected as a failure in the helper T cell response to
thymus-dependent antigens. This was first observed in randomly bred guinea pigs
using PLL as antigen (Table 12.2) (Levine *et al.*, 1963). Responder animals expressed
delayed hypersensitivity and a helper T cell response to PLL, whereas PLL non-
responders did not. The absence of PLL specific helper T cells for a response to
DNP–PLL can be bypassed by coupling a second thymus-dependent carrier (BSA) to
the DNP–PLL.

   In general *Ir* genes influence only the level of T cell help and not the specificity of
the antibody response. One of the few exceptions is the response of GA responder and
GA non-responder guinea pigs to GAT. The specificity of the antibody produced in
each case is different. The antibody to GAT in GA responders also reacts with GA
whereas in the GA non-responders none of the anti-GAT antibody reacts with GA

Table 12.2. Responses to PLL in guinea pigs

Response	Delayed hypersensitivity to PLL		Anti DNP	
	Strain 2	Strain 13	Strain 2	Strain 13
Antigen				
PLL	+	−		
DNP–PLL	+	−	+	−
DNP–PLL–BSA	+	−	+	+
DNP–PLL–BSA (guinea pigs tolerant to BSA)	+	−	+	−

Delayed hypersensitivity responses to PLL and anti-DNP responses to DNP–PLL in responder (strain 2) and non-responder (strain 13) guinea pigs. The PLL acts as a carrier for the anti-DNP response to DNP–PLL. The absence of PLL specific helper T cells in strain 13 is bypassed by coupling a second carrier (BSA) to the DNP–PLL.

(Bluestein *et al.*, 1972). The reason for this is not known but it may represent a failure of the GAT-specific helper T cells to interact with the GA-specific B cells.

For certain antigens non-responders fail to make antibody even on repeated immunization. For other antigens the non-responders eventually produce antibody levels comparable to that of the responder strain.

12.2.3 Ir genes and T cell proliferation

T cell proliferation is largely dependent on the activation of Lyt 1^+23^- helper T cells. *Ir* gene defects revealed by this assay parallel those for thymus-dependent antibody formation. A secondary proliferative response of cells primed *in vitro* is potentially useful to detect *Ir* genes in man (Hensen & Elferink, 1979).

12.2.4 Ir genes and Suppressor T cells

The capacity to generate antigen-specific suppressor T cells has also been shown to be under MHS *Ir* gene control. Mice normally produce antibody to GT polymers when given on an immunogenic carrier (GT on methylated BSA: GT–MBSA) but in certain strains, prior immunization with GT alone, suppresses the antibody response to GT–MBSA (Table 12.3). This suppression can be adoptively transferred with

Table 12.3. Suppression of response in mice of different haplotypes to GT–MBSA by prior injection of GT

| Strain | *H-2* | Response to challenge with GT–MBSA after priming with | | Suppression |
		Nothing	GT	
C57Bl/10	*b*	+ + + +	+ + + +	No
B10.D2	*d*	+ + + +	+	Yes
B10.BR	*k*	+ + + +	+	Yes
DBA/1	*q*	+ + + +	+ + + +	No
SJL	*s*	+ + + +	+	Yes
DBA/1 × SJL	*q/s*	+ + + +	+	Yes

Mice will respond to poly-glutamic acid; tyrosine (GT) when it is attached to methylated bovine serum albumin (MBSA) to give a GT-specific response. Prior injection of GT precipitated on alum leads to a failure of response to GT–MBSA. Note that in the F_1 the ability to generate suppressors for the antibody response is dominant. Based on Debre *et al.* (1975).

T cells. It is not certain if the defect in the generation of suppressor cells is in the suppressor cells themselves or in helper T cells required to generate the suppressors (see Chapter 10.4).

12.2.5 Ir *genes and Cytotoxic T cells*

Several MHS *Ir* genes are revealed as specific failures in cytotoxic T cell responses. A particularly interesting case is seen in the response to the minor histocompatibility antigen, H-Y, which is found on male but not female cells. H-Y-specific cytotoxic T cells can be obtained from female mice of certain strains following immunization with male cells. The generation of cytotoxic T cells requires helper T cells and a detailed analysis of the strain distribution of responses reveals *Ir* gene defects in both the helper and cytotoxic cells in this response (see §12.3.3).

12.3 Genetics of the MHS *Ir* genes

12.3.1 *Inheritance and arrangement of* Ir *genes*

The F_1 cross between a high and low responder is usually a responder. In many cases the level of the response in the F_1 is unpredictable compared to the parental phenotype, suggesting that more than one *Ir* gene may be involved. *Ir* gene complementation is an extreme example of this (see §12.3.3).

Linkage of MHS *Ir* genes to *H-2* was first shown by McDevitt and Chinitz (1969). By studying the response to (T,G)-A--L it was shown by back-cross analysis of F_1 to parent that the response phenotype segregated with the appropriate *H-2* haplotype. The pattern of response to a variety of antigens in *H-2* congenic mice is shown in Table 12.4.

12.3.2 *Mapping of* Ir *genes within* H-2

The majority of *Ir* genes determining helper T cell function map within *I-A* (Table 12.5) and a few map to the *I-E/C. Ir* genes determining the generation of cytotoxic T cells have been mapped to *K* or *D* and also to *I*. A summary of the current mapping of MHS *Ir* genes is shown in Table 12.6.

12.3.3 *Complementation of MHS* Ir *genes*

With some antigens the F_1 hybrids between two non-responder strains give a responder phenotype. This is known as complementation and is most easily explained by arguing that two (or more) different genes act together to determine a particular phenotype. Absence of the characteristic (in this case a specific immune response) is seen when a defect lies in either one of the two genes. In the F_1 hybrids, or in the appropriate recombinant strain, functional products of both genes will be present and the animal will be a responder. Table 12.7 shows this schematically for GLPhe where the response requires two genes which have been designated β and α in *I-A* and *I-E/C* respectively.

There are two distinct forms of complementation. The first is when the complementing genes are expressed on the same cell (Schwartz *et al.*, 1979). An example is in the complementation observed in the response to GLPhe which also shows the

Table 12.4. Distribution of responder and non-responder status amongst mice of different *H-2* type for a variety of antigens

Antigen[1]	Pattern of response in *H-2* haplotypes				
	b	*d*	*k*	*q*	*s*
(T,G)-A--L	+	+	−	−	−
(H,G)-A--L	−	+	+	−	−
(Phe,G)-A--L	+	+	+	+	−
GLPhe	−	+	−	+	−
GAT	+	+	+	−	−
Thyroglobulin	−	−	+	+	+

+ =responder, − =non-responder.
(1) For description of antigens see Table 12.2.

Table 12.5. Mapping of MHS-associated *Ir* genes controlling the response to (H.G)-A--L

Strain	*H-2*	K	*I-A*	*I-B*	*I-J*	*I-E*	*I-C*	S	D	Response to (H.G)-A--L
A	*a*	k	k	k	k	k	d	d	d	+++
A.SW	*s*	s	s	s	s	s	s	s	s	−
A.TL	*t1*	s	k	k	k	k	k	k	d	+++
A.TH	*t2*	s	s	s	s	s	s	s	d	−
B10	*b*	b	b	b	b	b	b	b	b	−
B10.A(4R)	*h4*	k	k	b	b	b	b	b	b	+++

Various strains of mice which are recombinant within the *H-2* region were challenged with (H.G)-A--L and antibody levels determined. Adapted from McDevitt *et al.* (1972).

characteristics of coupled complementation. This means that an apparently defective gene is only defective with some partners but functional with others. These properties of the GLPhe *Ir* genes suggest that the functional product of the genes is a complex of two or more polypeptide chains each coded by one of the complementing genes. It may not be coincidental that one of the *I* region proteins is a complex of two chains, one coded for by the *I-E/C* and the other by the *I-A* region (see Chapter 6).

The second form of complementation is seen in the generation of cytotoxic T cells. In this case each of the two complementing genes influence distinct T cell subpopulations (Table 12.10). The genes in the *I* region influence helper T cells whereas the genes in the *K* or *D* regions affect cytotoxic T cells. The mapping of these genes is shown in Table 12.8.

Table 12.6. Mapping of various MHS-associated *Ir* genes within the *H-2* region

Antigen	T cell function	Assay	K	*I-A*	*I-E/C*	D
(H.G)-A--L	Helper T cells	Antibody		●		
	?	T cell proliferation		●		
GLPhe	Helper T cells	Antibody		●	●	
	?	T cell proliferation		●	●	
H-Y	Cytotoxic T cells	Cytotoxic effectors	●			●
	Helper T cells			●		
GT	Suppressor and helper T cells	Generation of T_S to GT		●	●	

Table 12.7. Complementation of *Ir* genes for GLPhe

Strain	H-2	Chromosomes	Functional products	Response to G,L-Phe
B10	*b*	═══════╪═══ ══════	β	None
B10.A	*a*	═══ ══╪══════════	α	None
F₁ (B10 ×B10.A)	*b/a*	═══════╪═══ ─────	α and β	Yes
B10.A5R	Recombinant between *a* and *b*	═══════╪──────── ═══════╪────────	α and β	Yes

The table shows the *H-2* region of the chromosome schematically. The heavy line represents the *H-2ᵇ* haplotype. Mapping studies with recombinant strains have placed the α gene in the *I-C* or *I-E* subregions and the β gene in the *I-A* or *I-B* subregions. Adapted from Benacerraf and Dorf (1976).

Table 12.8. Complementation of MHS-associated *Ir* genes in the cytotoxic response to H-Y

Strain	H-2	K	I-A	I-B	I-J	I-E	I-C	S	D	Response to H-Y
		H-2 region and subregion								
B10	*b*	b̲	b	b	b	b	b	b	b̲	+ +
HTI		b̲	b	b	b	b	b	b	d	−
B10.A	*ia*	k	k	k	k	k	d	d	d	−
B10.A(4R)	*h4*	k	k	b	b	b	b	b	b̲	−
B10.A(5R)	*i5*	b̲	b	b	b	k	d	d	d	−
F₁ (4R×5R)	*h4/i5*	k̲/b	k/b	b/b	b/b	b/k	b/d	b/d	b̲/d	+ +

In each case the response is of female mice to male cells (H-Y⁺) of the same strain tested on syngeneic targets. From this table it can be seen that the response in *H-2ᵇ* mice depends on one gene in the *K* or *I-A* region and a second in the *D* region. Adapted from Simpson and Gordon (1977).

12.4 The cellular level of expression of MHS *Ir* genes

MHS *Ir* genes are revealed by specific failures in the T cell response. This can either be due to a failure in antigen presentation to T cells (presentation defect) or an absence of T cells with the appropriate specificity (repertoire defect). The former envisages that the MHS products on macrophages or other antigen-presenting cells are 'specifically' involved in processing or presenting antigen. The latter requires that the T cell repertoire is determined directly or indirectly by the MHS. There are many experiments which have attempted to distinguish between these two hypotheses but the phenomenon of MHS restriction can be used to destroy the arguments for either case. A detailed analysis of the specific interactions between T cells and macrophages illustrates this dilemma.

12.4.1 Ir genes and macrophages

The expression of *Ir* genes in macrophages has been investigated in guinea pigs. Strain 2 guinea pigs respond to GL but not to GT (GL$^+$GT$^-$) while strain 13 have the reverse phenotype (GL$^-$GT$^+$). F$_1$ (2 × 13) animals respond to both antigens (Shevach & Rosenthal, 1973). F$_1$ T cells can proliferate *in vitro* to either antigen if it is presented on F$_1$ macrophages but proliferate only to GL and not to GT if strain 2 macrophages are used, and only to GT and not to GL if strain 13 macrophages are used (Fig. 12.1). At first sight this experiment would suggest that the *Ir* genes function at the macrophage level. However, we know that the T cells in an F$_1$ consist of two populations (see Chapter 11): one that responds to antigen in the context of the MHS from one parent and the other that responds to antigen presented with the MHS of the other parent. Thus, a second way to interpret the experiment in Fig. 12.1 is to say that the subset of F$_1$ T cells which respond to antigen on strain 2 macrophages lacks receptors for GT (but not for GL) whereas the subset of T cells which responds to antigens on strain 13 macrophages lacks receptors for GL (but not for GT). This interpretation would imply that the MHS influenced the T cell repertoire.

Many other protocols have been used for analysing *Ir* gene defects in antigen presentation to T cells but they all suffer from the same ambiguity.

Fig. 12.1. Stimulation of (2 × 13) F$_1$ T cells using antigen-pulsed macrophages from F$_1$, strain 2 and strain 13 guinea pigs. The antigen used is shown underneath each set of histograms. Strain 2 is GL$^+$ GT$^-$ and strain 13 is GL$^-$ GT$^+$. The purified protein derivative of tuberculin (PPD) is used as a positive control. (Taken from Shevach & Rosenthal, 1973.) Mϕ=macrophage

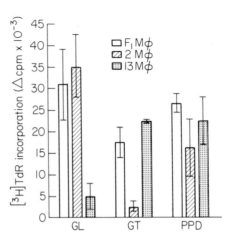

12.4.2 Ir genes and T cell development

The alternative explanation for *Ir* gene defects is that they represent repertoire defects in T cells. MHS restriction requires recognition of MHS molecules and this recognition is selected in the thymus (Chapter 11). It is possible, therefore, that the repertoire for antigen recognition is similarly selected by the thymus.

There are two types of experiments which appear to provide evidence for this but again when argued to their conclusion the question remains unresolved.

(a) Thymus-grafting experiments. In the response to GLPhe H-2^a and H-2^b mice are non-responders yet the $(H$-$2^a \times H$-$2^b)$ F_1 is a responder. If F_1 'B' mice are grafted with thymuses from either non-responder parent then the F_1 T cells which develop in the thymus graft acquire the non-responder phenotype (Table 12.9). Again at first sight this experiment suggests that *Ir* genes function at the level of the thymus. However, the phenomenon of MHS restriction can invalidate this conclusion. In F_1 responders, GLPhe is presented in association with the α/β structure—the product of the complementing genes on antigen-presenting cells. F_1 cells that have developed in a parental (non-responder) thymus may not have acquired the ability to recognize this structure and therefore fail to respond to antigen when presented with the α/β structure on F_1 macrophages. Consequently the F_1 B mouse grafted with the non-responder thymus will be a non-responder.

(b) Stem cell chimera experiments. A comparable experiment that shows the apparent influence of the MHS on the T cell repertoire has been described for cytotoxic T cells. F_1 T cells with the responder genotype acquire the non-responder phenotype if they have developed in either of the parental non-responder strains (Fig. 12.2,

Table 12.9. The rôle of the thymus in dictating the MHS-associated *Ir* gene response

Source of thymus graft	Response of F_1 (H-$2^{a/b}$) cells to GLPhe
H-2^b (non-responder)	−
H-2^a (non-responder)	−
H-$2^{a/b}$ (responder)	+++

The protocol for constructing thymus grafts is shown in Fig 11.2. The secondary antibody response to GLPhe was measured after priming and boosting with GLPhe in Freund's complete adjuvant. Adapted from Waldmann *et al.* (1979).

Table 12.10). Again this experiment cannot distinguish between defects in the repertoire or in antigen presentation.

However, this experiment demonstrates that the complementing *Ir* genes for the response to H-Y affect different cell populations. If T cells from both types of chimera are pooled and challenged in an irradiated F_1 recipient then the two apparently non-responder T cells will act together to generate a cytotoxic response.

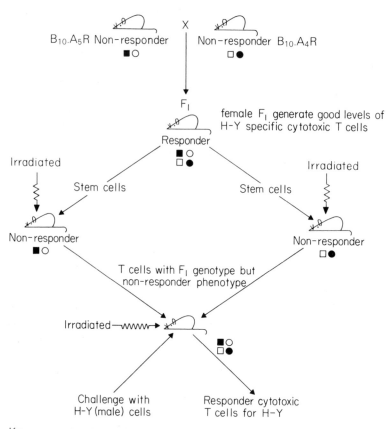

Fig. 12.2. Schematic representation of *Ir* gene complementation in the cytotoxic response to the male antigen, H-Y. (Based on von Boehmer *et al.*, 1979. See also Table 12.10.)

Table 12.10. Complementation of different T cell populations in the response to H-Y

Source of T cells	Cytotoxic response to H-Y
(B10.A(5R) × B10.A(4R)) F$_1$	+ + + +
B10.A(5R)	−
B10.A(4R)	−
F$_1$ developed in B10.A(5R)	−
F$_1$ developed in B10.A(4R)	−
1:1 mixture of F$_1$ cells developed in B10.A(5R) and B10.A(4R)	+ + + +

The haplotypes of the mice are shown in Table 12.8. Stem-cell chimeras were constructed as shown in Fig 11.3. The cells from chimeras or normal mice were transferred to irradiated F$_1$ mice (B10.A(5R) × B10.A(4R)) and challenged with H-Y antigens. After boosting *in vitro* the level of cytotoxic response to H-Y was measured. Adapted from von Bohmer *et al.* (1979).

12.5 *Ir* Genes and the T cell repertoire

At present it is impossible to distinguish if defects in the MHS *Ir* genes represent defects in presentation or defects in the repertoire. It is envisaged that the products of the MHS influence presentation either through some form of 'altered self' phenomenon or during antigen processing by macrophages (Benacerraf, 1978). It is less easy to envisage how the MHS may be responsible for repertoire defects. One view, for which there is no evidence, is that part of the T cell receptor is coded for by genes in the MHS. However, there are also ways in which the MHS may indirectly influence the T cell repertoire.

12.5.1 Cross-tolerance or negative selection

The concept behind cross-tolerance is that self molecules are similar to the test antigen. Thus self tolerance (see Chapter 13) leads to unresponsiveness to the test antigen. As an explanation for MHS *Ir* genes this view had little support since it predicted that, contrary to the findings, the F$_1$ between a responder and non-responder should be a non-responder, the F$_1$ having all the antigens present in both parents (Cohn, 1972).

Recently there has been a revival of interest in cross-tolerance (Schwartz, 1978; Matzinger, 1981). This has arisen through the discovery of the clonal nature of MHS restriction which implies that an F$_1$ animal is made up of two populations of T cells, each set reacting with antigen in the context of different MHS alleles. Consequently, if the recognition of self molecules during the induction of tolerance involves MHS restriction (a fact on which there is no information), then each set of T cells in the F_1 will be separately tolerant to self components and therefore separately cross-tolerant to different test antigens. In an F_1 between a responder and a non-responder the population restricted to the non-responder haplotype will have been cross-tolerized to the test antigen and the other set of T cells are responsible for the responder phenotype. The MHS-associated defects in response would then represent gaps in the T cell repertoire created as a consequence of unresponsiveness to self.

12.5.2 The MHS and the T cell repertoire

Long before MHS restriction was recognized, Jerne (1971) proposed that germ-line genes coded for receptors which were specific for the transplantation antigens of the species. During lymphocyte ontogeny auto-reactive cells would be driven to proliferate by the MHS products of the individual, and in the course of this proliferation mutations would arise in the T cell receptors. These mutant clones could be enriched if self-reactive clones were eliminated leaving mutated, non-self-reactive, clones as the T cell pool to react with external antigens (see Chapter 7).

If this hypothesis is correct, then the T cell repertoire for antigens will indirectly depend on the MHS of the individual. Certain MHS alleles may fail to generate particular specificities and these defects in specific response will show up as MHS-associated non-responders.

One attractive feature of the Jerne hypothesis is that it can explain not only MHS *Ir* genes, but also selection for the pattern of MHS restriction acquired by T cells in the thymus. Although these two phenomena are usually discussed separately they almost certainly represent two views of the same biological process. For a further discussion of this see von Boehmer *et al.* (1978) and Munro and Waldmann (1978).

References

BENACERRAF B. & DORF M.E. (1976) Genetic control of specific immune responses and immune suppression by *I*-region genes. *Cold. Spr. Harb. Symp. Quant. Biol.* **41**, 465.

BENACERRAF B. (1978) A hypothesis to relate the specificity of T lymphocytes and the activty of I-region specific. Ir genes in macrophages and B lymphocytes. *J. Immunol.* **120**, 1809.

BENACERRAF B. & McDEVITT H.O. (1972) The histocompatibility-linked immune response genes. *Science* **175**, 273.

BIOZZI G., STIFFEL C., MOUNTON D. & BOUTHILLIER Y. (1975) Selection of Lines of Mice with High and Low Antibody Responds to Complex Immunogens. In BENACERRAF B. (ed.), *Immunogenetics and Immunodeficiency*, pp. 179, 227. MT Press, Lancaster.

BLUESTEIN H.G., GREEN I., MAURER P.H. & BENACERRAF B. (1972) Specific immune response genes of the guinea pig. *J. exp. Med.* **135**, 98.

COHN M. (1972) Conference, evaluation and commentary. In (MCDEVITT H.O. & LANDY M., eds), *Genetic Control of the Immune Response*, pp. 370–448. Academic Press, New York.

DEBRE P., KAPP J.A., DORF M.E. & BENACERRAF B. (1975) Genetic control of specific immune suppression. *J. exp. Med.* **142**, 1447.

HENSEN E.J. & ELFERINK B.G. (1979) Primary sensitization and restimulation of human lymphocytes with soluble antigens *in vitro*. *Nature* **277**, 223.

JERNE N.K. (1971) The somatic generation of immune recognition. *Eur. J. Immunol.* **1**, 1.

LEVINE B.B., OJEDA A. & BENACERRAF B. (1963) The genetic control of the immune response to hapten poly-L-lysine conjugates in guinea pigs. *J. exp. Med.* **118**, 953.

MCDEVITT H.O. & CHINITZ A. (1969) Genetic control of antibody response, relationship between immune response and histocompatibility (*H-2*) type. *Science* **163**, 1207.

MCDEVITT H.O., DEAK B.D., SHREFFLER D.C., KLEIN H., STIMPFLING J.H. & SNELL G.D. (1972) Genetic control of the immune response, mapping of the *Ir-1* locus. *J. exp. Med.* **135**, 1259.

MATZINGER P. (1981) T cell behaviour: a one receptor viewpoint. *Nature*, in press.

MUNRO A. & WALDMANN H. (1978) The major histocompatibility system and the immune response. *Brit. Med. Bull.* **34**, 3, 253.

SCHWARTZ R.H. (1978) A clonal deletion model for *Ir* gene control of the immune response. *Scand. J. Immunol.* **7**, 3.

SCHWARTZ R.H., YANO A., STIMPFLING J.H. & PAUL W.E. (1979) Gene complementation in T lymphocyte proliferation response to GLPhe. *J. exp. Med.* **149**, 40.

SHEVACH E.M. & ROSENTHAL A.S. (1973) Role of macrophages in the regulation of the genetic control of the immune response. *J. exp. Med.* **138**, 1213.

SIMPSON E. & GORDON R.D. (1977) Responsiveness to H-Y antigen; *Ir* gene complementation. *Immunol. Rev.* **35**, 59.

VON BOEHMER H., HAAS W. & JERNE N.K. (1978) Major histocompatibility complex-linked immune responsiveness is acquired by lymphocytes of low responder mice differentiating in thymus of high responder mice. *Proc. Nat. Acad. Sci.* **75**, 2439.

WALDMANN H., MUNRO A. & MAURER D. (1979) The Role of MHS Gene Products in the Development of the T Cell Repertoire. In THIERFELDER S., RODT H. & KOLB H.J. (eds), *Recent Trends in the Immunobiology of Bone Marrow Transplantation*, Vol. 25 Suppl. to *Blut* p. 93.

Further reading

BENACERRAF B. & KATZ D.H. (1975) The histocompatibility-linked immune response genes. *Adv. Cancer Res.* **21**, 121.

BIOZZI G., MOUTON D., SANT'ANNA O.A., PASSOS H.C., GENNARI M., REIS M.H., FERREIRA V.C.A., HEUMANN A.M., BOUTHILLIER Y., IBANEX O.M., STIFFEL C. & SIQUEIRA M. (1979) Genetics of immunoresponsiveness to natural antigens in the mouse. *Curr. Topics in Microbiol. and Immunol.* **85**, 31.

ROSENTHAL A.S. (1978) Determinant selection and macrophage function in genetic control of the immune response. *Immunol. Rev.* **40**, 136 (MÖLLER G., ed.). Munksgaard, Copenhagen.

See also *Immunol. Rev.* (1978) **42**, Acquisition of the T cell repertoire (MÖLLER G. ed.). Munksgaard, Copenhagen.

Chapter 13
Immunological Tolerance

13.1 Introduction

The specific immune response to antigen can result either in the production of antibody and effector T cells, or in the specific failure to respond to secondary challenge with the same antigen. This is known as immunological tolerance or unresponsiveness and is an acquired characteristic. Tolerance to self antigens is not genetically inherited as the offspring of two histoincompatible parents inherit the capacity to recognize alloantigens of each parent but this potential is never expressed in the F_1.

There are two views as to the mechanism of tolerance. The first is that under appropriate circumstances antigen induces specific clonal deletion. The second is that tolerance is mediated by specific suppression and represents an exaggerated form of the normal regulatory control mechanisms. These two views are not mutually exclusive.

From the clinical viewpoint it is important to recognize the distinctions between the different forms of unresponsiveness. The rationale behind attempts to induce clinical unresponsiveness must consider whether clonal deletion is possible or whether specific suppression is more appropriate. This chapter is concerned with assessing the relative importance of these two mechanisms in various forms of immunological tolerance or unresponsiveness.

13.2 Tolerance induction in immature cells

Tolerance to transplantation antigens is a good model for self tolerance. The first real description of transplantation tolerance arose from the observations of Owen (1945) who showed that dizygotic cattle twins, which are naturally 'parabiosed' *in utero* as a result of placental fusion, are permanent chimeras with respect to their red cells, and other haemopoietic cells. They accept skin grafts from each other but not from unrelated cattle. It was concluded from this, that if the lymphoid tissue of immature animals was confronted with antigen at a critical period in its development, then tolerance would result. Billingham *et al.* (1953) subsequently showed that transplantation tolerance could be reproduced experimentally by injecting neonatal mice of one inbred strain (A) with haemopoietic stem cells from another partially histoincompatible strain $(A \times B)F_1$. The A strain mice were then able to accept skin grafts from the B strain, a situation referred to as classical transplantation tolerance.

It must be appreciated that in classical transplantation tolerance the critical factor is not the immaturity of the animal but the immaturity of the lymphoid cells since tolerance can be induced in *immature* cells from *adult* animals. This is clearly seen with bone-marrow chimeras. If $(A \times B)F_1$ animals are lethally irradiated and reconstituted with equal numbers of bone-marrow stem cells from adults of each parental strain (Fig. 13.1) then within 6–8 weeks the entire lymphoid tissue of the F_1 comprises equal numbers of mature A and B strain lymphocytes. The T cells are mutually tolerant of each other's alloantigens, function normally in the immune response and can reject third-party skin grafts. The 1:1 ratio of A:B lymphocytes is maintained over many months and since stem cells used for reconstitution the animals are chimeric for the entire haemopoietic system. Similarly tolerance to protein antigens is easily induced in immature B cells from adult bone marrow or neonatal spleen. This is not so for mature B cells in adult spleen (Nossal & Pike, 1975; Metcalf & Klinman 1976 (Fig. 13.2)). The mechanism for this is unknown but could be related to the observation that when surface immunoglobulin (sIg) of B cells is capped off by anti-immunoglobulin antibodies, then only the immature B cells fail to re-express sIg (Fig. 13.3). Comparable evidence for immature T cells is lacking.

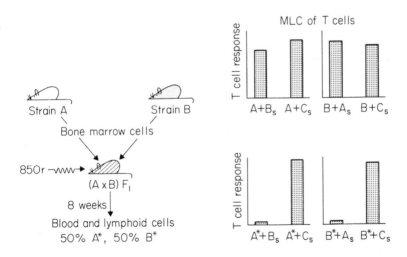

Fig. 13.1. Induction of classical transplantation tolerance in bone marrow chimeras. Irradiated $(A \times B)F_1$ recipients derived from two histoincompatible parents (A and B) are reconstituted with an equal mixture of A and B strain bone marrow cells. These give rise to mature A and B strain T cells designated A* and B* which are mutually tolerant. The A* T cells and B* T cells can be separated from each other and tested for their proliferative response to alloantigens in a mixed lymphocyte culture. A_s, B_s and C_s=mitomycin-treated A, B or C strain stimulator cells. (Based on von Boehmer et al., 1975.)

However, if whole organ cultures of fetal thymus are co-cultured in the presence of mitomycin-treated allogeneic cells, then the developing T cells acquire specific unresponsiveness (Robinson & Owen, 1978).

13.2.1 Kinetics of tolerance induction in immature cells

The kinetics of the induction and loss of tolerance in thymocytes and bone-marrow cells for soluble protein antigens has been defined by Weigle (1971). Since the response to a thymus-dependent antigen requires T–B cell cooperation then tolerance in either one of the populations should result in the absence of an antibody response. Tolerance to human gamma globulin (HGG) was induced in normal mice. Evidence that tolerance had been induced in either thymus or bone-marrow cells of these animals was shown by adoptive transfer of the tolerant cells into irradiated mice. T cell tolerance was established within 2 days and persisted for about 150 days (Fig. 13.4; Table 13.1). B cell tolerance took about a week to become established and was lost again by 50 days.

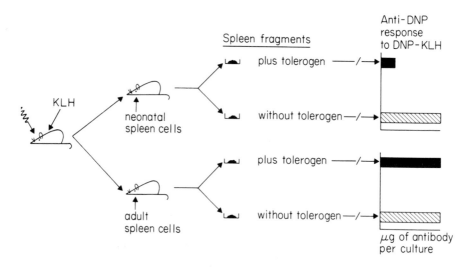

Fig. 13.2. System for comparing the tolerance susceptibility of immature and mature B cells from spleen. Mice were first primed with a carrier antigen (KLH) and then sub-lethally irradiated. This procedure provides recipients with carrier (KLH) primed T cells (which are radiation resistant with regard to their helper function) but without functional B cells. These animals are then reconstituted with neonatal or adult spleen cells and 24 hours later spleen fragments from these mice are challenged *in vitro* with tolerogenic concentrations (10^{-6} M) of DNP–MGG (mouse gamma globulin). After a further 24 hours the tolerogen is removed (—/→), the fragments now challenged with immunogenic concentrations of DNP–KLH and the anti-DNP response measured. With this system immature but not mature B cells were tolerized with 10^{-10} to 10^{-5}M DNP–MGG.

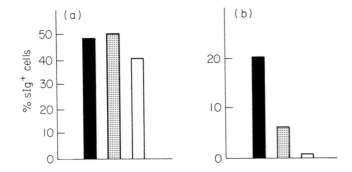

Fig. 13.3. Re-expression of surface immunoglobulin (sIg) after treatment of lymphocytes with rabbit anti-mouse Ig. Spleen cells from (a) mature or (b) young (6–9-day) mice were exposed to anti-mouse Ig for 1 hour (▦) or 24 hours (▢), the cells were then washed and sIg⁺ cells enumerated after a total period of 48 hours in culture. Untreated controls (■). (Based on Sidman & Unanue, 1975.)

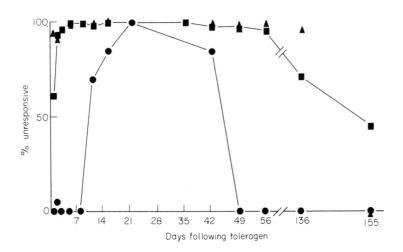

Fig. 13.4. Kinetics of the induction and loss of tolerance in mouse thymus and bone-marrow cells to HGG (Human Gamma Globulin). Mice were injected with tolerogenic amounts of HGG and at various times thereafter, either the thymus or bone-marrow cells were assayed for responsiveness in an adoptive transfer system. Tolerant thymus (or bone-marrow) cells were transferred with normal bone-marrow (or thymus) cells respectively. Recipients were challenged with immunogenic HGG and the percent unresponsive compared to animals receiving normal thymus and bone-marrow cells. (From Weigle, 1971.) Key: ■ Tolerant thymus; ● Tolerant bone marrow; ▲ Tolerant spleen.

Table 13.1. Reconstitution of the response of irradiated mice to protein antigens using thymus and bone-marrow cells from normal and tolerant mice

Cell population used for reconstitution		Antibody response to	
Thymus	Bone marrow	HGG	TGG
Normal	Normal	+	+
HGG tolerant	Normal	−	+
Normal	HGG tolerant	−	+
HGG tolerant	HGG tolerant	−	+

HGG=Human Gamma Globulin.
TGG=Turkey Gamma Globulin.
Data from Weigle *et al.* (1970).

13.2.2 Persistent antigen and the maintenance of tolerance

The primary lymphoid organs continuously generate new clones of lymphocytes. The maintenance of tolerance in these immature cells therefore requires persistent antigen as is well illustrated in classical transplantation tolerance. If A strain mice are tolerized by the neonatal injection of $(A \times B)F_1$ cells then the F_1 cells remain at levels of about 1–2 per cent in the tolerant mice. If these cells are experimentally eliminated then tolerance is broken as new clones of alloreactive T cells arise from the thymus (Lubaroff & Silvers, 1973). The pattern of recovery from tolerance seen in the experiments of Weigle may be explained by the effects of persisting antigen. With time the concentration of antigen falls below that required to tolerize newly emergent clones of antigen-reactive cells. The differential recovery rates (bone marrow before thymus) are a reflection that in this system helper T cells are preferentially tolerized with low doses of antigen.

13.2.3 The mechanism of tolerance induction in immature cells

The conventional view of tolerance induction in immature cells is that it occurs at critical stages of lymphocyte ontogeny when contact with antigen leads to clonal elimination. The recent vogue for suppressor T cells is an obvious challenge to this view, and so Brent *et al.* (1976) and Brooks (1975) have evaluated the rôle of suppressor cells in this form of tolerance. Tolerance was induced in neonatal A strain mice to B strain alloantigens by the injection of $(A \times B)F_1$ spleen cells. It was shown that serum or cells from the tolerant A strain mice did not prolong the survival of B strain skin grafts placed on normal A strain mice or facilitate tolerance induction to B strain alloantigens. Furthermore, the graft versus host (GVH) reaction produced in $(A \times B)F_1$ mice by small numbers of normal A strain spleen cells, was not abrogated by A strain cells tolerant to B alloantigens. If transplantation tolerance was maintained by suppressor cells then it was argued that tolerant cells would have reduced the GVH reactivity of the small number of normally reactive cells. Similarly von Boehmer *et al.* (1975) using the system described in Fig. 13.1 have been unable to find any evidence for suppressor mechanisms in chimeric mice.

Although these experiments argue against the involvement of suppressor mechanisms, they do not exclude the existence of suppressor T cells in classical transplantation tolerance. Roser and Dorsch (1979) have shown that suppressor T cells can be detected in the recirculating pool of DA strain rats made tolerant to PVA strain alloantigens. If the suppressor cells are adoptively transferred to lightly irradiated syngeneic recipients then they prevent the normal reappearance of host cells alloreactive to PVA alloantigens. It may be that in classical transplantation tolerance suppressor T cells act at a very early stage in T cell development. Their activity would have been missed in assays using mature T cells.

13.3 Tolerance induction in mature cells

Mature lymphocytes have passed the stage of development at which they are particularly susceptible to clonal elimination through contact with antigen. Consequently, tolerance induction in mature lymphocytes in peripheral lymphoid tissue is much more difficult to achieve. Two mechanisms operate in tolerance induction in mature cells; suppression and clonal elimination. Tolerance induction in mature lymphocytes is clinically more relevant since in most cases the problem is to eliminate an already ongoing immune response (e.g. hypersensitivities).

To produce tolerance in mature B cells the inductive events (see Chapter 10) for immune responses have to be bypassed or prevented. One way to do this is to use tolerogens based on thymus-independent antigens which act directly on B cells. Another is to manipulate the normal control mechanisms involved in active suppression.

13.3.1 Tolerogens based on thymus-independent antigens

High doses of many thymus-independent antigens can bring about specific B cell tolerance. The mechanism is unknown but is probably related to the polymeric nature of TI antigens and their persistence *in vivo* (see Chapter 8.4).

Cross-linking of B cell receptors is thought to be necessary for tolerance induction by these substances. Certain concentrations of polymeric flagellin, POL (8×10^6 M.W.) are immunogenic for B cells *in vitro* whereas the monomeric form, MON (4×10^4 M.W.) is not immunogenic at any concentration. At very high concentrations POL is tolerogenic while MON is not. This suggests that in this system, B cell inactivation requires some critical degree of epitope density at the B cell surface, possibly causing cross-linking of receptors. Artificial cross-linking of epitopes can be achieved with antibody. If B cells are first cultured with non-tolerogenic concentrations of POL or MON in the presence of appropriate concentrations of antibody to flagellin then tolerance can be induced with *both* forms (Fig. 13.5a). In this experiment F(ab')$_2$ antibody is as effective as whole IgG showing that the Fc part of the antibody is unimportant. Univalent Fab fragments are inactive stressing the requirement for cross-linking of determinants at the cell surface (Fig. 13.5b).

Haptens conjugated to TI antigens may induce hapten-specific tolerance. This was first shown in studies *in vitro* involving responses to various conjugates of POL; DNP$_1$ POL (one mole of DNP per monomer unit) is a good immunogen while DNP$_3$ POL is exclusively tolerogenic. If two different haptens are coupled to the same molecule of POL, then the immunogenic and tolerogenic response is dependent on the epitope density of each. For example, DANSYL$_1$ DNP$_4$ POL produces a good immune response to the DANSYL determinant but tolerance to the DNP determinant (Feldmann, 1972).

13.3.2 *Tolerance induction to thymus-dependent antigens*

In the case of thymus-dependent antigens the response of helper T cells can interfere with tolerance induction. Successful induction of tolerance requires presentation of antigen in such a way that T cell help is precluded. For some protein antigens (such as heterologous immunoglobulin or bovine serum albumin) this can be achieved using aggregate-free material. The cellular basis of tolerance induced with these antigens is critically dependent on the dose of tolerogen; high doses induce un-

Fig. 13.5a. Induction of tolerance with an immunogenic concentration of antigens in the presence of critical concentrations of specific antibody. Spleen cells were first incubated for 6 hours in the presence of immunogenic concentrations of polymeric flagellin (POL) and varying concentrations of anti-POL, washed free of complexes and then cultured for 4 days with immunogenic concentrations of POL. The anti-POL, PFC response for each culture was expressed as a percentage of the normal response. (Based on Diener & Feldmann, 1972.)

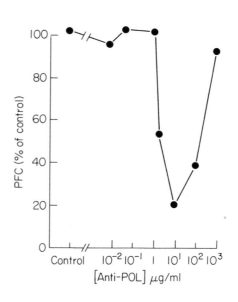

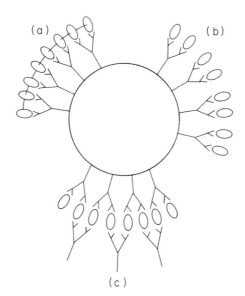

Fig. 13.5b. Schematic illustration of interactions between cell surface antigen receptors and antigen. (a) Latticing by a polymeric antigen—tolerogenic or immunogenic. (b) Binding of monomeric antigen—no response. (c) Latticing with monomeric antigen and bivalent antibody—tolerogenic.

responsiveness in T and B cells, low doses selectively tolerize T cells (Mitchison, 1964; Weigle, 1971). Several mechanisms have been suggested for this form of unresponsiveness: in the case of B cells it is not known whether they are eliminated or merely blocked by excess antigen; with T cell unresponsiveness in some but not all systems there is good evidence for the existence of specific suppressor T cells, though these need not be solely responsible for the unresponsive state (Weber & Kölsch, 1973).

13.4 Active suppression of specific cells

The experimental systems of active T cell suppression are discussed in Chapter 10. The distinguishing feature of this type of unresponsiveness is that it can be transferred from suppressed to normal recipients and is mediated by cells expressing Lyt 1^-23^+ and I-J sub-region determinants.

It is not understood why some antigens, or immunization protocols, should preferentially induce suppression rather than antibody formation. It is possible that the presentation of antigen to suppressor T cells differs from that to helper T cells and that this difference determines the subsequent response.

13.4.1 Suppression involving idiotype recognition

Anti-idiotypic T cells can deliver helper or suppressor signals and any imbalance in favour of suppressive anti-idiotypic cells will cause unresponsiveness (Chapter 10.7). Manipulation of the auto-anti-idiotypic response has been used to suppress the response to transplantation antigens in rats (Binz & Wigzell, 1976).

Lewis strain rats normally reject DA strain skin grafts in 12–15 days. Lewis T cells specific for DA strain alloantigens can be selectively expanded *in vitro* and then used as an enriched source of idiotype to immunize autologous Lewis rats (Fig. 13.6). This generates an auto-anti-idiotypic response directed against the receptors for DA alloantigens on Lewis T cells. Fifty per cent of these rats will accept DA strain grafts for longer than 5 weeks. Third-party grafts are rejected in the normal time. Comparable success has been achieved using anti-DA receptors isolated from the serum or urine of normal Lewis rats.

In principle it is surprising that this experiment should work at all since its success depends on generating an auto-anti-idiotypic response to all idiotypes on the Lewis anti-DA receptors. Success in 50 per cent of the animals implies either that the receptors on anti-DA clones are inheritable idiotypes or that the idiotypes on the receptors are extensively cross-reactive. Failure to induce transplantation tolerance in all animals could be due to the fact that the idiotypic determinants used for immunization do not represent the total repertoire of Lewis receptors against DA alloantigens and the anti-idiotypic suppression is therefore incomplete.

13.5 Breaking of tolerance

It is a well known observation that tolerance to certain antigens can be broken or circumvented by the injection of closely related antigens. A plausible explanation is

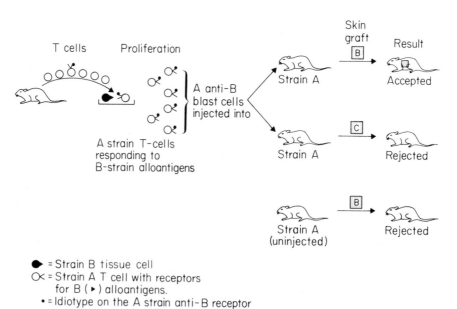

Fig. 13.6. The induction of an auto-anti-idiotypic response which permits prolonged acceptance of tissue grafts. A strain equals Lewis and B strain equals DA.

that although specific B cells are present they fail to respond due to absence of specific help. Tolerance to certain self antigens is an example of this (Fig. 13.7). In rabbits, tolerance to thyroglobulin is due to T cell tolerance alone. Injection of heterologous thyroglobulin or thyroglobulin coupled to an immunogenic carrier provides T cell help for the thyroglobulin-specific B cells which now make antibody. This mechanism of bypassing tolerant T cells is believed to operate in auto-antibody formation in certain auto-immune diseases.

Fig. 13.7. Breaking of tolerance to thyroglobulins. In the normal rabbit with self tolerance to rabbit thyroglobulin, T cells but not B cells are tolerant to thyroglobulin determinants a, b, c, d, e.

13.6 Clinical applications of tolerance

The three main areas of medicine which would benefit from successful induction of unresponsiveness are hypersensitivity reactions, auto-immune diseases and tissue transplantation. Tolerance induction for antibody-mediated hypersensitivities or auto-immune diseases would have to be induced in the presence of an ongoing response.

One possible approach in antibody-mediated hypersensitivities is the use of inert, non-degradable polymers expressing a high epitope density (Desaymard & Howard, 1975; Klaus & Humphrey, 1975). Chiorazzi et al. (1976) and Moreno et al. (1978) have induced unresponsiveness to benzyl penicillin (BP) in mice, using BP coupled to poly (D-glutamic acid, D-lysine) or Levan respectively. Ongoing IgE responses to simple haptens as well as complex allergens such as ragweed have similarly been eliminated in experimental animals (Liu & Katz, 1979; Lee & Sehon, 1978). It is encouraging that of the mature B cells those producing IgE are the most readily tolerized (Table 13.2). This approach is now being applied to man.

A different and more empirical approach is to chemically modify antigens such that they become tolerogenic. The ideal situation would be to alter the molecule such that the determinants recognized by T helper cells or antibody are destroyed leaving only the determinants recognized by suppressor cells. This situation would be analogous to that described for avian lysozymes (see Chapter 10.5). Three chemical

Table 13.2. Relative susceptibility of IgE memory cells to
tolerance induction by conjugates of DNP–Levan

Molar ratios and concentrations of DNP–Levan		Titre of secondary antibody response to DNP–KLH (titre $^{-1}$)	
		IgE	IgM+IgG
Nil		12,800	1,000
DNP$_{1.2}$LE	0.1 mg	3,200	800
	1.0 mg	1,600	3,400
DNP$_{1.7}$LE	0.1 mg	800	600
	1.0 mg	50	<10
DNP$_{2.5}$LE	0.1 mg	100	<10
	1.0 mg	<50	<10

Mice were primed with DNP–KLH and prior to secondary challenge with this antigen they were challenged with DNP–Levan of varying epitope density: DNP$_{1.7}$LE=1.7 mol DNP/40,000 M.W. polymer of Levan (from Desaymard, 1977)

treatments which may do this are acetoacetylation, denaturation with 8M-urea or cross-linking through polyethylene glycol (PEG).

Possibilities for inducing transplantation tolerance are more difficult to assess. Clonal elimination of immature cells alone would be worthless unless mature cells were also removed. Current interest centres on the use of drugs such as cyclosporin A which preferentially impairs the response of cells reacting to allo-antigen.

References

BILLINGHAM R.E., BRENT L. & MEDAWAR P.B. (1953) Actively allergized tolerance of foreign cells. *Nature* 172, 603.
BINZ H. & WIGZELL H. (1976) Specific transplantation tolerance induced by auto-immunization against the individual's own naturally occurring idiotypic, antigen-binding receptors. *J. exp. Med.* 144, 1438.
BRENT L., BROOKS C.G., MEDAWAR P.B. & SIMPSON E. (1976) Transplantation tolerance. *Brit. Med. Bull.* 32, 101.
BROOKS C.G. (1975) Neonatally induced transplantation tolerance: *in vitro* evidence supporting a clonal inactivation mechanism. *Eur. J. Immunol.* 5, 741.
CHIORAZZI N., ESHHAR Z. & KATZ D.H. (1976) Induction of immunological tolerance to the major antigenic determinant of penicillin: a therapeutic approach to penicillin allergy. *Proc. Nat. Acad. Sci. U.S.A.* 73, 2091.
DESAYMARD C. (1977) Role of epitope density in the induction of immunity and tolerance with thymus-independent antigens. IV. Selective tolerance of IgE response by the levan conjugates. *Eur. J. Immunol.* 7, 646.

DESAYMARD C. & HOWARD J.G. (1975) Role of epitope density in the induction of immunity and tolerance with thymus-independent antigens. II. Studies with 2,4 dinitrophenyl conjugates *in vivo. Eur. J. Immunol.* **5**, 541.

DIENER E. & FELDMANN M. (1972) Relationship between antigen- and antibody-induced suppression of immunity. *Transplant. Rev.* **8**, 76.

FELDMANN M. (1972) Induction of immunity and tolerance *in vitro* by hapten protein conjugates. I. The relationship between the degree of hapten conjugation and the immunogenicity of dinitrophenylated polymerized flagellin. *J. exp. Med.* **135**, 735.

KLAUS G.G.B. & HUMPHREY J.H. (1975) B cell tolerance induced by polymeric antigens. 1. Comparison of the dose and epitope density requirements for inactivation of primed and unprimed B cells *in vivo. Eur. J. Immunol.* **5**, 361.

LEE W.Y. & SEHON A.H. (1978) Suppression of reaginic antibodies. *Immunol. Rev.* **41**, 200.

LIU, FU TONG & KATZ D.H. (1978) Immunological tolerance to allergenic protein determinants. A therapeutic approach for selective inhibition of IgE antibody production. *Proc. Nat. Acad. Sci. U.S.A.* **76**, 1430.

LUBAROFF D.M. & SILVERS W.K. (1973) The importance of chimerism in maintaining tolerance of skin allografts in mice. *J. Immunol.* **111**, 65.

METCALF E.S. & KLINMAN N.R. (1976) *In vitro* tolerance induction of neonatal immune B cells. *J. exp. Med.* **143**, 1327.

MITCHISON N.A. (1964) Induction of immunological paralysis in two zones of dosage. *Proc. Roy. Soc. Lond. B.* **161**, 275.

MORENO C., HALE C. & HEWETT R. (1978) The use of hapten-polysaccharide conjugates for the induction of B cell tolerance involving IgE responses. I. Preparation, characterization and specific tolerogenic activity of penicilloyl-substituted levans affecting IgE responses in normal and sensitized mice. *Clin. exp. Immunol.* **31**, 499.

NOSSAL G.J.V. & PIKE B.L. (1975) Evidence for the clonal abortion theory of B lymphocyte tolerance. *J. exp. Med.* **141**, 904.

OWEN R.D. (1945) Immunogenetic consequences of vascular anastomoses between bovine twins. *Science* **102**, 40.

ROBINSON J.H. & OWEN J.J.T. (1978) Transplantation tolerance induced in fetal mouse thymus *in vitro. Nature* **271**, 758.

ROSER B. & DORSCH S. (1979) The cellular basis of transplantation tolerance in the rat. *Immunol. Rev.* **46**, 55.

SIDMAN C.L. & UNANUE E.R. (1975) Receptor-mediated inactivation of early B lymphocytes. *Nature* **257**, 149.

VON BOEHMER H., SPRENT J. & NABHOLZ M. (1975) Tolerance to histocompatibility determinants in tetraparental bone-marrow chimeras. *J. exp. Med.* **411**, 322.

WEBER G. & KÖLSCH E. (1973) Transfer of low zone tolerance to normal syngeneic mice by Thy 1 positive cells. *Eur. J. Immunol.* **3**, 767.

WEIGLE W.O. (1971) Recent observations and concepts in immunological unresponsiveness and autoimmunity. *Clin. exp. Immunol.* **9**, 537.

WEIGLE W.O., CHILLER J.B. & HABICHT G.J. (1970) Thymus and Bone-marrow Cells in Unresponsiveness. In MIESCHER P.A. (ed), *Immunopathology*, Vol. VI, p. 109. Schwabe & Co., Basel.

Further reading

Immunol. Rev. (1979) **43**, Mechanisms of B lymphocyte tolerance. MÖLLER G. (ed.). Munksgaard, Copenhagen.

Chapter 14
The Lymphoid System

14.1 Introduction

The principle aim of this chapter is to dispel any notion that lymphoid tissue is an *in vivo* artefact! On the contrary it provides the correct environment for all that has been said in Chapters 1–13.

The lymphon is a collective term for the primary and secondary lymphoid organs and their interconnecting blood vessels and lymphatics. Although anatomically discrete, lymphoid organs are strategically placed accumulations of the mobile lymphocyte pool. The main physiological functions of the lymphon—antigen recognition and dissemination of the immune response—are achieved by the constant recirculation of lymphocytes between and through secondary lymphoid organs. If recirculation were to be abnormal the lymphon would function poorly despite having a full repertoire of antigen-sensitive cells.

14.2 The organization of lymphoid tissue

The organized lymphoid system in mammals consists of the primary lymphoid organs, thymus and bone marrow, and the secondary lymphoid organs, spleen, lymph nodes and gut-associated lymphoid tissue (Fig. 14.1). Evolutionarily, the spleen was possibly the first lymphoid organ to arise and serves both as an erythroid and lymphoid organ. It is well positioned to cope with antigen in the circulation as it subtends the blood vascular system. Lymph nodes represent later adaptations and deal with antigen transported from the extravascular space. The gradual evolution of lymph nodes and the lymphatic system can be seen phylogenetically; amphibians have rudimentary lymphoid nodules which are not associated with lymphatics; birds have a widespread network of lymphatic vessels and possess only the equivalent of the central lymph nodes of mammals (lumbar and cervical nodes); and mammals have the most fully developed lymphoid system although there is variation between species. Pigs have lymph nodes which are 'inside out'—i.e. the paracortical regions lie outside the cortical regions.

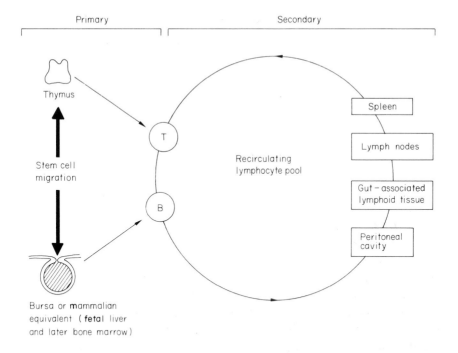

Fig. 14.1. The lymphon.

14.3 The anatomy of lymphoid tissue

14.3.1 Primary lymphoid organs

In mammals the fetal liver and bone marrow are sites of extensive lymphopoiesis (see Chapter 8). About 25 per cent of nucleated cells in the bone marrow are lymphocytes and of these about 20 per cent divide every 24–48 hours. They give rise to a less rapidly dividing population, some of which express the characteristic B cell surface phenotype (Fc receptor positive, Ia antigen positive, surface IgM positive). Pre-T cells, K and NK cells (see Chapter 15) are part of the surface IgM negative fraction of bone marrow cells. Thymic lymphopoiesis has been extensively discussed in Chapter 9. The thymus, particularly early in development, also contains macrophages which enter the thymus from the circulation.

14.3.2 Secondary lymphoid organs

In addition to the spleen, lymph nodes and gut-associated lymphoid tissue, the secondary lymphoid tissue includes lymphoid nodules organized at sites of antigen deposition in the tissues, e.g. at the site of injections of antigen in Freund's adjuvant.

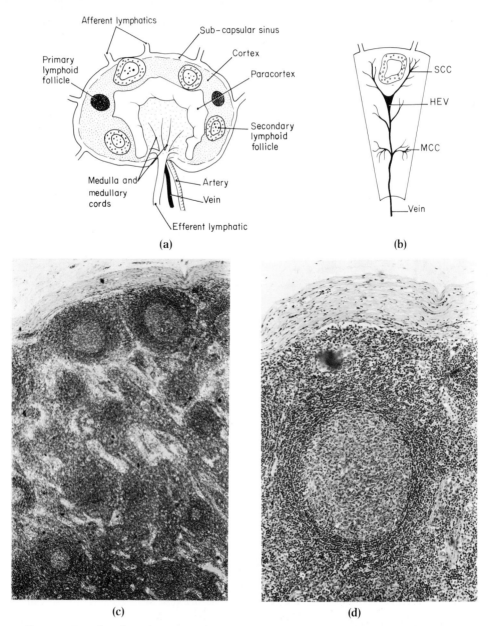

Fig. 14.2. Lymph node structure. (a) The node can be subdivided into the cortical (B-cell area), paracortical (T-cell area) and medullary region (both T and B cells). In an unstimulated node the cortex contains concentric accumulations of B lymphocytes (primary follicle) whereas in a stimulated node these follicles are larger and contain a pale staining area surrounded by B lymphocytes (secondary lymphoid follicle). (b) Depicts the venous drainage from a section of the node. There are two major capillary networks—the medullary cord capillaries (MCC) and the subcapsular capillaries (SCC). The high endothelial venule (HEV) is a specialized part of the post-capillary venule through which lymphocytes enter nodes. (c) Section of human lymph node showing cortical and paracortical regions (×65). (d) A secondary follicle in human lymph node (×260). (By courtesy of Dr J. Arno.)

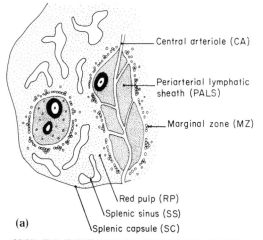

Central arteriole (CA)

Periarterial lymphatic sheath (PALS)

Marginal zone (MZ)

Red pulp (RP)

Splenic sinus (SS)

Splenic capsule (SC)

(a)

Fig. 14.3. (a) Schematic diagram of the spleen (adapted from Weiss, 1972)—description in text. (b) Spleen section showing central arteriole (top left) and periarteriolar lymphoid sheath with secondary follicle. (Courtesy of Dr J. Arno.) (c) Scanning electron micrograph of part of the central arteriole with attached germinal centre (arrowed) isolated from a 6-week-old chicken spleen. (By courtesy of Dr. K. Carr and Professor R. G. White.)

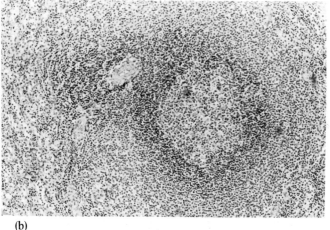

(b)

(c)

(a) *Lymph nodes.* These can be divided into an outer layer or cortex and an inner medulla all enclosed by a capsule (Fig. 14.2). The fixed tissue framework of the node comprises blood vessels, nerves, reticular cells and their fibres organized to form follicles and sinuses which radiate from the medulla to the subcapsular sinus. Lymph and lymphocytes enter the node either from the afferent lymphatics which drain into the subcapsular sinus or from the blood vessels. T and B cells accumulate in different areas in the cortex. In a resting, unstimulated node, B cells are found in follicles immediately beneath the subcapsular sinus (primary follicle) whereas T cells predominantly occur in the paracortical regions of the node, the thymus-dependent area. In an antigen-stimulated node small numbers of T cells are found in the B cell area which consists of concentric accumulations of cells. This structure is known as a germinal centre. Plasma cells do not occur in germinal centres and lie mainly within the chords of the medullary sinuses. All cells and macromolecules within the node leave via the efferent lymphatic.

(b) *Spleen.* The erythroid and lymphoid functions of the spleen are mainly restricted to the red and white pulp respectively. The white pulp consists of many oval or spherical accumulations of lymphocytes surrounding a central arteriole which is referred to as the periarteriolar lymphoid sheath or PALS (Fig. 14.3). The outer region of the periarteriolar lymphoid sheath, the marginal zone, contains a mixture of T and B cells and many macrophages. The B cell area and germinal centre lie to one side of the white pulp, adjacent to the marginal zone while the T cells are grouped around the central arteriole. Plasma cells are generally found in the red pulp.

(c) *The gut-associated lymphoid tissue.* This comprises the tonsils, Peyer's patches and appendix and is essential to mucosal immunity which is largely maintained by secretory IgA (Ottaway *et al.*, 1979). This is present in high concentrations in saliva, intestinal secretions (including bile) and is also synthesized by a large number of plasma cells distributed throughout the *lamina propria* of the intestinal villi. The secretory component is added by the epithelial cells of the gut which transport IgA into the gut lumen.

Peyer's patches are lymphoid structures located in the submucosal tissues of the gut which are particularly prominent in young animals. In a 3-month-old lamb the total mass of the Peyer's patch tissue (40 g) is about twice that of the thymus (Reynolds, 1980). The Peyer's patch contains both T- and B-dependent areas and germinal centres although the proportion of each cell type varies depending on age and antigenic experience. Adoptive transfer studies with Peyer's patch cells have shown that they contain a far greater proportion of IgA precursor cells than either spleen or lymph node (Craig & Cebra, 1971). The gut epithelial cells overlying the Peyer's patch are histologically distinct from normal gut epithelial cells in being non-columnar and lacking goblet cells. This may be a specialized type of epithelium which allows antigen transport. Immediately below the epithelium lies the 'dome' area of the Peyer's patch which is predominantly but not exclusively a T-dependent area (Parrott & Ferguson, 1974).

14.3.3 *Lymphoid tissue macrophages*

The cells of the mononuclear–phagocyte system associated with lymphoid tissue show marked functional and morphological heterogeneity (Humphrey, 1981). They are primarily involved in the uptake and presentation of antigen to lymphocytes and include sinus lining macrophages, dendritic reticular cells and Langerhans cells (see 14.5).

14.4 Lymphocyte traffic

The migration pattern and tissue distribution of different types of lymphocytes has been followed by first labelling the cells with appropriate radioactive precursors such as ${}^{3}H$ thymidine or ${}^{3}H$ adenosine. Their overall tissue distribution can then be determined once they have been returned to the original donor or following adoptive transfer to syngeneic recipients (Gowans & Knight, 1964; Ford, 1975). Details of the flow of cells through different parts of the lymphon can be gained by cannulating lymphatics such as the thoracic duct, the major posterior lymphatic trunk. In larger animals (sheep, pigs, cattle) efferent lymphatics from single lymph nodes can be

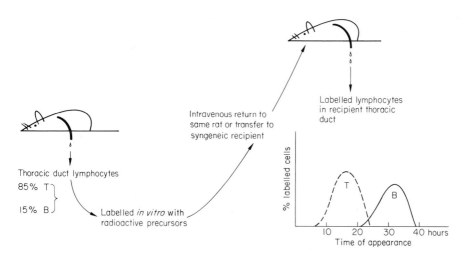

Fig. 14.4. Experimental model for analysing lymphocyte traffic in rats.

cannulated and lymph collected for several weeks. This system has provided information on the immunological events occurring in single lymph nodes (Hall &
Morris, 1965).

There are two patterns of lymphocyte movement *in vivo*. The first is the migration
or homing of lymphocytes from one site to another and the second is the continuous
recirculation between, and through, the lymphoid tissues. Migrating thoracic duct
lymphocytes can be easily distinguished from recirculating thoracic duct cells by
adoptive transfer experiments. If thoracic duct cells are labelled and adoptively
transferred to a second (syngeneic) recipient then only the recirculating lymphocytes will appear in this animal's thoracic duct lymph (Howard, 1972) (Fig. 14.4).
The cell surface characteristics which distinguish the migrating from the recirculating cell are not known. One factor is that blast cells do not recirculate to any marked
degree but have a predilection to home and stay at certain sites (see 14.5.3).

14.4.1 Lymphocyte lifespan

Estimates of the frequency with which lymphocytes divide *in vivo* can be derived by *in vivo* labelling studies (Sprent, 1977). Rapidly dividing cells are labelled following a
short exposure *in vivo* to ^{3}H thymidine whereas infrequently dividing cells require a
much longer exposure to the isotope. The average interval between cell divisions for
the labelled cells can be estimated by following their rate of loss from the recirculating pool. These studies have shown that in rodents resting recirculating T cells have
an average intermitotic period of 4–5 months whereas resting recirculating B cells
divide every 2–3 months. Studies on radiation-induced chromosome damage in man
have suggested an intermitotic interval of at least 10 years.

The persistence of immunological memory, often for the lifetime of an individual,
implies that memory cell clones are long lived. Although long-lived, non-dividing
lymphocytes must contribute to immunological memory it is also likely that memory
is in part maintained by continuous divisions at a low frequency of clones of
lymphocytes driven via idiotype or anti-idiotypic recognition (see Chapter 10).

14.4.2 Lymphocyte recirculation between secondary lymphoid organs

The traffic routes of lymphocytes are shown in Fig. 14.5. This circulation is considerable and in the adult rat or sheep about 1–2 per cent of the total pool of recirculating
lymphocytes emerge into the blood from the thoracic duct each hour. This output
from the thoracic duct balances the number of lymphocytes which have left the
blood in the lymph nodes, gut or tissues in the rear two-thirds of the animal.

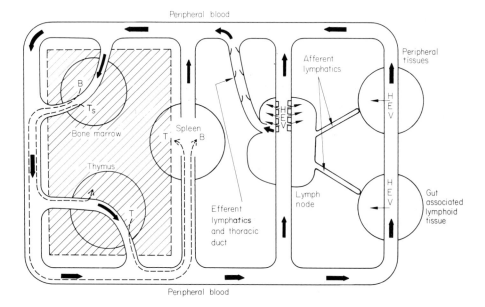

Fig. 14.5. Major lymphocyte traffic patterns within the mature lymphon: in this figure T_s represents the migration of lymphoid stem cells (precursor T cells) to the thymus. T and B lymphocytes leaving these primary lymphoid organs are believed to preferentially migrate to the spleen where, after a further maturation stage, they give rise to recirculating T and B lymphocytes. Lymphocytes entering the spleen return to the circulation via the splenic vein, but lymphocytes entering the lymph nodes either from the tissues or the GALT return to the blood via the major lymphatic ducts. Key: □ recirculating lymphocyte pool (RLP); ▨ not part of the RLP; HEV=high endothelial venule.

14.4.3 Lymphocyte recirculation through the spleen

Lymphocytes enter and leave the spleen in the blood. Although there is afferent lymphatic drainage from the spleen to local nodes this is a minor part of splenic lymphocytic traffic. The marginal zone of the white pulp contains a rich plexus of capilliaries (the marginal sinus) and studies with labelled cells have shown that lymphocytes which leave the marginal sinus first appear in the marginal zone where both T and B lymphocytes are mixed (Nieuwenhuis & Ford, 1976). T lymphocytes move directly into the PALS and within 5–6 hours they leave this area via the marginal zone bridging channels entering the red pulp and leaving the spleen via the splenic veins. B lymphocytes have a much longer transit time through the white pulp (about 20 hours) and may have to cross the thymus-dependent area before reaching the B cell area (Fig. 14.6).

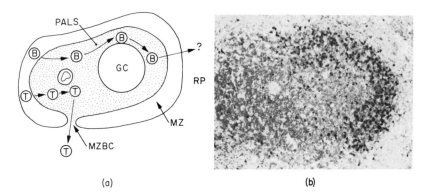

(a)   (b)

Fig. 14.6. (a) Schematic cross-section of splenic white pulp showing routes of traffic of T and B cells (PALS—periarteriolar lymphoid sheath; MZ—marginal zone; MZBC—MZ bridging channels; GC—germinal centre; RP—red pulp). (b) Rat B lymphocytes were isolated, labelled with ³H-uridine and injected. 24 hours later the labelled cells were seen to be concentrated around the germinal centre. (From Ford, 1975; Nieuwenhuis & Ford, 1976.)

14.4.4 Recirculation through the lymph nodes

The overall arrangement of lymph nodes is such that the direction of lymph flow is centripetal with lymph first passing through the peripheral nodes (popliteal, brachial, precapsular) and then the central nodes (lumbar, inguinal, mediastinal) finally gaining the thoracic duct via the major lymphatic vessels. Although all lymph nodes receive most of their lymphocytes from the blood, central nodes have a far greater afferent input than peripheral nodes, whose afferent supply comes entirely from the tissues and not from another node. This may lead to differences in lymphocyte traffic through central nodes (see 14.5.2).

The kinetics of lymphocyte traffic through single lymph nodes is well understood in sheep (Fig. 14.7). Using ^{85}Sr-labelled microspheres it has been shown that a resting lymph node in sheep receives 0.014 per cent of the cardiac output which produces a blood flow of about 24 ml/hour through a single node. This represents a lymphocyte throughput in the blood of about 1.10^8 lymphocytes per hour. The output of lymphocytes in the efferent lymph is about 3.10^7 per hour and since only 5 per cent of this is derived either from the afferent input or from *de novo* synthesis within the node, then about one in every four lymphocytes passing through the node in the blood actually enters the lymphoid compartment (Hay & Hobbs, 1977).

The cells which reach a peripheral node via the afferent lymphatics are qualitatively different from those which enter the node directly from the blood. Afferent lymph in both sheep and humans contains few surface immunoglobulin-positive (sIg$^+$) B lymphocytes and the sIg$^-$ lymphocytes (presumably T cells) respond poorly to histocompatibility antigens compared to efferent lymphocytes (Scollay *et al.*, 1976).

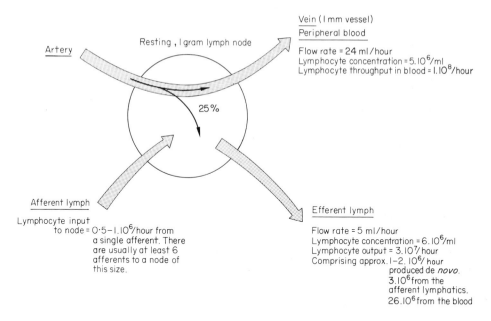

Fig. 14.7. Approximate flow of lymphocyte to and from a single lymph node in sheep.

An important physiological fact about lymph nodes is that irrespective of whether macromolecules or cells enter the node from the blood or via the afferent lymphatic, their only apparent route back to the circulation is via the efferent lymphatic (see 14.5.4).

14.4.5 Lymphocyte recirculation through the gut-associated lymphoid tissue

The gut-associated lymphoid tissue is largely responsible for maintaining immunity at mucosal surfaces. Lymphocytes enter the Peyer's patches from the blood via high endothelial venules (see 14.4.6) situated between the T- and B-dependent areas. They then travel via afferent lymphatics (lacteals) to the mesenteric node finally reaching the blood via the thoracic duct. Many of the plasma cells in the *lamina propria* are derived from activated IgA precursor cells generated either in the Peyer's patch or mesenteric node which migrate to the lamina propria as well as other mucosal surfaces (e.g. salivary gland, mammary gland) via the thoracic duct and blood. Antigen plays no rôle in this selective migration, the mechanism of which is unknown.

14.4.6 *High endothelial cells*

The entry of lymphocytes into lymph nodes is highly selective. Erythrocytes and polymorphonuclear leucocytes do not normally enter the node in substantial numbers since efferent lymph does not contain these cell types. Entry occurs at the cortical/paracortical junction across a specialized part of the post-capillary venule known as the high endothelial venule (HEV) (Fig. 14.8). In rats and humans (but not sheep) HEV cells are distinguished by their more extensive cytoplasm. These cells synthesize a sulphated proteolipoglycan in greater concentration than flat endothelium and can be differentially labelled *in vivo* with ^{35}S sulphate (Fig. 14.8) (Andrews *et al.*, 1980). Lymphocytes first adhere via their microvilli to the luminal surface of the high endothelial venules and then actively migrate between the high endothelial cells. It is not known what surface structures on the lymphocyte and the high endothelial cells are involved in this type of cell–cell recognition. Only metabolically active lymphocytes adhere to the high endothelium. This adhesion is calcium but not magnesium dependent and does not occur if microtubule function is inhibited. Studies *in vitro* have shown that lymphocyte adhesion to the high endothelium is a feature of mature lymphocytes since thymus or bone-marrow cells adhere poorly to HEV (Stamper & Woodruff, 1976, 1977; Woodruff & Kuttner, 1980).

High endothelial cells are not restricted to lymph nodes. They occur in tonsil, Peyer's patches, can be induced to appear in granulomas and are characteristically associated with sites where lymphocytes preferentially leave the blood.

14.5 Uptake of antigen by lymphoid tissue

The reticuloendothelial system plays a major rôle in the uptake and presentation of antigen to lymphocytes. A substantial fraction of injected antigen never reaches lymphoid tissue but is destroyed by liver and lung macrophages. In unprimed animals soluble antigen is first seen within the phagolysomes of macrophages lining the subcapsular and medullary sinuses in lymph nodes and marginal zone and red pulp of the spleen.

Antigen which enters via the gut can localize in the Peyer's patch or go via lacteals to the mesenteric node. Much of the antigen which reaches the portal vein is degraded by Kupffer cells in the liver. The importance of these different routes and whether they lead to systemic immunity, local and mucosal immunity or tolerance are poorly understood (see 14.5.3). It has been estimated that 0.01 per cent of antigenic material in the gut can reach the systemic circulation.

There is considerable heterogeneity in the macrophage populations associated with lymphoid tissue. Although many of these cells have a phagocytic function there is increasing evidence that others are more involved in antigen presentation and possibly in determining the migration patterns of lymphocytes within lymphoid tissue (Haston, 1979; Humphrey, 1980).

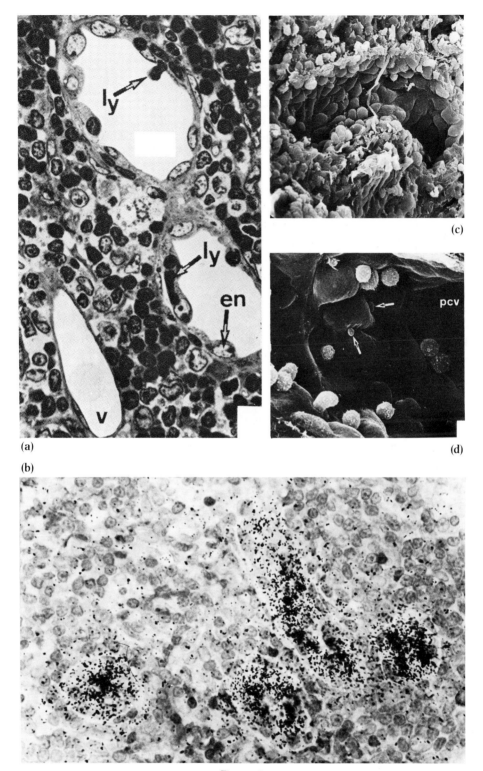

(a)

ly

ly

en

v

(b)

(c)

(d)

pcv

Fig. 14.8

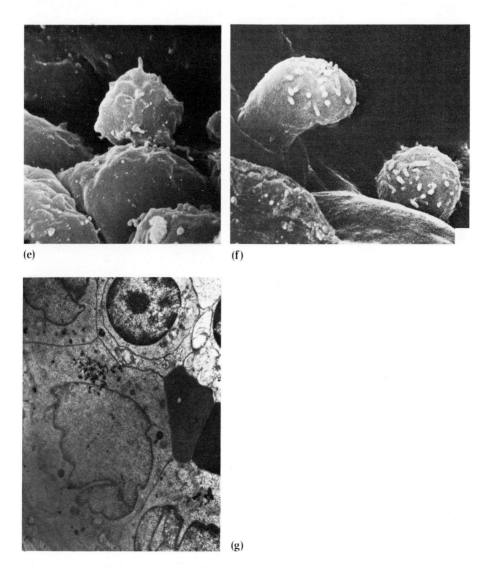

(e)

(f)

(g)

Fig. 14.8. The journey across the high endothelial venule. (a) Post-capillary venule in the paracortex of a lymph node. Ly = lymphocytes; en = high endothelial cells; v = vein (×920). (b) Radioautograph showing four high endothelial venules in section. High endothelial cells were labelled *in vivo* by injecting ³⁵S-sulphate into the drainage area of the node 15 minutes earlier. (From Andews *et al.*, 1980.) (c) Scanning electron micrograph of the high endothelial venule seen from the blood vessel side. The high endothelial cells have a 'cobblestone' appearance and elaborate basement membrane. (d) Attachment of lymphocytes to the HEV (arrowed). (e) and (f) The lymphocyte and the high endothelial cell-contact (e) and penetration (f). Lymphocytes appear to lose their surface microvilli on inserting themselves between the high endothelial cells. (g) Transit. The EM radioautograph shows an erythrocyte in the lumen of the HEV, a high endothelial cell labelled with ³⁵S-sulphate (grains occur over the Golgi), and a lymphocyte in transit. (Figs a, d, f by courtesy of Dr W. van Ewijk, see van Ewijk 1977; Figs b, c and g by courtesy of Professor W. L. Ford and Dr P. Andrews, see Andrews *et al.*, 1980.)

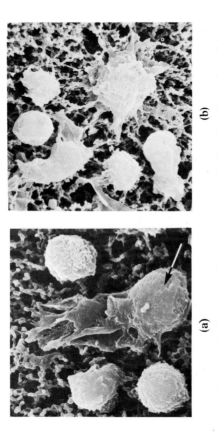

(a)

(b)

Fig. 14.9. Electron micrographs of cells (arrowed in 14.9a) commonly found in afferent lymph (a—scanning electron micrograph. ×4,000: b—transmission electron micrograph. ×8,000). They are large mononuclear cells with characteristic long and active cytoplasmic processes or veils. They are weakly phagocytic but carry surface-associated antigen from the periphery to the draining node where they probably give rise to interdigitating cells in the paracortex. The other cells in (a) are lymphocytes. (Courtesy of Drs H. A. Drexhage and B. M. Balfour; Drexhage H. A. et al. (1979).)

14.5.1 Dendritic reticular cells

These cells are predominantly located in the B cell dependent areas, notably the primary and secondary follicles in lymph nodes and germinal centres in spleen. They possess long cytoplasmic processes interweaved between B cells and can retain small amounts of membrane-attached antigen for several weeks. This type of antigen localization follows gross localization of antigen in medullary and sinus lining macrophages and after the appearance of plasma cells in the medulla. It is likely that dendritic cells can localize antigen in the form of an immune complex adhering via Fc and C3b receptors.

If antigen is given as an immune complex or if it has the capacity to directly activate the alternative pathway of complement (DNP-Levan) then localization to the surface of the dendritic reticular cells occurs immediately. Further evidence that localization to these cells can be complement dependent is shown by the fact that DNP-Levan fails to localize within primary follicles in C3-depleted mice (Klaus & Humphrey, 1977). Since the dendritic reticular cells are in close contact with B lymphocytes it has been suggested that they play an important rôle in initiating thymus-independent responses and in the development of B cell memory.

14.5.2 Langerhans cells

Rediscovered by immunologists after 100 years. They were first described by Paul Langerhans in 1868 and in being closely associated with epidermal cells were first thought to be either neural cells or melanocytes. Their importance to the immune system has only recently been recognized. Langerhans cells are derived from the bone marrow and although they express the characteristic surface markers of cells of the mononuclear–phagocyte system such as membrane-associated Fc and C3b receptors and many hydrolytic enzymes, they are non-phagocytic and in certain species have a characteristic raquet shaped structure in the cytoplasm known as the Birbeck granule.

Langerhans cells are a highly mobile population. If parental skin is grafted onto an F_1 recipient within 3 weeks all the Langerhans cells in the graft are of host origin. These cells travel in the afferent lymph along with other cells of the mononuclear–phagocyte system and on reaching lymph nodes give rise to the interdigitating cells (Fig. 14.9) These occur in the T-dependent areas and outer regions of the secondary follicles and like dendritic reticular cells possess long cytoplasmic processes interweaved and forming close contact with the T cells. It is proposed that they ferry antigen in a membrane-bound form from the periphery and being Ia positive are likely to be involved in antigen presentation within lymphoid tissue (Hoefsmit et al., 1980). Recent studies have shown that if a contact sensitizing agent is applied to an area of skin depleted of Langerhans cells by ultraviolet irradiation then tolerance to the antigen is readily induced (Toews et al., 1980).

14.5.3 Non-specific effects of antigen on lymphoid tissue

The non-specific effects of antigen on lymphoid tissue are well characterized in sheep where the characteristic changes seen in the efferent lymph reflect events which have occurred within the node. With most antigens and particularly in antigen-primed animals secondary challenge of the node produces an immediate drop in the lymphocyte output—a phenomenon known as cell shutdown (Fig. 14.10). This is followed by a biphasic increase in the lymphocyte output with resting small lympho-cytes appearing in the first peak and blast cells in the second. The term cell shutdown obscures the fact that quite dramatic changes occur in the node during this time (Cahill et al., 1976). There is a four fold increase in blood supply to the node, a four fold increase in lymphocyte entry into the node and no reduction in the efferent lymph flow which can contain large amounts of the soluble products of activated T cells. The first wave of lymphocytes leaving the node after shutdown are those which entered during shutdown. Recent studies suggest that shutdown is mediated by prostaglandin E_2 synthesized by cells in the node which may inhibit the active locomotion of cells along intranodal pathways (Hopkins et al., 1981). The physiological significance of cell shutdown is unknown but it may provide a mechanism for promoting the early stages of antigen–cell or cell–cell interactions.

14.5.4 Depletion of antigen-reactive cells from the recirculating lymphocyte pool by antigen

It has been shown both in rats and mice that 24 hours after antigen has localized in the spleen or lymph nodes the appropriate antigen-specific cells become specifically depleted from the recirculating pool and are absent from the thoracic duct. They are thought to be retained in the tissues by antigen. This negative selection can be

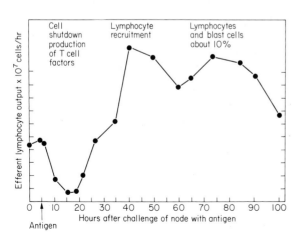

Fig. 14.10 Kinetics of lymphocyte output in afferent lymph from a cannulated popliteal node in sheep following secondary challenge of the node with antigen. During cell shutdown substantial amounts of T-cell factors and prostaglandin can be detected in the efferent lymph. (From McConnell et al., 1980.)

achieved with a wide variety of antigens including allogeneic lymphocytes, applies equally well to T and B lymphocytes, and is a useful method of producing populations of cells depleted of specific antigen-reactive cells. After 3 or 4 days the specifically activated blast cells appear in the thoracic duct (Ford & Atkins, 1971).

The conventional view of lymphocyte recirculation through lymph nodes is that lymphocytes enter nodes randomly across the high endothelial venule and only regain the circulation via the efferent lymphatic and thoracic duct. However, studies on lymphocyte traffic through antigen-stimulated lymph nodes in sheep have indicated that this may not be the whole story (Hopkins *et al.*, 1980). If a single lymph node in sheep primed to several antigens is cannulated and the node then repeatedly challenged with one antigen, the entire animal eventually becomes specifically unresponsive to this antigen. Since all the cells entering the node are removed from the sheep via the efferent cannula, the result cannot be explained in terms of random entry of specific cells into the node. If so depletion would have been non-specific.

There are two possible mechanisms to explain this result. Either antigen can be 'presented' by the high endothelial cells thereby enhancing the entry of specific cells, or alternatively, lymphocytes enter the node at random and cells not specifically stimulated by the antigen return to the blood within the node. Either mechanism would result in a specific depletion. Although studies with isolated, perfused lymph nodes in rats have indicated that there is no direct entry of cells into the blood from resting nodes (Sedgley & Ford, 1976), the situation for antigen-stimulated nodes may be quite different, particularly in view of the marked changes in blood flow and lymphocyte traffic which occur after antigenic stimulation.

Another accepted view of lymphocyte traffic is that recirculation of resting T cells throughout the lymphon is random. This is challenged by recent studies in sheep which show that if efferent lymphocytes from the mesenteric nodes and peripheral nodes are separately labelled with different isotopes, pooled and reinjected into the same animal then the labelled cells preferentially recirculate through the nodes from which they had originally come (Cahill *et al.*, 1977). This implies that there is some selectivity in the migration of resting T cells through the gut/mesenteric node axis compared to peripheral nodes. This type of non-random recirculation of resting T cells does not occur in fetal sheep (Cahill *et al.*, 1980). B cells of the IgA class similarly traffic through the gut/mesenteric node axis. It is possible that the nonrandom recirculation of T cells and IgA B cells is related but the mechanism is not known.

14.5.5 *Traffic of antigen-activated cells*

The migration of antigen-activated cells is the mechanism whereby specific memory cells and activated blast cells are disseminated throughout the lymphoid tissue. This is well defined in sheep where several days after challenge of a lymph node with antigen, the cells in the efferent lymph contain a very high proportion of primed and active blast cells, many of the latter containing specific antibody. If all these cells are removed from the body, despite a vigorous response in the lymph node, priming of the whole animal for a secondary response fails to take place. On the other hand, if cells are washed free of antigen and returned intravenously, priming for a secondary response does take place, proving that lymphocytes in efferent lymphatics can be the carriers of immunological memory (Hall & Morris, 1965). If the activated cells in the efferent lymph are labelled and returned via an afferent lymphatic to the next node in the chain then in some cases these cells give rise exclusively to the germinal centre in the second node. It is possible that in nodes the immune response may be confined to isolated zones within the node (Fahy *et al.*, 1980).

The seeding of activated cells throughout the tissues is also seen in the immune response of the gut lymphoid tissue. Isolated loops of the small intestine (Thiry–Vella loops) can be constructed with or without a Peyer's patch (Husband & Gowans, 1978). Challenge of a loop with cholera toxoid results in the appearance of specific antibody-forming cells in the thoracic duct. If the loop lacks a Peyer's patch no activated cells appear in the thoracic duct. (In these experiments the mesenteric lymph node was removed before challenge.) Furthermore, the IgA blast cells in the thoracic duct migrate to the *lamina propria* of the small intestine via the blood. The homing of IgA blast cells to the gut is antigen independent and essential in maintaining immunity throughout the entire gut (Hall *et al.*, 1977). It has been suggested that this is the mechanism for producing IgA-secreting cells at a wide variety of mucosal surfaces such as the lungs. Oral challenge with *E. coli* in pregnant women or lactating sows produces marked antibody levels in the milk, but not in serum, suggesting that IgA-secreting cells generated in the gut can home to the mammary gland. If there is non-random traffic of activated cells generated in the Peyer's patches or mesenteric node to all mucosal surfaces then this would have wide implications with respect to vaccination for mucosal immunity.

Another ill understood function of gut-associated lymphocytes is in tolerance induction. It is well known that feeding large amounts of a contact-sensitizing agent can induce tolerance to the hapten (the Schulzberger-Chase phenomenon). The traditional view is that after gut immunization most of the antigen goes to the liver since tolerance induction does not occur if the portal vein is bypassed. However, there is recent evidence to suggest that suppressor T cells both for contact sensitivity and for the IgE response can be more easily generated in the Peyer's patches than in spleen or lymph nodes. If correct, this finding might have important therapeutic implications (Asherson *et al.*, 1977).

References

ANDREWS P., FORD W.L. & STODDART R.W. (1980) Metabolic studies of high-walled endothelium of post-capillary venules in rat lymph nodes. In 'Blood Cells and Vessel Walls; Functional Interactions'. *CIBA Foundation Symposium 71*, p. 211. Excerpta Medica, Amsterdam.

ASHERSON G.L., ZEMBALA M., PERERA M.A.C.C., MAYHEW B. & THOMAS W.R. (1977) Production of immunity and unresponsiveness in the mouse by feeding contact-sensitizing agents and the role of suppressor cells in Peyer's patches, mesenteric nodes and other lymphoid tissues. *Cell. Immunol.* **33**, 145.

CAHILL R.N.P., FROST H. & TRNKA Z. (1976) The effects of antigen on the migration of recirculating lymphocytes through single lymph nodes. *J. exp. Med.* **143**, 870.

CAHILL R.N.P., HERON D.I., POSKITT D.C. & TRNKA Z. (1980) Lymphocyte recirculation in the sheep fetus. In 'Blood Cells and Vessel Walls; Functional Interactions'. *CIBA Foundation Symposium 71*, p. 145. Excerpta Medica, Amsterdam.

CAHILL R.N.P., POSKITT D.C., FROST H. & TRNKA Z. (1977) Two distinct pools of recirculating T lymphocytes: migratory characteristics of nodal and intestinal T lymphocytes. *J. exp. Med.* **145**, 420.

CRAIG S.W. & CEBRA J.J. (1971) Peyer's patches; an enriched source of precursors for IgA-producing immunocytes in the rabbit. *J. exp. Med.* **134**, 188.

DREXHAGE H.A., MULLINK H., DE GROOT J., CLARKE J. & BALFOUR B.M. (1979) A study of cells present in peripheral lymph of pigs with special reference to a type of cell resembling the Langerhans cell. *Cell and Tissue Res.* **202**, 407.

FAHY V.A., GERBER H.A., MORRIS B., TREVELLA W. & ZUBOSKI C.F. (1980) The function of lymph nodes in the formation of lymph. *Mongr. in Allergy* **16**, 82.

FERGUSON A. (1977) Intraepithelial lymphocytes of the small intestine. *Gut* **18**, 921.

FORD W.L. (1975) Lymphocyte migration and immune responses. *Progr. Allergy* **19**, 1.

FORD W.L. & ATKINS R.C. (1971) Specific unresponsiveness of recirculating lymphocytes after exposure to histocompatibility antigens in F_1 hybrid rats. *Nature (New Biol.)* **234**, 178.

GOWANS J.L. & KNIGHT E.S. (1964) The route of recirculation of lymphocytes in the rat. *Proc. Roy. Soc. Lond. B.* **159**, 257.

HALL J.G., HOPKINS J. & ORLANS E. (1977) Studies on the lymphoblasts of the sheep. III. The destination of lymph-borne immunoblasts according to their tissue of origin. *Europ. J. Immunol.* **7**, 30.

HALL J.G. & MORRIS B. (1965) The origin of the cells in the efferent lymph from a single lymph node. *J. exp. Med.* **121**, 901.

HASTON W. (1979) A study of lymphocyte behaviour in cultures of fibroblast-like lympho-reticular cells. *Cell. Immunol.* **45**, 74.

HAY J.B. & HOBBS B.B. (1977) The flow of blood to lymph nodes and its relation to lymphocyte traffic and the immune response. *J. exp. Med.* **145**, 31.

HOEFSMIT E., KAMPEROTIZK E.W.A., HENDRIKS H.R., BEELEN R.H.J. & BALFOUR B.M. (1980) Lymph Node Macrophages. In *The Reticuloendothelial System, Vol. 1. Morphology*. CARR I. & KNIGHT W.J. (eds), Plenum Press, New York.

HOPKINS J., McCONNELL I. & LACHMANN P.J. (1981) Specific selection of antigen reactive lymphocytes into antigen stimulated lymph nodes in sheep. *J. exp. Med.* (in press).

HOPKINS J., McCONNELL I. & PEARSON J.D. (1981) Lymphocyte traffic through lymph nodes. II. Role of prostaglandin E_2 as a mediator of cell shutdown. *Immunology* **42**, 225.

HOWARD J.C. (1972) The life span and recirculation of marrow-derived small lymphocytes from the rat thoracic duct. *J. exp. Med.* **135**, 185.

HUMPHREY J.H. (1980) Macrophages and the differential migration of lymphocytes. In 'Blood Cells and Vessel Walls; Functional Interactions'. *CIBA Foundation Symposium 71*, p. 287. Excerpta Medica, Amsterdam.

HUMPHREY J.H. (1981) The Fate of Antigens. In LACHMANN P.J. & PETERS D.K. (eds), *Clinical Aspects of Immunology*. Blackwell Scientific Publications, Oxford.

HUSBAND A.J. & GOWANS J.L. (1978) The origin and antigen-dependent distributions of IgA-containing cells in the intestine. *J. exp. Med.* **148**, 1146.

KLAUS G.G.B. & HUMPHREY J.H. (1977) The generation of memory cells. 1. The role of C_3 in the generation of B memory cells. *Immunology* **33**, 31.

McCONNELL I., HOPKINS J. & LACHMANN P.J. (1980) Lymphocyte traffic through lymph nodes during cell shutdown. In 'Blood Cells and Vessel Walls; Functional Interactions.' *CIBA Foundation Symposium 71*, p. 167. Excerpta Medica, Amsterdam.

NIEUWENHUIS P. & FORD W.L. (1976) Comparative migration of B and T lymphocytes in the rat spleen and lymph nodes. *Cell. Immunol.* **23**, 254.

OTTAWAY, C.A., ROSE, M.L. & PARROTT D.M.V. (1979) The gut as an immunological system. *Int. Rev. Physiol. Gastrointestinal Physiology* III, **19**, 323.

PARROTT D. & FERGUSON A. (1974) Selective migration of lymphoblasts within the small intestine. *Immunology* **26**, 571.

REYNOLDS J. (1980) Gut-associated lymphoid tissues in lambs before and after birth. *Monogr. in Allergy* **16**, 187.

SCOLLAY R., HALL J.G. & ORLANS E. (1976) Studies on sheep lymphocytes. II. Some properties of cells in various compartments of the recirculating lymphocyte pool. *Europ. J. Immunol.* **6**, 121.

SEDGLEY M. & FORD W.L. (1976) The migration of lymphocytes across specialized vascular endothelium. 1. The entry of lymphocytes into the isolated mesenteric lymph node of the rat. *Cell Tissue Kinet.* **9**, 231.

SPRENT J. (1977) Migration and Lifespan of Lymphocytes in B and T Cells in Immune Recognition. In LOOR F. & ROELANTS G.F. (eds), p. 59. J. Wiley, New York.

STAMPER H.B. & WOODRUFF J.J. (1976) Lymphocyte homing into lymph nodes: *in vitro* demonstration of the selective affinity of recirculating lymphocytes for high-endothelial venules. *J. exp. Med.* **144**, 828.

STAMPER H.B. & WOODRUFF J.J. (1977) An *in vitro* model of lymphocyte homing. 1. Characterization of the interaction between thoracic duct lymphocytes and specialized high endothelial venules of lymph nodes. *J. Immunol.* **119**, 772.

TOEWS G.R., BERGSTRASSER P.R., STREILIN J.W. & SULLIVAN S. (1980) Epidermal Langerhans cell density determines whether contact hypersensitivity or unresponsiveness follows skin painting with DNCB. *J. Immunol.* **124**, 445.

WOODRUFF J.J. & KUTTNER B.J. (1980) Adherence of lymphocytes to the high endothelium of lymph nodes *in vitro*. In 'Blood Cells and Vessel Walls; Functional Interactions'. *CIBA Foundation Symposium 71*, p. 243. Excerpta Medica, Amsterdam.

Further reading

CIBA SYMPOSIUM (1977) Immunology of the Gut. *CIBA Foundation Symposium 46*. Excerpta Medica, Amsterdam.

VAN EWIK W. (1977) *Microenvironments of T and B lymphocytes: a light and electronmicroscopic study.* (Doctoral Thesis, University of Rotterdam.)

WEISS L. (1972) *The Cells and Tissues of the Immune System. Strucure, Fuctions, Interactions* (eds. Osler G. & Weiss L.). Prentice-Hall Inc., Englewood Cliffs, New Jersey.

Section 3
Clinical Immunology

This section is concerned with the relationship of the immune system to disease. Immunological effector mechanisms and their rôle both in immunity and causation of disease form the basis of Chapter 15. Readers will be pleased to note that there is more to immunity than T and B cells. Although there are a widespread number of immunity mechanisms their deployment by the host is selective and geared to the particular type of invading pathogen. The contribution which studies on immunity deficiency syndromes have made to our understanding of the biology of the immune system is emphasized in Chapter 16. Chapter 17 discusses the diseases associated with breakdown of self tolerance. The final chapters underline the clinical relevance of the MHS. In 'HLA and Disease' we discuss why certain diseases might be associated with particular haplotypes together with some of the problems associated with this area. The concluding chapter is an appraisal of graft rejection—the immunologist's chestnut. Although we are still far from inducing specific unresponsiveness to allogenic MHS molecules it can be claimed that advances in tissue typing, immunosuppressive therapy and organ preservation have made clinical organ transplantation less of a hope and more of a reality.

Chapter 15
Mechanisms in Immunity
and Hypersensitivity

15.1 Introduction

Immunity to pathogenic micro-organisms is rarely mediated by antibody and lymphocytes alone. Effective defence mechanisms rely on interactions between the specific components of the immune system and a variety of non-specific effector mechanisms involving accessory cells and serum factors. The inappropriate activation of these mechanisms can result in hypersensitivity and tissue damage rather than immunity.

There are several problems in trying to synthesize this area of immunology. Much of the literature on immunity mechanisms is phenomenological and except in the case of selective immune deficiency states it is not easy to determine which of the many mechanisms are involved in resistance to infection. Further, the particular mechanism involved varies depending on the type of micro-organism, its route of entry, site of replication in the host, mechanism of causing disease and so on.

To be comprehensive is clearly beyond the scope of a single chapter and we shall therefore concentrate on the basic mechanisms involved in immunity and hypersensitivity using clinical examples where appropriate. We hope that the reader will then be able to apply the basic rules to the many other well-described clinical situations.

15.2 Innate resistance

The mammalian host can eliminate most potentially pathogenic organisms by non-immunological means. Although the mechanisms of innate resistance are not precisely known, they can be broadly divided into those wherein the potential pathogen is incapable of growing in the host and those wherein primitive, non-specific defence mechanisms operate (Table 15.1). When the latter are impaired, either congenitally or as a result of concomitant disease or drug treatment, then some, but not all, organisms become pathogenic (see Chapter 16).

15.2.1 Incompatibility between host and parasite

In most cases, the reason for the failure of a potential pathogen to grow in a host is unknown, whilst in some cases it is known. For example, the merozoites of *Plasmo-*

Table 15.1. Non-specific defence mechanisms

Physical	Chemical
Skin Barrier	Skin-associated unsaturated fatty acids
Mucociliary system (lungs)	
Tears, saliva	Lysozyme
Intestinal motility	Acid pH of stomach
Temperature (rhinoviruses replicate at 35°C but not at 37°C)	
	Antibacterial substances released by normal gut flora

dium knowlesi only penetrate red cells expressing Duffy blood groups; those of *P. vivax* may also require the Fy antigen, while other plasmodia fail to parasitize red cells expressing the sickle-cell trait. Thus, in areas where malaria is endemic, there is an increase in the number of individuals expressing sickle-cell haemoglobin. Similarly, the presence or absence of particular cell surface receptors for viruses will determine the range of cell types which they can infect (see Mögenson, 1979).

15.2.2 Phagocytosis and intracellular killing mechanisms

Phagocytosis and intracellular killing by hydrolytic and other enzymes is the most primitive type of defence mechanism. Although many unicellular organisms are phagocytic, in the primitive multicellular organisms phagocytosis is a property of specialized cells. In mammals the two principal classes of phagocytic cells are macrophages and neutrophils although other cells do have phagocytic activity.

Cells of the macrophage/monocyte series are derived from bone-marrow precursor cells—promonocytes. They contain a wide variety of hydrolytic enzymes and are heterogeneous both in function and morphology (Table 15.2). They are released from the bone marrow as immature cells, survive for long periods in the tissues and accumulate at sites of chronic inflammatory reactions. Their intrinsic bactericidal activity can be enhanced by T cell lymphokines.

Neutrophils are produced in the bone marrow in large numbers (8.10^7 cells per minute in man) and in contrast to macrophages are short-lived (2–3 days). Their intrinsic bactericidal activity is not affected by T cell lymphokines, and although they have no immunological specificity whatsoever, they are involved in many immunological reactions via interaction with antibodies and complement (Table 15.3).

Micro-organisms adhering to the plasma membrane of phagocytic cells rapidly

Table 15.2. Mononuclear
phagocytes

Produced in	Bone marrow
Maturation	Bone marrow and other tissues
Mainly present in	Liver, spleen, lymph nodes, lungs, peritoneum, blood
Main products	Lysosomal (hydrolytic) enzymes Lysozyme Complement components Interferon
Main function	Antigen 'presentation' Ingestion and digestion of pathogens and abnormal cells Accumulate in inflammatory reactions
Sub-classes	Monocytes Kupffer cells Histiocytes Langerhans cells Peritoneal macrophages Alveolar macrophages Sinusoid lining cells Osteoclasts Microglial cells

become interiorized within the phagocytic vacuole (phagosome) and killing occurs when these fuse with lysosomes within the cell (phagolysosome). These contain a wide variety of hydrolytic enzymes and pathogens resistant to these can become established as intracellular parasites, e.g. *Brucella abortus*.

There are a number of killing mechanisms generated in phagolysosomes:

(a) *Cationic (basic) proteins.* These proteins bind to and destroy the bacterial cell.

(b) *The oxidative microbicidal pathway.* Neutrophil granules contain myeloperoxidase which interacts with hydrogen peroxide in the phagosome in the presence of a halide co-factor to kill bacteria. This is associated with the generation of superoxide, singlet oxygen and the hydroxyl radical, (see 10.3.2a) and with emission of light (chemiluminescence) by the cell. The importance of the oxidative mechanism in killing bacteria is demonstrated in chronic granulomatous disease where the neutrophils fail to generate H_2O_2, show no chemiluminescence and fail to kill certain bacteria. Catalase will substitute for myeloperoxidase in tissue macrophages.

15.2.3 *Complement*

The importance of the complement system in immunity centres around C3 and C5. C3b is chiefly involved in mediating adherence reactions between C3b-coated micro-

Table 15.3. Some properties of neutrophils and macrophages

| Cell | Maturation | Life-span | Factors influencing activity | | Sensitizing | |
			Chemotactic		Target (opsonization)	Effector cell (arming)
Neutrophils	Released fully mature	2 days	Complement derived		IgG, C$_3$	—
Macrophages	Released immature	Months or years	T lymphocyte-derived lymphokines		IgG, C$_3$, T cell factors	Lymphokines
	Activated by lymphokines					

organisms and the wide variety of cells which express C3b receptors, such as polymorphonuclear cells, macrophages, monocytes and platelets in certain species. Adherence of C3b-coated micro-organisms to any accessory cell expressing C3b receptors results in the enhanced phagocytosis and killing of the organism or in some cases the exocytosis of the cell contents (e.g. vasoactive amines released from platelets). The released amines will kill bacteria and in some cases produce local tissue damage. The small molecular weight fragments of cleaved C3 and C5, C3a (9,000 M.W.) and C5a (15,000 M.W.), as well as the trimolecular complex, C$\overline{567}$, also have widespread effects on accessory cells; C3a and C5a (the anaphylatoxins) produce degranulation of mast cells and basophils by interacting with distinct C3a and C5a receptors on the cell surface. Both these anaphylatoxins are readily inactivated by serum carboxypeptidase B which, being of high molecular weight (300,000 M.W.) does not reach the tissue until there is an increase in capillary permeability. C5a, as well as C$\overline{567}$, are also potent chemotactic factors for neutrophils and eosinophils.

The involvement of the complement system in immunity does not necessarily depend on the terminal pathway of complement activation since C5-deficient mice, C6-deficient rabbits are all perfectly healthy (see Chapter 16). Apart from a few C3 or Factor I deficient individuals, no other genetic deficiencies of the alternative pathway have been detected, suggesting that such deficiencies are life threatening.

There are a variety of micro-organisms which directly activate complement without involving antibody. Certain rough strains of gram-negative bacteria, as well as many animal oncornaviruses interact directly with C1 in normal human serum, thereby producing classical pathway activation. Cells transformed with certain viruses (Epstein–Barr virus, Mareks' disease virus and measles virus), trypanosomes, schistosomula and many other parasites produce alternative pathway activation, possibly via some kind of protected surface phenomenon (Fig. 15.1) (see Chapter 3.4). Following activation, the organisms or transformed cells become coated with C3 and are then removed by the reticuloendothelial system or lysed. Antibody-independent activation of the alternative pathway can prevent overwhelming infections by certain micro-organisms in patients with antibody deficiencies.

15.2.4 Interferons

The interferons (IFN) are important components of non-specific immunity to viruses. IFNα and IFNβ (Table 15.4) are generated by viral infection or non-viral inducers (poly I:C) whereas IFNγ is a T cell lymphokine. Their anti-viral effects are unclear and probably multifactorial. IFNα and IFNβ can bind to ganglioside receptors on cells triggering the synthesis of ribosomal binding proteins which block translation of viral but not host RNA. Interferons also act on certain accessory cells of the immune system and enhance the cytotoxicity of natural killer (NK) cells (see below; Sonnenfeld & Merigan, 1979).

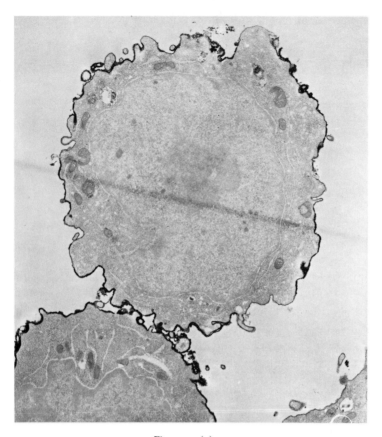

Fig. 15.1 (a)

Efforts are now being made to produce interferons on a large scale for treatment of certain infections and possibly cancers. Monoclonal antibodies to interferon are being used for its purification from bulk human leucocyte cultures (Secher and Burke, 1980). Ultimately it is hoped that bacteria carrying human interferon genes will produce the substance in large quantities (Nagata *et al.*, 1980).

15.2.5 *Natural killer cells*
Natural killer (NK) cells kill target cells in the absence of any known antigenic stimulation and in the absence of antibody to the target cell (Keissling & Wigzell, 1979; Heberman *et al.*, 1979). It is unknown how NK cells recognize their targets. One speculation is that their specificity is directed at carbohydrate determinants on the target cells, their rôle being to destroy cells with incompatible or incomplete glycoproteins. The range of susceptible targets is broad but there are certain general rules. NK activity is greater with homologous mixtures of effector and target cells

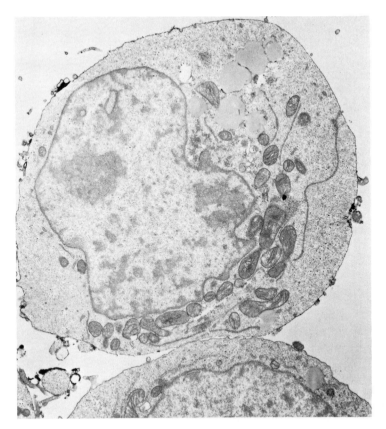

Fig. 15.1 (b)

Fig. 15.1. (a) Epstein–Barr (EB) virus-positive and (b) EB virus-negative cells after incubation in normal human serum and staining with peroxidase-labelled anti-human C_3. The EB virus-positive cells but not the EB virus-negative cells spontaneously activate the alternative complement pathway which results in the deposition of C_3 on the surface of the EB virus-positive cell. (By courtesy of Dr S. Patterson.)

(human NK and human targets) than with heterologous mixtures. There is no evidence for any MHS restriction since NK cells can kill heterologous targets. Cells of lymphatic or haemopoietic origin are the most susceptible targets and killing activity can be enhanced by interferon. NK cells are widely regarded as playing a major rôle in tumour surveillance.

The cell lineage of NK cells is not known but active NK cells have receptors for the Fc part of IgG. Recently, a mutant strain of mouse (beige mutant) has been shown to lack NK cell activity, although these mice have cells which bind to target cells in the NK assay *in vitro* (Roder & Duve, 1979). The absence of a killing mechanism in the

Table 15.4. Some properties of human interferons (Hu IFN)

Interferon	Susceptibility		Produced by	Target cell specificities	M.W.
	Acid pH	Heat			
IFN-α	−	+	leucocytes and fibroblasts	Human only	18,000 38,000
IFN-β	−	+		Human, bovine, porcine, feline	
IFN-γ	+	−	activated T lymphocytes	Human only	30,000– 100,000

Many different animal interferons have variable target-cell specificity and M.W.s ranging from 15,000 to 100,000. *E. coli* carrying the IFN-α and IFN-β genes have been constructed which can synthesize a polypeptide with functional and immunological similarities to Hu IFN-α and Hu IFN-β (Nagata *et al.*, 1980). See Nature, (1980) **286**, 110; for report on new nomenclature of interferons.

mutant mice may be related to the fact that beige mice carry a lysosomal defect similar to that seen in Chediak–Higashi disease in man (see Chapter 16). The mice also lack K cell activity, although they have normal levels of cytotoxic T lymphocytes, suggesting that the K/NK lineage may be distinct from that of T cells. NK cells are not mature T cells since athymic (nude) mice have normal levels. The possibility that they are immature T cells cannot be excluded.

15.3 Specific immunity

In situations in which organisms escape from, or overcome, innate resistance, recovery from a primary infection or development of resistance to reinfection, depends on a specific immune response. This may act alone (e.g. antibody neutralization of viruses or T cell killing of virus-infected cells) or, more commonly, together with the primitive defence mechanisms. This localizes and enhances the response at the appropriate site. Potential pathogens vary in their ability to evade the primitive defence mechanisms and the nature of the specific response varies widely for each host–pathogen combination.

15.3.1 Antibody alone

Antibodies alone can be effective by binding to critical sites on toxins, bacteria and viruses, thereby preventing their attachment to target cells. Local production of IgA at mucosal surfaces can prevent the attachment of polio virus or *vibrio cholera* to gut epithelial cells.

15.3.2 *Antibody with accessory cells, with or without complement*

The primitive capacity of all phagocytic cells to ingest and destroy micro-organisms is enhanced when the target organisms are coated with antibody or with antibody and complement. In such cases, the interaction of the bound Fc or C3b with the Fc or C3b receptors on the cell's surface leads to increased phagocytosis.

In addition to this simple enhancement of a primitive function, the accessory cells interact with each other and with the immune system in complex ways.

(a) *Eosinophils.* This is particularly well illustrated in immunity to schistosomiasis in which, in common with many helminth infections, there is an association between increased levels of eosinophils in the peripheral blood and high IgE responses. In mice, depletion of eosinophils *in vivo*, by treatment with an anti-eosinophil serum, ablates immunity to schistosomes, suggesting a crucial rôle for the eosinophil in this disease. Although by no means certain, the following summary reflects a reasonable view of the involvement of eosinophils in immunity to schisto-somiasis and demonstrates the complexity of the response (Mahmoud, 1980).

First, both the development of a specific IgE response and the increase in peripheral blood eosinophils, are T cell dependent reactions. These two reactions may be inter-related, possibly via the numerous lymphokines which influence eosinophils (Fig. 15.2). Second, the specific IgE bound to mast cells, in the skin at the site of larval penetration, leads to the release of mast cell mediators (see 15.4.1 and Table 15.5). These mediators increase capillary permeability, thereby allowing the entry of specific IgG antibodies and complement at the site of the reaction. In addition, mast cell mediators are chemotactic for various cell types, especially eosinophils, which will start to accumulate at the site of the reaction. Third, eosinophils arriving at the site of invasion exert a toxic effect on the organism in that they adhere to and damage schistosomula coated with specific IgG antibodies. This reaction is complement independent and is associated with the degranulaton of the

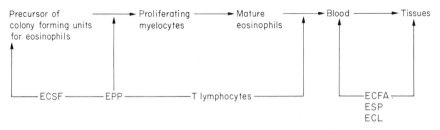

Influence of eosinophil directed humoral factors

Fig. 15.2. Possible sites of action of T cells and lymphokines which promote eosinophil maturation.   ECSF=Eosinophil colony stimulating factor;   EPP=Eosinophilopoietin; ECFA=Eosinophil chemotactic factor of anaphylaxis.

Table 15.5. Mast cell mediatiors with effects on eosinophils

Category	Mediator	Structure	Action on eosinophil
Preformed	Histamine	M.W. 111	Enhanced expression of C_3b receptors. Chemotactic. Increases chemotaxis to other factors
	Eosinophil chemotactic factor of anaphylaxis (ECFA)	Val/ala-gly-ser-glu M.W. 360–390	Chemotactic (neutrophils also). Enhanced expression of C_3b receptors. Inactivates response to subsequent exposure to ECFA. Increases helminth killing
Newly formed	Lipid chemotactic factor (LCF)	M.W. 300–500 Cycloxygenase product	Chemotactic. Production inhibited by indomethacin
	Monohydroxyeicosatetranoic acids (HETES)	M.W. 320 Lipoxygenase product	Chemotactic. Increases expression of C_3b receptors (neutrophils also)
	Heptadecatrenoic acid (HHT) PGE_2 (a prostaglandin)	M.W. 280 Cycloxygenase product	Chemotactic Chemotactic

Adapted from Goetzl and Austen (1980) and Kay and Anwar (1980).

eosinophils. The release of the contents of the granules, especially the eosinophil major basic protein, leads to the death of the schistosomula. In contrast, under the same conditions, adherent neurophils fail to degranulate and do not damage the parasite (Butterworth *et al.*, 1980). In addition to the major basic protein the granules in eosinophils contain enzymes which can neutralize the biological activities of some of the mast cell mediators (Table 15.6). Consequently degranulation of eosinophils reduces the inflammatory reactions, and reduces the number of eosinophils accumulating at the site of the invasion. The eosinophil enzymes that participate in this negative feed back include histaminase, arylsulphatase, phospholipase D and lysophospholipase, and their biological effects are described in 15.4.

Finally the schistosumula specific IgE, which is important in conjunction with mast cells in facilitating the accumulation of serum components and eosinophils at the invasion site, may be more directly involved in immunity to schistosomes. Macrophages, incubated in the presence of immune complexes containing IgE and schistosomula antigen, have altered functional properties such that they adhere to and damage young schistosomula (Dessaint *et al.*, 1979).

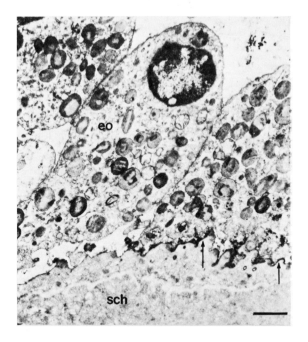

Fig. 15.3. Electron micrograph showing the early stages of the interaction between human eosinophils and antibody coated schistosomula. Eosinophils (eo) are shown in the process of making contact with the surface of the schistosomula (sch) and one of the eosinophils shows a characteristic extensive close contact with the surface of the antibody-coated parasite. Scale bar 1 μm. (From Glauert *et al.*, 1978.)

Table 15.6. Eosinophil 'mediators'

Substance	Proposed biological activities
Eosinophil peroxidase	Possesses antimicrobial activity (bacteria and helminths) when combined with H_2O_2 and halide ions
Major basic protein	Localized to core of eosinophil granules. Toxic to trichinella and schistosomula and also to normal mammalian cells
Phospholipase D	Inactivates PAF (platelet aggregating factor). Inactivates histamine
Arylsulphatase B	Inactivates SRS-A from mast cells
Histaminase	Inactivates histamine
Lysophospholipase	Inactivates lysophosphatides

Adapted from Gleich, Klebanoff, Goetzl and Austen (see Mahmoud & Austen, 1980).

In summary, the destruction of the young schistosomulum in the skin of the immune host involves a wide variety of responses and interactions, including the T cell dependent production of IgE and IgG, T cell dependent effects on eosinophils, the interaction of eosinophils with the products of mast cell degranulation and the interaction of macrophages with immune complexes containing IgE.

(b) *K cells*. K cells are non-phagocytic mononuclear cells which recognize the Fc part of IgG antibodies reacting with target cells and then kill the target cells (MacLennan, 1972; Perlmann *et al.*, 1972). There is little restriction as to the range of susceptible targets which include antibody-coated tissue cells, bacteria (meningococci), fungi (cryptococcus neoformans) and parasites (Makwananzi *et al.*, 1976). The lack of involvement of the MHS in K cell killing points to a fundamental distinction in the activation mechanisms of cytotoxic lymphocytes and K cells.

There is some confusion as to the exact nature of the K cell. This is complicated by the fact that many other cells with Fc receptors can bind to antibody-coated cells and if these cells have intrinsic killing mechanisms, target cell cytotoxicity occurs. However, killing by K cells can occur with as little as a few hundred molecules of IgG per target cell, whereas that mediated by other Fc receptor-positive cells cannot. So far, there is no defining marker for K cells and, although they are highly cytotoxic *in vitro*, their significance *in vivo* remains to be established.

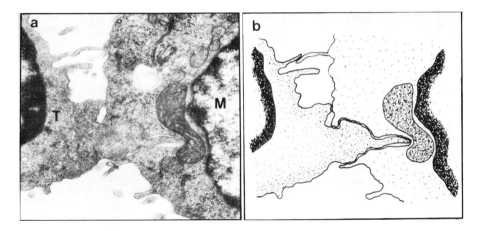

Fig. 15.4. 'T cell killing.' (a) A single-pointed projection from a cytotoxic T cell extending into a P815 (mastocytoma) target cell (M). (b) Schematic diagram of (a). (From Sanderson & Glauert, 1979.)

15.3.3 *Cytotoxic T lymphocytes*

Cytotoxic T cells are a distinct T cell subset which recognize and kill cells expressing foreign antigens. Killing of the target cell is initiated by recognition of both the antigen and the products of the MHS on the target cell and if these MHS products are absent then no T cell killing occurs. Time lapse photography has shown that having once made contact with a target cell, cytotoxic T cells can move away to kill other targets leaving an apparently normal target cell which later undergoes lysis (Fig. 15.4).

15.3.4 *Activated macrophages*

There are a wide range of micro-organisms which are not killed following phagocytosis by resting macrophages. These organisms, which include bacteria (*Listeria*, *Mycobacteria*), fungi and protozoa (*Leishmania*) replicate within normal macrophages and may eventually kill the cell. These intracellular parasites can be killed following 'activation' of the macrophages by T cells or T-cell lymphokines.

A good example of enhanced immunity following macrophage activation is seen in *Listeria monocytogenes* infection in mice and rats (Mackaness and Blanden, 1967; Nelson, 1976). This organism replicates within the macrophages of the liver and spleen, and non-immune animals succumb to high doses. Animals which have recovered from a sublethal inoculum are resistant to subsequent challenge with a dose that would be lethal for non-immune animals. This resistance is due to antigen specific T cells which, in the presence of antigen, will activate macrophages to kill a variety of organisms.

15.4 Hypersensitivity reactions

Hypersensitivity occurs when immune mechanisms cause tissue damage. Coombs and Gell (1975) have defined four types of initiating mechanisms involved in hypersensitivity reactions (Fig. 15.5). It must be remembered that many of the hypersensitivity reactions are not restricted to a particular type, and they are usually mixed responses.

15.4.1 Type 1 reactions

These reactions are elicited by the interaction of antigen with tissue mast cells or basophils passively sensitized with reaginic antibodies (IgE in man) resulting in the release of a variety of pharmacologically active substances.

Classical Type 1 reactions in man can occur to harmless antigens such as pollen. Both T cell help and suppression are involved in the development and control of IgE synthesizing B cells. The balance between helper and suppressor cells which selectively control the extent of the IgE response, is affected by many parameters. These include the route of administration of antigen, its chemical composition, physical nature, adjuvants employed and the genetic makeup of the animal. For example, it has been suggested that low levels of mucosal IgA predispose to sensitization for an IgE response.

In man, familial tendencies towards high IgE responses indicate the involvement of genetic factors, although the nature of these is unknown. For example, family studies on ragweed hypersensitivity have suggested the involvement of at least two genes. One of these, linked to HLA, determines a heightened response to ragweed antigen while the second (unassigned) controls the IgE nature of the response. The presence of both genes predisposes to ragweed hypersensitivity.

IgE responses are characteristically directed against antigens which enter through epithelial surfaces, whether mucosal membranes or skin. In evolutionary terms, the selective advantage of such responses is therefore probably against pathogens which enter through such surfaces, in that the hypersensitivity reaction permits the rapid accumulation in the tissues of other components of the immune response (see 15.3.2).

The mediators released by mast cells and basophils in Type 1 reactions are numerous (Table 15.5). Although histamine has been the most extensively studied, others which may be important include the slow-reacting substance of anaphylaxis (SRS-A), platelet-aggregating factors (PAF) and factors chemotactic for leucocytes, especially eosinophils. The active components of the low molecular weight eosinophil chemotactic factors of anaphylaxis (ECF-A) reside in two preformed tetrapeptides, ala-gly-ser-glu and val-gly-ser-glu. Eosinophils localized at the site of the reaction inactivate the residual mast-cell mediators (Table 15.6), thus switching off the reaction.

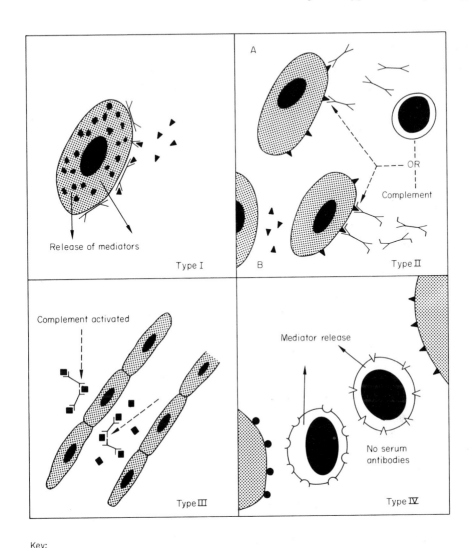

Release of mediators

Type I

A

OR

Complement

B   Type II

Complement activated

Mediator release

No serum
antibodies

Type III   Type IV

Key:

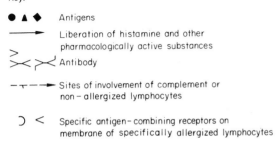

● ▲ ◆   Antigens

⟶   Liberation of histamine and other
          pharmacologically active substances

≍ ⤝   Antibody

− ⊤ − ⟶   Sites of involvement of complement or
          non − allergized lymphocytes

⊃ <   Specific antigen− combining receptors on
          membrane of specifically allergized lymphocytes

Fig. 15.5. Classification of hypersensitivity reactions. (From Gell, Coombs & Lachmann, 1975.)

15.4.2 *Type 2 reactions*

These are initiated by antibody reacting with antigen which is part of the cell membrane or with antigens which have become secondarily associated with the cell surface. The consequences depend on whether complement or accessory cells become involved (polymorphonuclear cells, K cells) and on the anatomical location of the target membrane.

Type 2 reactions involving intravascular complement activation occur in incompatible blood transfusions, and certain autoimmune haemolytic anaemias involving anti-Rh antibodies or IgM 'cold' autoantibodies to the I blood group. In the latter case, the autoantibody binds better in the cold than at 37°C and hence intravascular haemolysis occurs in the peripheral tissues especially where they are below body temperature. Many of the drug-induced anaemias occur because the drugs (α-methyl-dopa, chlorpromazine, sedormid) are antigenic and can become secondarily attached to cells *in vivo*. Antibodies to the modified cells then cause lysis of the cells causing anaemia, neutropaenia and thrombocytopaenia.

Antibodies to the glomerular basement membrane (GBM) can result in complement fixation and/or accessory cell activation within the renal glomerulus. This can produce extensive tissue destruction and renal failure. This situation occurs in Goodpasture's syndrome and can be induced experimentally by injecting anti-GBM antibodies in guinea-pigs. The accessory cells which accumulate at the site adhere via their Fc or C3b receptors to the antibody and/or complement coated basement membrane. Since the opsonized membrane cannot be phagocytosed, the activated polymorphonuclear cells exocytose their granules, releasing tissue-damaging enzymes (proteases, cathepsins, lysosomal enzymes, etc.). Type 2 reactions may also involve critical receptor sites·on cells causing thyrotoxicosis and myasthenia gravis (see Chapter 17).

15.4.3 *Type 3 reactions*

These reactions are due to the presence of immune complexes either in the circulation or extravascular space and are classically represented by serum sickness and the Arthus reaction. Immune complexes (depending on size) may localize in capillary networks (lungs, kidney, joints) where together with accessory cells and complement, they produce extensive tissue damage. For example, in Arthus reactions immune complexes may form at the site of second or third injections of antigen-producing haemorrhagic vasculitis and necrosis.

Type 3 reactions can sometimes be associated with persistent virus infections where, although antibody is present, it fails to eliminate the virus because it is of too low affinity. Failure to eradicate virus because of low affinity antibody occurs in certain strains of mice infected with lymphocytic choriomeningitis (LCM) virus. The production of low affinity antibodies in susceptible strains is not restricted to LCM but also occurs in response to other antigens possibly because of a failure in the normal maturation of the response. These mice have high levels of circulating immune complexes which mediate many of the pathological lesions.

Dengue haemorrhagic shock in man is a good example of a severe Type 3 reaction occurring in the intravascular space. It occurs in patients who have previously made an uncomplicated recovery from a primary infection with Dengue virus. Although these patients have high levels of IgG antibody to the infecting strain of virus, this does not protect against infection with other strains. A massive viraemia occurs and because the variants react weakly with antibody produced during the first infection, immune complexes are formed within the intravascular space. These may interact with platelets to produce severe thrombocytopenia and intravascular complement consumption which, if severe enough, can produce intravascular coagulation and shock.

15.4.4 Type 4 (delayed) hypersensitivity reactions

These reactions are initiated by antigen specific T cells reacting with antigen and releasing lymphokines that affect a variety of accessory cells, especially macrophages. Antibody and complement are not necessary, although many delayed hypersensitivity reactions seen clinically are mixed reactions, with antibodies also being involved. Histologically, delayed hypersensitivity reactions are an infiltrate of lymphocytes, macrophages, and eosinophils. Persistent lesions lead to necrosis and fibrosis.

Type 4 reactions may be directed against a wide range of antigens including viral, bacterial, protozoal and metazoal antigens, as well as contact sensitizing agents, drugs, self antigens and alloantigens. The clinical effects vary depending on the site and extent of the reaction and persistence of the antigen. The reactions range from the small and transient lesions, seen in intradermal skin tests (Mantoux test), to necrosis and fibrosis of the lungs seen in chronic tuberculosis. The reactions seen in leprosy illustrate the relationship between hypersensitivity and immunity (Turk, 1976).

Leprosy varies markedly in its presentation and Ridley and Jopling (1966) proposed the idea of a spectrum of disease, based on clinical and on histological appearances. At one end of the spectrum, the polar tuberculoid form presents as a slowly-progressive disease, characterized by nodular lesions of the skin and peripheral nerves. These lesions are composed of lymphocytes, macrophages and giant cells, containing a few extracellular bacilli. Antibody titres to *Mycobacterium leprae* are low. At the other extreme, lepromatous leprosy is seen as a rapidly progressive, disseminated disease. Lymphocytes are rare in the lesions and the macrophages present are abnormal in appearance ('foamy' cells) and contain many intracellular bacilli. Antibody levels are high and the drug therapy causes release of antigens and development of local or circulating immune complex disease.

These differences are also reflected in immune response of the patients. In tuberculoid leprosy, lymphocyte transformation to irrelevant antigens or mitogens is normal, but responses to *M. leprae* antigens are particularly high. Macrophages from such patients, in the presence of autologous lymphocytes, can be activated to kill the organism. In contrast, patients with lepromatous leprosy show a reduction in the *in vitro* T cell transformation to irrelevant antigens or mitogens and a complete absence of T cell responses to *M. leprae* antigens. Their macrophages cannot be activated to kill the organism.

In addition to these two groups of leprosy patients, together with those showing intermediate forms, a third and considerably larger group of individuals have been infected with *M. leprae* and are immune to repeated infections.

References

BLANDEN R.V. (1974) T-cell responses to viral and bacterial infection. *Transplant. Rev.* **19**, 000.

BUTTERWORTH A.E., VADAS M.A. & DAVID J.R. (1980) Mechanisms of Eosinophil-mediated Cytotoxicity. In MAHMOUD A.A.F. & AUSTEN K.F. (eds), *Proceedings of the Eosinophil Centennial, Brook Lodge, Michigan.* Grune & Stratton Inc., New York.

COOMBS R.R.A. & GELL P.G.H. (1975) Classification of Allergic Reactions Responsible for Clinical Hypersensitivity and Disease. In GELL P.G.H., COOMBS R.R.A. & LACHMANN P.J. (eds), *Clinical Aspects of Immunology*, 3rd ed., p. 761. Blackwell Scientific Publications, Oxford.

DESSAINT J.-P., TORPIER G., CAPRON M., BAZIN H. & CAPRON A. (1979) Binding characteristics of IgE on the surface of macrophages in the rat. *Cell. Immunol.* **45**, 1.

GLAUERT A.M., BUTTERWORTH A.E., STURROCK R.F. & HOUBA V. (1978) The mechanism of antibody-dependent, eosinophil-mediated damage to schistosomula of *Schistosomula mansoni in vitro*: a study by phase contrast and electron microscopy. *J. Cell Sci.* **34**, 173.

GOETZL E.J. & AUSTEN K.F. (1980) Natural Eosinophilactic Peptides: Evidence of Heterogeneity and Studies of Structure and Function. In MAHMOUD A.A.F. & AUSTEN K.F. (eds), *Proceedings of the Eosinophil Centennial, Brook Lodge, Michigan.* Grune & Stratton Inc., New York.

HEBERMAN R.B., DJEU J.Y., KAY D., ORTALDO J.R., RICCARDI C., BONNARD G.D., HOLDEN H.T., FAGNANI R., SANTONI A. & PUCCETTI P. (1979) Natural killer cells. *Immunol. Rev.* **44**, 43.

KAY A.B. & ANWAR A.R.E. (1980) Eosinophil Surface and Receptors. In MAHMOUD A.A.F. & AUSTEN K.F. (eds), *Proceedings of the Eosinophil Centennial, Brook Lodge, Michigan.* Grune & Stratton Inc., New York.

KEISSLING, R. & WIGZELL, H. (1979) An analysis of the immune NK cell as to structure, function and biological relevance. *Immunol. Rev.* **44**, 105.

KLEBANOFF S.J., JONG E.C. & HENDERSON W.R., JR (1980) The Eosinophil Peroxidase: Purification and Biological Properties. In MAHMOUD A.A.F. & AUSTEN K.F. (eds), *Proceedings of the Eosinophil Centennial, Brook Lodge, Michigan.* Grune & Stratton Inc., New York.

MACKANESS G.B. & BLANDEN R.V. (1967) Cellular immunity. *Progr. Allergy* **11**, 89.

MACLENNAN L.C. (1972) Antibody in the induction and inhibition of a lymphocyte cytotoxicity. *Transplant. Rev.* **13**, 67.

MAHMOUD A.A.F. (1980) Eosinophilopoiesis. In MAHMOUD A.A.F. & AUSTEN K.F. (eds), *Proceedings of the Eosinophil Centennial, Brook Lodge, Michigan*. Grune & Stratton Inc., New York.

MAKWANANZI J.B., FRANKS D. & BAKER J.R. (1976) Cytotoxocity of antibody-coated trypanosomes by normal human lymphoid cells. *Nature* **259**, 403.

MÖGENSON S.C. (1979) Role of macrophages in natural resistance to virus infections. *Microbiol. Rev.* **43**, 1.

NAGATA S., TAIRA H., HALL A., JOHNSRUD L., STREULI M., FESODI J., BALL W., CANTELL K. & WEISSMAN C. (1980) Synthesis in *E. coli* of a polypeptide with human leucocyte interferon activity. *Nature* **284**, 316.

NELSON D.S. (ed.) (1976) *Immunobiology of the Macrophage*. Academic Press, New York.

PERLMANN P., PERLMANN H. & WIGZELL H. (1972) Lymphocyte-mediated cytotoxicity *in vitro*. Induction and inhibition by humoral antibody and nature of effector cells. *Transplant. Rev.* **13**, 91.

RIDLEY D.S. & JOPLING W.H. (1966) Classification of leprosy according to immunity. A 5 group system. *Int. J. Leprosy* **34**, 255.

RODER J. & DUVE A.K. (1979) The beige mutation in the mouse selectively impairs natural killer function. *Nature* **278**, 451.

RODER J.C., HALIOTIS T., KLEIN M., KOREC S., JETT J.R., ORTALDO J., HEBERMAN R.B., KATZ P. & FAUCI A.S. (1980) A new immunodeficiency disorder in humans involving NK cells. *Nature* **284**, 558.

SANDERSON L.J. & GLAUERT A.M. (1979) The mechanism of T-cell mediated cytotoxicity. IV. T-cell projections and their role in target cell killing. *Immunology* **36**, 119.

SECHER D.S. & BURKE D.C. (1980) A monoclonal antibody for large-scale purification of human leucocyte interferon. *Nature* **285**, 446.

SONNENFELD G. & MERIGAN T.C. (1979) The role of interferon in virus infections. *Springer Seminars in Immunopath.* **2**, 311.

TURK S.L. (1976) Leprosy as a model of sub-acute and chronic immunologic diseases. *J. Invest. Dermat.* **67**, 457.

Chapter 16
Immunity Deficiency

16.1 Introduction

Undue susceptibility to infection is often the first indication of an immunity deficiency syndrome. The spectrum of defects ranges from major constitutional abnormalities which are life-threatening to relatively minor deficiency states. The latter are compatible with health in hygienic environments but in communities where there is malnutrition and frequent contact with pathogens they can prove fatal.

Studies on immunity deficiency diseases have added greatly to our understanding of the immune system and its many effector mechanisms. As our understanding of immunology has improved it has become possible to define the precise nature of the defects in immune deficiency.

16.2 Clinical tests useful in the detection of immunity deficiency

The diagnosis of immunity deficiency rests largely on the clinical findings of recurrent fungal and bacterial infections, septicaemia, failure to thrive and poor response to antibiotic therapy. The precise nature of the defect can be determined by a variety of tests of immunological function which are briefly discussed below. For further details see Brown (1981).

16.2.1 Immunoglobulin levels

All the immunoglobulin classes can be easily detected and quantified in most tissue fluids using immunoelectrophoresis, single radial diffusion or radioimmunoassay. The latter method can detect levels as low as 50 pg/ml and is the preferred assay for detecting IgE.

Infants in the first few months of life can synthesize all the immunoglobulin classes but only IgM and IgA levels can be satisfactorily measured since any IgG made is masked by the high (but declining) levels of maternal IgG (Fig. 16.1). Immunoglobulin levels vary with age and it is usual to make several measurements at different intervals comparing them to a normal growth curve. This is especially true for IgA which can show a twofold increase in concentration around puberty.

The ability to make specific antibodies can be determined either from the levels of natural blood group antibodies or following immunization with antigens such as tetanus toxoid or bacteriophage.

16.2.2 B lymphocyte levels and function

Cells of the B lymphocyte lineage in bone marrow, lymphoid tissue and peripheral blood can be distinguished at different stages of maturation. Pre-B cells can be detected in bone marrow as they have a high spontaneous uptake of thymidine and contain cytoplasmic but not surface immunoglobulin. Mature B cells and their surface immunoglobulin isotypes can be detected by techniques based on the binding of suitably labelled class-specific antibody to the B lymphocyte surface. By applying these tests to patients with hypogammaglobulinaemia the various blocks in B cell differentiation have been defined.

There are several assays for B cell function most of which rely on stimulating B lymphocytes with mitogen or specific antigen. The response is measured either in terms of the number of antibody-secreting cells generated (usually by some form of haemolytic plaque assay) or by detecting newly synthesized antibody in the superna-

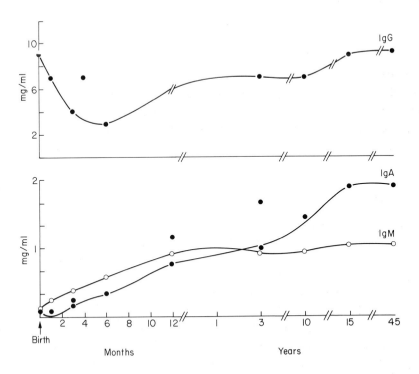

Fig. 16.1. Serum immunoglobulin levels in normal individuals of different age groups. (Adapted from Hobbs (1975), see Turner, 1977.)

tant. Pokeweed mitogen is the most used mitogen for human B lymphocytes and acts as a T-dependent polyclonal B-cell activator. Although polyclonal activation is a measure of B-cell function it may not represent the normal pathway of T–B cell cooperation in response to specific antigen. In the mitogen response there is no difference in the T-cell help given either by allogeneic or syngeneic T cells. Growth factors derived from stimulated T cells (see Chapter 10.3.2) have also been used to augment the human B lymphocyte response *in vitro*.

16.2.3 T lymphocyte levels and function

The most widely used assay for enumerating human T cells is the sheep cell rosette assay wherein human T cells form rosettes *in vitro* with sheep erythrocytes. Heteroantisera, alloantisera and monoclonal antibodies directed against T cell subsets, however, are proving more useful. In addition to enumerating T cells they can be used to isolate distinct T cell subsets which can then be functionally tested *in vitro*. Both helper and suppressor T cells in humans have been defined by this approach.

Delayed hypersensitivity as measured by intradermal skin tests is the most reliable assay for the detection of defects in cell-mediated immunity. Patients are designated anergic if they fail to produce a delayed skin reaction to intradermal inoculation of a range of antigens such as tuberculin (PPD), candida antigen, streptokinase–streptodornase and mumps test antigen. It is important to realize that the full expression of delayed hypersensitivity is the last step in a number of events involving antigen–lymphocyte–macrophage interactions and positive skin tests indicate that the entire T cell/macrophage axis is intact. Patients have been known to fail to give a good skin reaction because of a macrophage defect and yet have functional antigen-specific T cells which can proliferate to antigen *in vitro*.

16.2.4 Tests of complement and phagocytic function

Repeated bacterial infections are often an indication of a phagocytic defect. This may be extrinsic and due to defective complement function or low numbers of polymorphonuclear cells induced by other disease processes or drugs. Intrinsic defects in phagocytic cells may vary from a failure to undergo proper chemotaxis, phagocytosis or to induce intracellular killing of phagocytosed bacteria.

Most of the serum complement components can be readily assayed both antigenically and functionally. The levels of the individual components can be detected antigenically by rocket electrophoresis using antisera specific for the individual components. Functional assays are based on haemolytic techniques usually involving haemolytic radial diffusion assays in agarose gels containing red cells. By appropriate choice of haemolytic indicator system the total classical pathway, total alternative pathway and individual components can be separately measured (Lachmann & Hobart. 1976).

There are a number of tests for the detection of intrinsic phagocytic defects. These range from relatively simple assays which measure phagocytosis of labelled particles, chemotaxis or ability to produce intracellular killing. A useful diagnositc test which correlates with the ability of cells to produce intracellular killing is the nitroblue tetrazolium dye reduction test. Nitroblue tetrazolium is a clear compound which, on reduction within polymorphonuclear cells, forms a blue dye. This can be extracted and measured spectrophotometrically. The amount of reduction is correlated with the intracellular level of metabolic activity and oxidative capacity. Failure to reduce nitroblue tetrazolium is characteristic of the neutrophils of patients with chronic granulomatous disease (see 16.3.3).

16.3 Immunity deficiency syndromes

Immunity deficiency syndromes exhibit a variety of genetic and immunological features which have permitted a preliminary classification of the various disorders (Cooper et al., 1974; Hayward, 1980). They have been broadly classified into primary

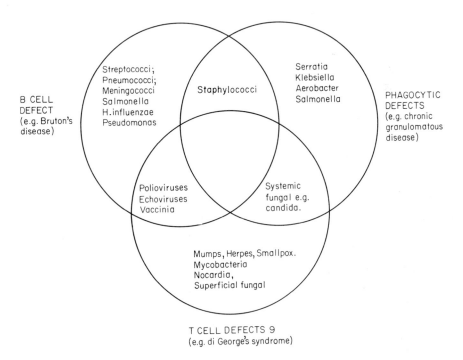

Fig. 16.2. A summary of the types of infection commonly associated with immunity deficiency states.

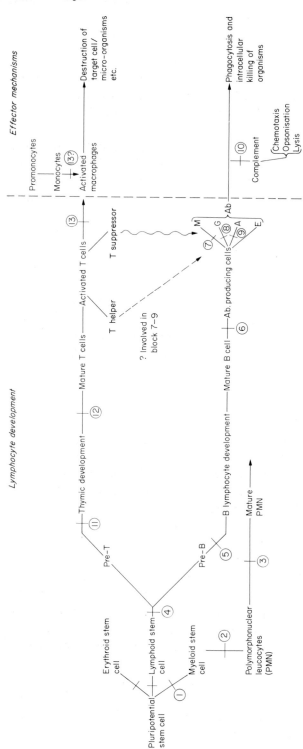

Fig. 16.3. Sites of defects in lymphocyte development and in effector mechanisms associated with defects in immunity.

immunodeficiency states where there is a major defect in the development of particular aspects of an immunity mechanism either in lymphocytes, macrophages, complement or polymorphonuclear cells. Immune response gene defects in man may also be involved in the specific failure or hyporesponsiveness to certain pathogens. Secondary immunity deficiency usually arises through a variety of different causes, including infections, malignant diseases, malnutrition, drug-induced and other autoimmune responses. Infection with measles virus, for example, is often associated with a transient depression of T cell function thought to be due to the destruction of lymphocytes during the viraemic phase. It must be stressed that secondary immunity deficiency diseases are far more common than primary immunity deficiency.

The pattern of infection depends on the nature of the immune defect. Severe impairment of the cell-mediated immune axis (macrophages/T cells) predispose to overwhelming viral and fungal infections usually associated with diarrhoea and a failure to thrive. Defects in the humoral immune axis (antibody/complement/polymorphonuclear leucocytes) often result in infections with pyogenic bacteria, particularly staphylococci and streptococci (Fig. 16.2). The various deficiency states are best discussed in terms of the blocks which occur in the development of the specific components of the immune system and their associated effector mechanisms. All the blocks described below are indicated on Fig. 16.3.

16.3.1 General haemopoietic deficiency (Fig. 16.3, Block 1)

Reticular dysgenesis is a familial defect in which all types of leucocytes (lymphocytes, granulocytes, macrophages) are greatly reduced in number or absent. Affected infants usually die of overwhelming infection after birth and none have been reported to survive longer than 90 days. Bone-marrow transplantation offers hope for the successful treatment of this abnormality.

16.3.2 Selective defects of polymorphonuclear leucocytes (Fig. 16.3, Block 2)

Patients with neutrophil defects suffer predominantly from stomatitis, vaginitis, otitis, mastoiditis and skin infections which suggest that these cells are particularly important for the protection of exposed surfaces. Several varieties of hereditary neutropenias have been described, some of which have a fluctuating neutropenia. These patients are capable of monocyte production and some may have monocytosis. Infections usually appear if blood neutrophils remain below 500 per mm^3.

An interesting example of an extrinsic neutrophil disorder has been reported in patients with periodontal disease caused by *Capnocytophaga*, a gram-negative anaerobe. Neutrophils from these patients have abnormal morphology and function although their ability to phagocytose particles and reduce nitroblue tetrazolium is normal. A dialysable substance recovered from sonicates of the capnocytophaga was found to irreversibly induce the same defect in normal neutrophils *in vitro*. After elimination of the micro-organism from the patients their neutrophils returned to normal. Since a substantial fraction of the daily turnover of neutrophils takes place via the oral cavity the ability of certain micro-organisms to secrete substances which depress neutrophil function can clearly predispose to periodontitis and possibly affect neutrophil functions at other sites (Shurin *et al.*, 1979).

The lazy leucocyte syndrome is characterized by a moderate neutropenia and a decrease in random mobility and chemotactic responsiveness of PMN leucocytes. Phagocytic and bacteriocidal capacity of the cells is normal. The underlying biochemical defect is unknown.

Syndromes associated with monocyte defects have not yet been clearly defined (see Wiscott–Aldrich syndrome 16.3.8). One family with severe acquired monocytopenia has been reported where the predominant symptoms were chronic fungal infections, recurrent chest infections and giant warts (Kaur *et al.*, 1972).

16.3.3 *Phagocytic defects (Fig. 16.3, Block 3)*

There are a number of phagocytic defects some of which are due to intrinsic defects in phagocytosis or the killing mechanisms of phagocytic cells (Table 16.1). Others arise through abnormalities in the complement system which may lead to a failure of chemotaxis or opsonization.

Chronic granulomatous disease is an X-linked recessive disorder in which all

Table 16.1. Combined phagocyte defects in man

Disease	Comments
Chronic granulomatous disease (CGD)	Lack of H_2O_2 production, all patients clinically affected, carriers normal
Chediak–Higashi syndrome	Giant lysosomes, decreased killing power, function improved by ascorbate
Myeloperoxidase deficiency	Most patients healthy
Glucose-6-phosphate deficiency	Lack of H_2O_2 production, clinically similar to CGD
Lipochrome histiocytosis	Phagocyte defect similar to CGD, patients have rheumatoid arthritis as well as recurrent infections

phagocytes fail to generate superoxide O_2^- and H_2O_2. The most frequent infections in these patients are with catalase-producing bacteria rather than the encapsulated pyogenic bacteria which are common in other defects in the 'humoral axis'. The disease is characterized by recurrent skin infections, chronic lymphoadenopathy with discharging sinuses, osteomyelitis, pneumonia and liver abscesses. Affected boys may survive beyond adolescence if carefully treated with antibiotics.

Chediak–Higashi disease is an autosomal recessive disorder characterized by giant lysosomes in granulocytes, macrophages and other cells. The patients are moderately neutropenic and suffer from pyogenic infections which can be fatal. Intracellular killing mechanisms are poor. Phagocytic function is greatly improved by ascorbic acid and preliminary clinical experience suggests that the patients may also benefit from treatment with high doses of ascorbic acid. These patients also lack natural killer cells (NK) which may play a rôle in tumour surveillance (Roder et al., 1980). Although Chediak–Higashi disease is rare 85 per cent of the patients recorded in the literature develop lymphoma-like tumours during the later stages of the disease (Blume & Wolff, 1972).

Myeloperoxidase deficiency of PMN leucocytes and monocytes has been reported to be an autosomal recessive disorder which in some patients predisposes to systemic candidiasis (Lehrer & Cline, 1969).

16.3.4 Combined deficiency of B and T lymphocytes (SCID) (Fig. 16.3, Block 4)

These diseases have been claimed to cause a significant proportion of post-natal mortality. In severe form there is profound depletion of lymphocytes to less than 1,000 per mm^3, but normal phagocytic function. Some patients may have considerable numbers of B lymphocytes and foci of lymphocytes in the gut, spleen and lymph nodes. The disease often presents during the first 3 months of life with diarrhoea and failure to thrive. Fungal infections are usually prominent. Other common pathogens in these children include E. coli, staphylococci, and pneumocystis carinii. The patients usually die before the age of 2 years unless effective treatment can be given, e.g. bone-marrow grafts or adenosine deaminase replacement (see below).

Both x-linked and autosomal recessive forms of SCID have been reported and approximately 35–50 per cent of patients with the latter lack adenosine deaminase (Giblett et al., 1972 and 1979). This is an enzyme of the purine metabolic pathway which converts adenosine into inosine. About 90 per cent of heterozygous carriers have significantly lower levels than normals. Since adenosine deaminase is absent from all the tissues in the homozygote prenatal diagnosis can also be made. The absence of the enzyme causes a lymphocyte maturation defect although other types of cells differentiate and function normally in these patients. The reason for this is unknown but there is some evidence that the deoxyadenosine which accumulates in these patients is selectively metabolized by lymphocytes by virtue of a kinase found only in these cells. This kinase converts the deoxyadenosine into deoxyadenosine triphosphate which is present in very high levels in lymphocytes from patients with severe combined immunodeficiency. The high level of deoxyadenosine triphosphate prevents the formation of the other three deoxyribonucleotides thus stopping lymphocyte DNA synthesis. Lymphocytes lacking adenosine deaminase can respond to antigen *in vitro* if adenosine deaminase is added to the culture. In one study 5 out of 10 adenosine deaminase-deficient patients responded to treatment with adenosine deaminase and in several other cases marked improvement has followed transfusion with red cells which contain high levels of the enzyme. These are challenging findings for they clearly indicate that there is a relationship between biochemical events and immunological function. Much effort is presently being directed to see if other immunity deficiency states are similarly related to enzymatic abnormalities (see CIBA Symposium, 1979).

16.3.5 Antibody deficiency (Fig. 16.3. Blocks 5–9)

X-linked hypogammaglobulinaemia (Bruton's disease) was the first immunity deficiency disease to be identified. Levels of all five classes of immunoglobulin are low or absent, particularly IgA and IgM. Antibody responses are undetectable but patients have normal T cell function and effective T cell immunity to viruses. Their lymphoid tissue is hypoplastic; tonsils, adenoids and lymph nodes being characteristically small and lacking any germinal centres or plasma cells. Since these patients have normal levels of pre-B cells in the bone marrow the block in B cell development (Fig. 16.3, Block 5) occurs after the pre-B cell stage and before the development of mature B cells expressing surface IgM (Pearl, 1978). Infections usually occur between the age of 6 months and 2 years and commonly involve pyogenic bacteria. Passive administration of whole gammaglobulin or whole plasma keeps most of these patients relatively free of infection.

Variable hypogammaglobulinaemia is different from the above in that patients with this disease have normal levels of B lymphocytes but these fail to differentiate into plasma cells (Fig. 16.3, Block 6). The block in B cell maturation in these patients may also be selective for given immunoglobulin classes (Fig.16.3. Blocks 7, 8, 9).

16.3.6 Complement deficiencies (Fig. 16.3, Block 10)

In view of the importance of the complement system in the opsonization, chemotaxis and lysis of pathogens it is not surprising that complement deficiencies are often detected in patients with repeated infections or septicaemia. The severity and nature of the immunity defect in patients with isolated complement deficiencies varies

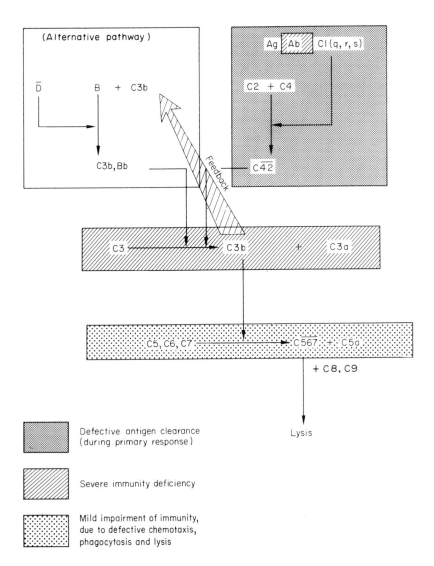

Fig. 16.4. Functional disturbances arising from inherited complement deficiencies. Group 1 (fine stippling): deficiencies of the classical pathway at the C1, C4 or C2 level predisposes to defective antigen clearance (or handling). Group 2 (cross-hatched): primary or secondary deficiency of C3 results in severe immunity deficiency resembling agammaglobulinaemia. Group 3 (coarse stippling): deficiency of C5, C6 or C7 found in healthy individuals, but sometimes associated with immunity impairment, possibly due to phagocytic or chemotactic defects.

depending on which component is missing (Fig. 16.4) (see Chapter 5.5). Deficiencies of the early components of the classical pathway (C1, C4 and C2) are usually associated with defective antigen clearance. The commonest deficiency is in C2 and although about half the affected individuals are healthy the remainder suffer from immune complex disease, notably systemic lupus erythematosus. Although the overall incidence of C2 deficiency in the normal healthy population is low (about 1/10,000) the incidence in patients with systemic lupus erythematosus is about 1/200. No deficiencies of the alternative pathway have yet been described. Although it can be argued that such deficiencies would be life threatening it must be pointed out that routine screening of patients for alternative pathway components is not widely practised.

Since C3 occupies a central role in the biological functions of complement, deficiencies in this component result in severe immunity deficiency. C3 deficiency can be due to either a primary defect in the synthesis of C3 or be indirectly associated with Factor I deficiency. In the latter group of patients absence of the control protein results in uncontrolled activation of the alternative pathway via the C3b feedback cycle (see Chapter 3.4) which results in low levels of C3 and Factor B. Deficiencies of the terminal pathway in both man and animals is compatible with survival. In man such deficiencies are often associated with repeated infections by Neisseria (usually meningococcal meningitis or septicaemia). Association of these deficiencies with Neisseria infections is probably due to the fact that these organisms are normally lysed in the circulation.

16.3.7 Isolated failure of T lymphocyte differentiation (Fig. 16.3, Block 11 and 12)

Several clinical types of selective T lymphocyte deficiency have been identified and are listed in Table 16.2.

di George's syndrome (Fig. 16.3, Block 11) is an abnormality of the embryogenesis of the third and fourth pharyngeal pouches. It results in failure to develop the thymus and parathyroid glands as well as severe cardiovascular abnormalities. T lymphocyte levels are low and cell-mediated immunity defective. Although the anatomical defect is similar to that of nude or thymectomized mice, in some patients

Table 16.2. Different types of selective T lymphocyte deficiency

Complete di George's syndrome (thymic aplasia)
Partial di George's syndrome (thymic hypoplasia)
T cell dysfunction:
   associated with nucleoside phosphorylase deficiency
   associated with short-limbed dwarfism
   associated with autoimmune haemolytic anaemia
? lymphokine deficiency syndrome(s) (e.g. late onset hypogammaglobulinaemia)

the serum IgA level is normal and their ability to produce antibodies is only marginally affected, suggesting that the T cell defect is only partial.

The first symptoms are neonatal tetany brought on by the parathyroid defect, usually followed by candidiasis and other infections characteristic of deficiency of the 'cellular axis'. Correction of the immunological defect by thymus grafting has been reported. Variants with minor degrees of T cell deficiency have also occured, sometimes with spontaneous improvement.

In ataxia telangectasia there is also thymic hypoplasia with defective T cell function and a selective IgA deficiency.

Purine nucleoside phosphorylase (Fig. 16.3, Block 12) catalyses the interconversion of adenine, hypoxanthine and guanine into their respective nucleosides. The discovery that many cases of severe combined immunity deficiency were due to adenosine deaminase deficiency stimulated a search for defects in enzymes of the purine, pyrimidine or nucleic acid metabolic pathways. Surprisingly several patients with defective T cell functions but normal B cell function were discovered (Giblett, 1975; Stoop et al., 1977) and there are now at least nine patients with homozygous deficiency of this enzyme. They develop increasingly severe T lymphocyte deficiency which starts to give rise to infections between the age of 2 and 5 years. In contrast to adenosine deaminase deficiency, B cells are not significantly affected in patients with purine nucleoside phosphorylase deficiency, and their antibody responses are normal. Purine nucleoside phosphorylase is less than 1 per cent of normal in all tissues studied and heterozygous carriers have approximately half normal levels. The mechanism whereby lack of purine nucleoside phosphorylase causes immune deficiency is unknown. It is possible that high intracellular levels of deoxyguanosine triphosphate inhibit DNA synthesis. It is not clear why purine nucleoside phosphorylase deficiency should only affect maturation of T lymphocytes. Preliminary clinical experience suggests that administration of the enzyme either native or in the form of irradiated red cells from normal donors may prevent the deterioration of T-cell function in patients deficient in purine nucleoside phosphorylase (Polmar et al., 1976; Zegers et al., 1979).

16.3.8 Lymphokine deficiency (Fig. 16.3, Block 13)

Patients with chronic mucocutaneous candidiasis are sometimes incapable of producing T-cell lymphokines (e.g. MIF) in vitro. Although this may explain their condition it is a poorly worked out area of immunity deficiency whose future development will await the immunochemical characterization of lymphokines.

16.3.9 Combined T and B lymphocyte dysfunction of unknown causes

The Wiscott–Aldrich syndrome, an X-linked recessive condition, is characterized by eczema, thrombocytopenia and recurrent infection. The thrombocytopenia is caused by autoantibodies and can be improved by splenectomy.

Except for IgM which may be low, serum immunoglobulin levels are normal but the patients fail to make antibodies to polysaccharide antigens. There is indirect evidence that the defect is at the level of antigen presentation (Blaese *et al.*, 1968). The lymphocytes of these patients fail to respond to antigens even though their responses to non-specific mitogens may be normal. There is also a progressive loss of cell-mediated immunity.

Finally certain antibody deficiencies and autoimmune disorders are associated with dysfunction of both T and B lymphocytes, but it is by no means clear whether these are primary or secondary abnormalities.

References

BLAESE R.M., STROBER W., BROWN R.S. & WALDMANN T.A. (1968) The Wiskott–Aldrich syndrome, a disorder with a possible defect in antigen processing or recognition. *Lancet* i, 1054.

BLUME R.S. & WOLFF S.M. (1972) The Chediak–Higashi syndrome: studies in four patients and a review of the literature. *Medicine* 51, 247.

BROWN D.L. (1981) Interpretation of tests of immune function. In LACHMANN P.J. & PETERS D.K. (eds), *Clinical Aspects of Immunology*, 4th ed. Blackwell Scientific Publications, Oxford.

CIBA SYMPOSIUM (1979) *Enzyme Defects and Immune Dysfunction. CIBA Foundation Symposium No. 68* (NS). Excerpta Medica, Amsterdam.

COOPER M.D., FAULK W.P., FUDENBERG H.H., GOOD R.A., HITZIG W., KUNKEL H.G., ROITT I.M., ROSEN F.S., SELIGMANN M., SOOTHILL J.F. & WEDGEWOOD R.J. (1971) Primary immunodeficiencies, Meeting report of the 2nd International Workshop on Primary Immunodeficiency Diseases in Man. *Clin. Immunol. & Immunopathol.* 2, 416.

GIBLETT E.R. (1979) Adenosine deaminase and purine nucleoside phosphorylase deficiency: how they were discovered and what they may mean. In *Enzyme Defects and Immune Dysfunction. CIBA Foundation Symposium No. 68* (NS), p. 3. Excerpta Medica, Amsterdam.

GIBLETT E.R., AMMANN A.J., WARA D.W., SANDMAN R. & DIAMOND L.K. (1975) Nucleoside–phospholipase deficiency in a child with severely defective T-cell immunity and normal B-cell immunity. *Lancet* i, 1010.

GIBLETT E.R., ANDERSON J.E., COHEN F., POLLARA B. & NEUWISSEN H.J. (1972) Adenosine deaminase deficiency in two patients with severely impaired cellular immunity. *Lancet* ii, 1067.

HAYWARD A.R. (1977) Immunodeficiency. In TURK J. (ed.), *Current Topics in Immunology*. Arnold Publishers Ltd., London.

HAYWARD A.R. (1981) Immunity Deficiency. In LACHMANN P.J. & PETERS D.K. (eds), *Clinical Aspects of Immunology*, 4th ed. Blackwell Scientific Publications, Oxford.

KAUR J., CATOVSKY D., VALDIMARRSSON H., JENSSON O. & SHIERS A.F.D. (1972) Familial acute myeloid leukaemia with acquired Pelger-Huët anomaly and aneuploidy of C group. *Brit. Med. J.* 4, 327.

LACHMANN P.J. (1979) Complement. In SELA M. (ed.), *The Antigens*, Vol. 5, p. 6. Academic Press, New York.

LACHMANN P.J. & HOBART M.J. (1976) Complement Technology 1.6. In WEIR D.M. (ed.), *Handbook of Experimental Immunology*. Blackwell Scientific Publications, Oxford.

LEHRER R.I. & CLINE M.J. (1969) Leucocyte myeloperoxidase deficiency and disseminated candidiasis. The role of myeloperoxidase in resistance to *Candida* infection. *J. Clin. Invest.* **48**, 1478.

PEARL E.R., VOGLER L.B., OKOS A.J., CRIST W.M., LAWTON A.R. & COOPER M.D. (1978) B lymphocyte precursors in human bone marrow: an analysis of normal individuals and patients with antibody deficiency states. *J. Immunol.* **120**. 1169.

POLMAR S.H., STERN R.C., SCHWARTZ A.L., WETZLER E.M., CHASE P.A. & HIRSCHORN R. (1976) Enzyme replacement therapy for adenosine deaminase deficiency and severe combined immunodeficiency. *New Engl. J. Med.* **295**, 1337.

RODER J.C., HALIOTIS T., KLEIN M., KOREC S., JETT J.R., ORTALDO J., HEBERMAN R.B., KATZ P. & FAUCI A.S. (1980) A new immunodeficiency disorder in humans involving NK cells. *Nature* **284**, 553.

SHURIN S.B., SOCRANSKY S.S., SWEENEY E. & STOSSEL T.P. (1979) A neutrophil disorder induced by capnocytophaga, a dental micro-organism. *New. Engl. J. Med.* **301**, 849.

STOOP J.W., ZEGERS B., HENDRICKX G.F., SIEGENBEEK D., VAN HENKELOM L.H., STAAL G.E.J., DE BREE P.K., WADMAN S.K. & BALLILIEUX R.E. (1977) Purine nucleoside phosphorylase deficiency associated with selective cellular immunodeficiency. *New Engl. J. Med.* **296**, 651.

TURNER M.W. (1977) The Immunoglobulins. In HOLBOROW E.J. & REEVES W.G. (eds), *Immunology in Medicine*, p. 81. Academic Press, New York.

ZEGERS B.J.M., STOOP J.W., STAAL G.E.J. & WADMAN S.K. (1979) An approach to the restoration of T-cell function in a purine nucleoside phosphorylase-deficient patient. In *Enzyme Defects and Immune Dysfunction. CIBA Foundation Symposium No. 68* (NS), p. 231. Excerpta Medica, Amsterdam.

Chapter 17
Autoimmune Disease

17.1 Introduction

There are at least two mechanisms for maintaining unresponsiveness to self. The first is by specific deletion of self-reactive clones and the second is by suppression (see Chapter 13). Autoimmune disease is thought to occur when either or both these mechanisms fail.

17.2 Mechanisms for breaking self tolerance

Since many responses are thymus dependent, tolerance will exist if the helper T cell population alone is absent. In normal healthy individuals antigen-binding, self-reactive B cells and low titres of autoantibodies are not uncommon. The origin of self-reactive B cells is not clear but they may represent cells which have failed to meet self antigen at a critical phase in ontogeny or alternatively represent somatic mutants of mature B cells specific for foreign antigens. There are four ways in which these self-reactive B cells may become activated.

17.2.1 Polyclonal activation

High concentrations of polyclonal activators such as lipopolysaccharides and high molecular weight dextrans will activate B cells irrespective of the specificity of the immunoglobulin receptor on the B cell surface (see Chapter 8.4 to 8.6). Injection of mice with LPS results in the production of IgM autoantibodies to a wide variety of antigens including such self antigens as single-stranded DNA, IgG, thymocytes and red cells. The spectrum of autoantibody produced reflects the specificities present in the population of cells which react with the polyclonal activator.

Polyclonal activation *in vivo* is not a perversion of the cellular immunologist since a similar activation can occur during certain infections. Epstein–Barr (EB) virus is a T cell independent polyclonal activator of human B lymphocytes and following infection (infectious mononucleosis) a wide spectrum of antibodies are produced. Only a small fraction of the IgM and IgG elevation is specific antiviral antibody and autoantibodies to smooth muscle, nuclear proteins, lymphocytes and red cells can also be detected.

Polyclonal activation occurs in parasitic infections. Grossly elevated IgM levels and a high incidence of rheumatoid factors and antinuclear antibodies are commonly found in patients (and mice) with protozoal infections (e.g. infection with *Plasmodium berghei yoelli* in mice).

17.2.2 Non-specific helper factors

T cell activation results in the production of a variety of lymphokines (see Chapter 10.3.2 and Table 10.3). Lymphokines can replace T cells in the antibody response to certain T cell-dependent antigens. Thus in situations where there is excessive T cell activation a wide variety of autoreactive B cells may become activated.

17.2.3 Cross-reactive antigens

Autoreactive B cells may also be activated by foreign antigens which carry epitopes cross-reactive with self. The foreign epitopes act as helper determinants for the T cell dependent activation of autoreactive B cells. In man, high titre cold agglutinins to the I blood group arise as an occasional complication of *Mycoplasma pneumoniae* infections. The autoantibody persists for only a few days but is associated with a short-lived and sometimes severe haemolytic episode. The cold agglutinin is thought to be a cross-reacting autoantibody arising from the response to I-like determinants on the mycoplasma. Anti-I cold agglutinins also develop in rabbits injected with group C streptococcal vaccine. Here there is clear evidence of cross-reactivity of the anti-I for both the I blood group substance and the immunodominant sugar moiety of the group C carbohydrate.

17.2.4 Absence of T-cell suppression

Although there is come evidence that T cell suppression is involved in maintaining self tolerance the mechanisms are not well characterized. In systemic lupus erythematosus in mice it has been claimed that absence of a suppressor T cell subset leads to B cell hyperreactivity and elevated levels of autoantibodies (see 16.4.1). In mice autoreactivity to bromelin-treated mouse red cells arise spontaneously in cultures of spleen cells (Cunningham, 1975; Ramshaw *et al.*, 1979). One explanation for the spontaneous development of autoreactivity may be the relative instability of suppressor cells which disappear in culture thus allowing autoreactive B cells to mature. Clinical situations which result in the abrogation of the normal suppressive control could conceivably result in enhanced antibody formation.

17.3 Autoreactivity and pathogenesis

There is a large and ever growing list of diseases in man which are associated with the presence of autoantibodies to self antigens (Table 17.1). In many cases the rôle of the autoantibody in the pathogenesis is not proven. It is important to distinguish between those cases, where the autoantibodies arise after a primary tissue-damaging event (e.g. anti-myocardial antibodies after myocardial infarction) and where the pathology is directly due to cytotoxic autoantibody or autoreactive T cells. Early studies of both thyrotoxicosis and myasthenia gravis in man showed that many of the clinical features of these diseases could be passively transferred to mice by serum IgG from affected individuals. More convincing proof has been derived from the detection of the autoimmune disease in neonates following the passive transfer of maternal IgG to the fetus during the last trimester of pregnancy. Neonatal thyrotoxicosis, myasthenia gravis and idiopathic thrombocytopenic purpura can all result from the placental transfer of maternal IgG although only a minority of infants from diseased mothers are usually affected. Since maternal IgG is catabolized the autoimmune syndrome is transient and disappears in 6–12 weeks. A rare example of this 'experiment of nature' is the placental transfer of nephritic factor (autoantibody to the C3b, Bb complex, see Chapter 3.4.2) which produces the expected complement abnormalities in the neonate (Davis *et al.*, 1978; see Chapter 3.4.2).

With many autoimmune haemolytic anaemias there is no doubt that the autoantibody itself causes the disease since immunosuppressive therapy results in the cessation of red-cell destruction. The remaining series of autoantibodies to serum and tissue antigens such as anti-globulins, immunoconglutinins, anti-endocrine cell antibodies, antimyocardial antibodies, anti-actin and antinuclear components, have yet to be shown to be more than just autoreactive phenomena.

17.4 Types of autoimmune diseases

Clinically, the wide spectrum of autoimmune diseases can be considered as 'non-organ specific' and 'organ specific'. In non-organ specific the disease process is widespread and examples include systemic lupus erythematosus (SLE), rheumatoid arthritis and Sjögren's syndrome. Organ-specific diseases include autoimmune endocrine diseases and autoimmune haemolytic anaemia.

SLE is a spontaneously occurring autoimmune disease in some species (mice, dogs and man). Because there are extensive clinical and serological similarities in murine and human SLE this disease will now be considered in some detail.

17.4.1 *Autoimmune (SLE-like) mice*

Four strains of mice die prematurely from severe systemic autoimmune disease (see review by Dixon, 1979).

(a) *The New Zealand black mouse.* The dominant feature in this strain is an

Table 17.1. Self antigens eliciting the formation of autoantibodies in man

Antigen	Main disease associations
1. *Plasma proteins*	
IgG	Rheumatoid arthritis, Sjögren's syndrome, SLE, scleroderma, chronic immune complex diseases
Thyroglobulin	Chronic (allergic) thyroiditis, thyrotoxicosis
*Factor VIII	SLE (acquired haemophilia syndrome)
C3b, C4b	Rheumatoid arthritis
$\overline{C3b,Bb}$	Dense deposit disease (mesangiocapillary glomerulonephritis)
2. *Gut secretion*	
*Intrinsic factor	Pernicious anaemia
3. *Cell membrane antigens*	
*Red cells	Autoimmune haemolytic anaemias
*Platelets	Idiopathic thrombocytopenic purpura
*Neutrophils	Autoimmune neutropenia, SLE
Lymphocytes	SLE, juvenile rheumatoid arthritis
Neurons	Cerebral SLE
Cardiac muscle	Acute rheumatic fever
*Epidermal cells	Pemphigus vulgaris
*Spermatozoa	Post-vasectomy, male and female infertility
Zona pellucida of ovum	Female infertility
4. *Functional membrane receptors*	
*TSH receptor	Thyrotoxicosis
*Insulin receptor	Insulin-resistant diabetes (associated with acanthosis nigricans)
*Acetyl choline receptor	Myasthenia gravis
Parathyroid hormone receptor	Uraemia
5. *Extracellular antigens*	
*Renal and alveolar basement membranes	Goodpasture's syndrome
*Epidermal basement membrane	Bullous pemphigoid
*Ocular proteins	Sympathetic ophthalmia
6. *Intracellular antigens*	
ss-DNA	SLE, rheumatoid arthritis, chronic active hepatitis, malaria and many chronic inflammatory and infective diseases

Table 17.1 cont.

Antigen	Main disease associations
6. *Intracellular antigens cont.*	
ds-DNA	SLE, chronic active hepatitis
Ribonucleoprotein	Mixed connective tissue disease
Acidic nucleoproteins	SLE
Nucleosomes (the DNA–histone subunits of chromatin)	SLE
Actin	Chronic active hepatitis (smooth muscle antibodies)
Mitochondria	Primary biliary cirrhosis, Sjögren's syndrome, SLE
Microsomal	
(i) Thyroid	Chronic (allergic) thyroiditis
(ii) Parietal cell	Chronic gastritis and pernicious anaemia
Adrenal	Addison's disease
Islet cell cytoplasm	(i) Diabetes mellitus as part of the 'polyendocrine syndrome' (ii) Recent onset juvenile diabetes mellitus
Melanophores	Vitiligo

* In these diseases there is either unequivocal or very strong presumptive evidence that the antibody is the cause of the disease.

IgG-mediated autoimmune haemolytic anaemia which proves fatal by 20 months. There is marked lymphoid hyperplasia (as there is in all lupus mice) and a tendency to lymphoma. Autoantibodies to DNA, antinuclear antibodies and immune complex damage to the renal glomerulus are minor features.

(b) *The New Zealand black–New Zealand white hybrid mouse (NZB × NZW)* F_1. The disease in this F_1 hybrid closely resembles severe human SLE. Autoantibodies to nuclear antigens, double- and single-stranded DNA and antibody to the envelope glycoprotein of murine retroviruses begin to arise at about 6 months of age. The high levels which are reached give rise to circulating immune complexes which localize both in vessel walls and the renal glomerulus to produce type II and type III tissue-damaging reactions (see Chapter 15). The mice usually die at about 9–12 months of age from membranoproliferative glomerulonephritis. Males survive about 6 months longer and show less severe pathological changes than females, thus showing that sex hormones modulate the pace of the disease. Similarly, if female mice are ovarectomized and given 5-α dihydrotestosterone implants they achieve male longevity (Roubinian *et al.*, 1979), though there is no sustained reduction in antinuclear or

DNA antibodies. The mechanism of the testosterone-induced protection is not yet understood but the higher incidence of the disease in females parallels the situation with SLE in man.

(c) *The MRl/1 and B×SB mice*. Two further lupus strains have recently been described (Andrews *et al.*, 1978). Autoimmune disease in both male and female MRL/1 and male B×SB progresses more rapidly than in the F_1 described in 16.4.1(b), with mice dying within 5 months from proliferative glomerulonephritis. The MRL/1 strain have high levels of circulating immune complexes, cryoglobulins and rheumatoid factors. They also develop a chronic arthritis of the hind legs and feet which has histological resemblance to rheumatoid arthritis in man. Like the NZB and the (NZB×NZW) F_1 the new strains develop marked lymphoid hyperplasia, and half the MRL/1 mice develop monoclonal immunoglobulins.

The most consistent immunological finding in all the lupus strains is a markedly elevated IgM level (5–10 times normal) due to B cell hyperreactivity. The spectrum of elevated IgM antibodies (anti-hapten, anti-DNA) is consistent with polyclonal B cell activation arising from an intrinsic B cell defect. It has also been claimed that the NZB mouse lacks a T cell subpopulation (Lyt 123^+, Qa 1^+) which is involved in suppressing helper T cells (see review by Cantor & Gershon, 1979; and Chapter 10.4). It is not clear whether the absence of this T cell subset is the primary cause of the disease or whether it is secondary as a result of the formation of autoantibody to these T cells.

There is no simple genetic explanation for the susceptibility of these four genetically distinct strains of mice to SLE. Each strain seems to have a series of non-complementary defects and cross-breeding experiments often result in healthy rather than sick offspring. There is no single disease marker and the conclusion is that there are multiple gene dosage effects.

Another characteristic feature in SLE-like mice is the presence of high levels of antibodies to the envelope glycoproteins (gp 70) of xenotropic retroviruses. This has led to the suggestion that SLE has a viral aetiology, but there is no direct association between endogenous retroviruses and the disease. Retrovirus infection is common in many non-autoimmune strains and crosses between NZB, which are 'high-virus' mice and SWR which are 'non-virus' mice have shown that the virus genes segregate independently of the ability to make anti-DNA antibodies and to develop proliferative glomerulonephritis (Datta *et al.*, 1978). The accelerating factor in the disease is not the virus itself but the enhanced antibody response to gp 70 which in the presence of antigen results in immune complex disease.

17.4.2 SLE in man

There are many clinical and serological similarities between human and murine SLE (Quimby & Schwartz, 1978). In man, SLE is a multi-autoantibody disease and much of the pathology arises from immune complex damage. Immune complexes localize in small vessels causing vasculitis, non-erosive polyarthritis and membranoproliferative glomerulonephritis. Many studies have tried to establish which immune complexes, as defined by antigen specificity, class and affinity, are nephritogenic or vasculitogenic. Current evidence points to the involvement of non-precipitating IgG antibodies to double-stranded DNA. High titre antibody to double-stranded DNA is found only in SLE and can be considered diagnostic. Other antinuclear antibodies, especially antibodies to single-stranded DNA, occur with varying frequency and titre in other rheumatic diseases. In SLE there are also anti-red cell and anti-platelet antibodies which cause haemolytic anaemia and thrombocytopenia. Cytotoxic antibodies to T lymphocytes can also be detected.

There is much evidence to show that the consistent immunological aberration in human SLE is related to a B cell hyperreactivity. There is progressive hypergamma-globulinaemia during the active phase of the disease (IgG levels of 40–80 g/l), elevated antibodies to common viruses and a high proportion of IgG and IgA plasma cells in the peripheral blood. There is evidence to suggest that T cell function is abnormal and that suppressor T cells are difficult to detect. It is not clear whether such T cell defects are secondary to the autoantibodies produced to T cells or to the steroid treatment of the patients or both.

There is a high familial incidence of SLE the ratio of affected females to males being 9 : 1. Concordance for SLE in identical twins is about 70 per cent and overall about 12 per cent of SLE patients have an affected relative. Many healthy female relatives and identical twins have some of the serological features of the disease such as hypergammaglobulinaemia and raised levels of antinuclear antibodies. HLA typing has not revealed any strong association between any of the HLA-A, B, C or D alleles and SLE (see Chapter 18).

17.5 Autoantibodies to receptor sites in organ-specific autoimmune disease

There are three, organ-specific, autoimmune diseases which are in part mediated by autoantibody interacting with critical receptor sites on the target organ. The autoantibodies may either be specific for the active site of the receptor and mimic the action of the hormone or neurotransmitter, or bind to other parts of the receptor to produce receptor blockade.

17.5.1 Thyrotoxicosis (Graves' disease)

Hyperthyroidism, the main feature of this disease, is caused by IgG autoantibody to the receptor for thyroid-stimulating hormone (Rees-Smith & Hall, 1974). The antibody binds to the receptor on thyroid follicular cells triggering increased breakdown of thyroglobulin and excessive production of T3 and T4 iodothyronines.

The stimulating effects of the autoantibody can be shown using tissue slices or isolated thyroid follicular cells *in vitro*. Whole IgG, F(ab')$_2$ and Fab' fragments all equally stimulate adenyl cyclase activity in thyroid cells. The ability of the Fab' fragment to do this suggests that the antibody is directed at the active site of the receptor for thyroid-stimulating hormone and mimics its action. Autoantibodies against other parts of the receptor are also produced and these may act to produce receptor blockade.

17.5.2 *Insulin resistance and hyperinsulinaemia*

Severe insulin resistance, hyperinsulinaemia and acanthosis nigricans is a rare syndrome seen in non-Caucasoid females and associated with the production of an IgG autoantibody to the insulin receptor on tissue cells (Kahn, 1979). The autoantibody stimulates glycogen metabolism within fat cells *in vitro* but unlike the autoantibody in thyrotoxicosis this only occurs with whole IgG or F(ab')$_2$ but not Fab' fragments. One of the paradoxical effects of the antibody is to produce hyperglycaemia *in vivo*.

17.5.3 *Myasthenia gravis*

In myasthenia gravis an autoantibody can be detected which binds to the postsynaptic membrane of the motor end plate of voluntary muscle. Studies *in vitro* using α-bungarotoxin (a snake neurotoxin which is a specific ligand for the acetylcholine receptor) have shown that the antibody does not bind to the active site of the acetylcholine receptor since pretreatment of muscle preparations with this antibody does not block the uptake of ^{125}I-labelled α-bungarotoxin. It seems that the whole antibody or F(ab')$_2$ fragments induce a three-fold increase in the turnover of the acetylcholine receptor at the motor end plate. Fab' antibody fails to do this, suggesting that the effect of divalent antibody is via cross-linking of receptors or other structures at the motor end plate. These findings may explain why muscle from myasthenics contains only about 20 per cent of the normal number of acetylcholine receptors. Passive transfer to mice of IgG from myasthenics causes a reduction in the muscle acetylcholine receptors and the development of a myasthenic syndrome within about 10 days.

Acute, subacute and chronic myasthenic syndromes can be induced in laboratory animals by injections of heterologous or homologous motor end plates in complete Freund's adjuvant. The chronic syndromes most closely resemble human myasthenia. The ultrastructural appearance of the motor end plate in the chronic syndromes is like typical myasthenia with widening of the synaptic gap, simplification of the post-synaptic clefts and absence of cellular infiltrates.

Receptor loss does not explain the entire clinical picture (Drachman, 1979). There is a poor correlation between titre of anti-receptor antibody and severity of symptoms; placental transmission of the disease from myasthenic mothers is un-predictable and infrequent.

17.6 Experimental autoimmune disease

Much of the experimental work on autoimmune disease has centred on the induction of the disease following injection of autoantigens in complete Freund's adjuvant. This type of immunization is designed to overcome the normal homeostatic mechanisms and the resulting pathology is clearly due to the production of autoreactive T cells and/or antibody. Although spontaneous clinical autoimmune disease is not associated with immunization in Freund's complete adjuvant this type of approach is nonetheless relevant since it demonstrates the type of pathology which can arise when the normal homeostatic mechanisms are overcome and autoreactive T cells and antibody arise.

There are three classic types of experimental autoimmune diseases which can be induced in experimental animals (Table 17.2). Experimental autoimmune encephalomyelitis is predominantly T-cell mediated and can be induced following immunization with a polypeptide of 9–14 amino acids derived from sequences within the myelin basic protein. The critical amino-acid sequence for the encephalitogenic peptide differs for different species. Onset occurs 15–21 days after immunization and is associated with lymphocytes and macrophage infiltration of Schwann cells and progressive demyelination. The nerve axon remains intact but non-conducting. Passive transfer experiments have shown that the disease is mediated by autoreactive T cells. Rats can be made unresponsive to the induction of experimental encephalomyelitis by prior immunization with the encephalitogenic peptide in incomplete Freund's adjuvant or saline. This mechanism of resistance may be due to tolerance induction in the autoreactive T cells or to the selective stimulation of suppressor cells. The latter possibility is supported by the observation that resistance can be transferred to normal susceptible animals with spleen and lymph node cells. (See review by Paterson, 1977.)

The major clinical interest in experimental autoimmune orchitis in rabbits derives from the fact that some of the clinical findings are similar to those occurring following vasectomy. Experimental autoimmune orchitis is predominantly associated with autoantibodies to sperm and the pathology is due to immune complex tissue damage. Sperm autoantibodies are also present in about 50 per cent of post-vasectomized men but there is no evidence that these cause disease.

Experimental autoimmune thyroiditis appears to be mediated by autoantibody and effector cells, possibly K cells and macrophages, although a rôle for cytotoxic T cells can not be excluded. Experimentally, there is a good correlation between the severity of the infiltration of the thyroid follicles and interstitial tissue with lymphocytes and macrophages and the titre of anti-thyroglobulin antibodies. Furthermore,

Table 17.2. Experimental autoimmune disease

Disease	Inducing antigen	Autoreactivity		Pathology	Other features
		T cells	Auto-antibody		
Experimental autoimmune encephalomyelitis (EAE)	CNS homogenous myelin basic protein (MPB) Encephalitogenic peptide from MBP	+	–	Progressive demyelination and paralysis	Largely T-cell mediated; EAE cannot be induced in 'B' rats; can be passively transferred to normal rats by T but not B cells
Experimental autoimmune orchitis (EAO)	Autologous or homologous testicular extracts	+	+	Damage to sperm-forming cells	In guinea pigs EAO can be transferred by T cells. In rabbits EAO is mainly antibody/K-cell mediated and associated with immune complex disease
Experimental autoimmune thyroiditis (EAT)	Thyroglobulin	–	+	Infiltration of thyroid follicles with lymphocytes and macrophages. High titres of anti-thyroglobulin antibodies	EAT can be passively transferred with antibody and may be K-cell mediated. Analogous to spontaneous thyroiditis in obese strain chickens

experimental autoimmune thyroiditis has been successfully transferred by early sera taken from thyroglobulin-immunized donors to untreated recipients. Spontaneous autoimmune thyroiditis in the obese strain of White Leghorn chicken has many similarities to the experimentally-induced disease in other species. Autoantibodies to thyroglobulin and iodothyronines appear 2 weeks after hatching and a progressive thyroiditis occurs. This is associated with a myxoedema-like state characterized by lethargy, overweight and poor feather formation. The thyroiditis is autoantibody dependent, abrogated by bursectomy and exacerbated by neonatal thymectomy suggesting a form of partial T cell control. The disorder has several similarities to Hashimoto's thyroiditis in man where progressive thyroid failure can be correlated with high levels of anti-thyroid antibodies.

References

ANDREWS B.S., EISENBERG R.A., THEOFILOPOULOS A.N., IZUI S., WILSON C.B., McCONAHEY P.J., MURPHY E.D., ROTHS J.B. & DIXON F.J. (1978) Spontaneous murine lupus-like syndromes. Chemical and immunopathological manifestations in several strains. *J. exp. Med.* **148**, 1198.

CANTOR H. & GERSHON R.K. (1979) Immunological circuits: cellular composition. *Fed. Proc.* **38**, 2058.

CLAGETT J.A. & WEIGLE W.O. (1974) Roles of T and B lymphocytes in the termination of unresponsiveness to autologous thyroglobulin in mice. *J. exp. Med.* **139**, 643.

CUNNINGHAM A.J. (1975) Active suppressor mechanisms maintaining tolerance to some self components. *Nature* **254**, 143.

DATTA S.K., MANNY N., ANDRZEJEWSKI C., ANDRE-SCHWARTZ J. & SCHWARTZ R.S. (1978) Genetic studies of autoimmunity and retrovirus expression in crosses of New Zealand black mice. I. Xenotropic virus. *J. exp. Med.* **147**, 854.

DAVIS A.E., ARNAOUT M.A., ALPER C.A. & ROSEN F.S. (1978) Transfer of C3 nephritic factor from mother to foetus. *New Engl. J. Med.* **297**, 144.

DIXON F.J. (1979) The pathogenesis of murine systemic lupus erythematosus. *Amer. J. Path.* **97**, 10.

DRACHMAN D.B. (1979) Immunopathology of myasthenia gravis. *Fed. Proc.* **38**, 2613.

KAHN C.R. (1979) Auto-antibodies to the insulin receptor: clinical and molecular aspects. *Fed. Proc.* **38**, 2607.

PATERSON P.Y. (1977) Autoimmune neurological disease: experimental animal systems and implications for multiple sclerosis. In TALAL N. (ed.), *Autoimmunity* p. 153. Academic Press, New York.

QUIMBY F.W. & SCHWARTZ R.S. (1978) The etiopathogenesis of systemic lupus erythematosus. *Pathobiol. Ann.* **8**, 35.

RAMSHAW I.A., WOODSWORTH M. & EIDINGER D. (1979) The *in vitro* suppression of spontaneous erythrocyte autoimmune responses with lymphocytes activated with Concanavalin A. *J. Immunol.* **122**, 265.

REES-SMITH B. & HALL R. (1974) Thyroid-stimulating immunoglobulins in Graves' disease. *Lancet* **ii**, 427.

ROUBINIAN J.R., TALAL N., GREEN-SPAN J.S., GOODMAN J.R. & SIITERI P.K. (1979) Delayed androgen treatment prolongs survival in murine lupus. *J. Clin. Invest.* **63**, 902.

Chapter 18
HLA and Disease

18.1 Introduction

The main impetus to the study of the association between the MHS and disease originated from the observations by Lilly (1966) that resistance to viral leukaemogenesis in certain inbred strains of mice was controlled by genes located to the *K* end of the *H-2* complex. Since then, an enormous catalogue of tissue types and disease has been compiled which in humans ranges from such diseases as arthritis to manic depression. In a few cases there is a strong correlation between a particular tissue type and disease susceptibility but in many cases the correlations are less apparent and more difficult to analyse. This is largely due to the fact that conventional tissue typing for the serologically detectable alleles of the MHS is a very imprecise tool with which to approach problems such as infectious disease in an outbred population. This chapter describes some of the principles and pitfalls in this type of work—enthusiasts should turn to the HLA disease registry.

18.2 Detection of HLA disease association

18.2.1 Family studies

Many diseases have a familial history. This could either be due to environmental factors such as food and infections shared by the family or to the inheritance of genes which predispose to the disease. In the latter case a higher frequency of the same disease in identical twins or HLA identical siblings compared to other family members clearly indicates that a genetic element is involved. Family studies can reveal MHS disease association not apparent from population studies. For example, in tuberculoid leprosy, family studies have shown that affected siblings within families often shared HLA alleles whilst at the population level no correlation between tuberculoid leprosy and any HLA allele could be convincingly demonstrated. One explanation is that it is not the HLA specificities themselves which are involved in this disease but some other gene(s) closely linked to *HLA* (van Rood *et al.*, 1980).

283

18.2.2 Population studies

The commonest way to determine MHS disease association at the population level is to compare HLA antigen frequencies between diseased and normal populations. It is important that, in this apparently simple experiment, the same HLA typing sera are used for the test and control groups and that both groups are matched for age, sex and racial origin. If these precautions are not taken then factors other than predisposition to the disease will bias the results.

18.2.3 Expression of results

Two calculations can be made using the data collected from a population study. The first is the significance of any difference found between the patient and the control group and the second is the size of the difference which is often expressed as the relative risk. The latter is a measure of the increased risk of getting the disease if you carry the associated *HLA* gene and is derived as follows:

$$\text{relative risk} = \frac{P_d (1 - P_c)}{P_c (1 - P_d)}$$

where P_d=the frequency of a particular HLA gene in patients and P_c = the frequency of the same gene in the controls. The measurement of the significance of the difference determines if the difference is real. Disease associations with a small increase in relative risk can be highly significant but can only be detected if large numbers of patients and controls are studied. For example, the association of blood group A with cancer of the stomach is highly significant but only has a relative risk of 1.2 compared to group O (Mourant *et al.*, 1978). In determining the significance of a difference in the frequency of the HLA antigens between a normal and disease group one must remember that the usual level of significance of p=0.05 (i.e. that the results could have happened by chance with a probability of one in twenty) is not always sufficiently stringent. An acceptable level of significance is p = 0.05/N where N is the number of different HLA antigens compared between the two groups using one set of data. For a fuller account of statistical methodologies see Svejgaard and Ryder (1977).

18.2.4 Properties of the HLA system and interpretation of disease association

One of the striking features of the HLA system is the occurrence of linkage disequilibrium between certain alleles. For example, in the normal populations the haplotype *HLA-A1-B8* occurs with a much higher frequency (0.088) in Caucasoids than would be expected (0.019) from the product of the frequencies of these two genes. The effect of this in studies on MHS disease association makes it impossible to be sure that the allele being typed for is involved in the disease or whether it is in linkage disequilibrium with another gene at a different locus which predisposes to the disease. For example,

Table 18.1. Linkage disequilibrium and disease association

Disease	Allele	Relative risk
Graves' disease	A1	1.5
	B8	2.3
	DR3	3.7
Coeliac disease	B8	8.3
	DR3	10.8
Multiple sclerosis	A3	1.4
	B7	1.8
	DR2	4.80
Dermatitis herpetiformis	A1	4.0
	B8	8.7
	DR3	56.4
Idiopathic haemochromatosis	A3	8.2
	B7	3.0

The alleles A1, B8 and DR3 show linkage disequilibrium with respect to each other and similarly the alleles A3, B7 and DR2. (Data adapted from Ryder et al., 1979.)

certain autoimmune diseases were initially associated with HLA-B8 but were subsequently shown to be more strongly associated with HLA-DR3 which is in linkage disequilibrium with HLA-B8 (Table 18.1). It is generally assumed that the relative risk increases the nearer the marker gene is to the gene responsible for increased susceptibility to the disease. A second problem associated with linkage disequilibrium is that particular haplotypes may appear to be associated with certain diseases when in fact it is only one of the alleles which is involved. Although in a few diseases there is some evidence to suggest that the haplotype is more important than any individual allele, this is a difficult point to establish and in this chapter we shall discuss alleles rather than haplotypes. (For a fuller discussion of linkage disequilibrium see Bodmer & Bodmer, 1978.)

An additional problem in trying to understand the rôle of the MHS in disease is that we do not fully understand the biological functions of the products of the MHS. We know from studies on MHS restriction and MHS Ir genes that the products of the MHS are involved in the antigen-specific clonal expansion of T cells (see Chapters 11 and 12). It is possible that MHS disease associations are manifestations of the same phenomenon and in fact reflect MHS Ir genes. Conventional typing sera react with only a small number of determinants on the HLA-A, -B, -C and -DR molecules and it is possible that other parts of these molecules or of molecules coded for by genes in linkage disequilibrium with *HLA* genes, are more directly involved in the disease. This is supported by the fact that certain diseases are associated with different antigens in different populations making it unlikely that the serologically defined parts of the HLA molecules are involved, for example with Graves' disease.

18.3 Diseases associated with HLA

A representative sample of HLA-associated diseases is given in Tables 18.2 and 18.3 (for a complete list refer to the HLA disease registry; Ryder *et al.*, 1979; and to Batchelor, 1981). Some of these diseases have immunological connotations and are probably due to the presence of particular HLA-A, -B, -C or -D alleles. Others have no immunological basis and result from the actions of genes at different loci within the MHS which themselves have no relevance to the functions of the MHS. A clear example of such a disease is congenital adrenal hyperplasia which is due to a deficiency of the enzyme 21-hydroxylase. Family studies have shown that the deficiency is very closely linked to *HLA* (Dupont *et al.*, 1977). Idiopathic haemochromatosis is similarly thought to be a recessive defect in the gene involved in iron metabolism which is closely linked to *HLA* (Lipinski *et al.*, 1978). From the relative risk figures it would appear to be closer to *HLA-A* than *HLA-B* (Table 18.3). In mice it is known that genes associated with *H-2* affect a wide variety of diverse biological

Table 18.2. Diseases associated with HLA-DR

Disease	Allele	Relative risk
Chronic active autoimmune hepatitis	DR3	13.9
Coeliac disease	DR3	10.8
Dermatitis herpetiformis	DR3	56.4
Graves' disease (thyrotoxicosis)	DR3	3.7
Juvenile diabetes	DR3	5.7
	DR4	2.8
	DR2	0.24
Idiopathic Addison's disease	DR3	6.3
Myasthenia gravis	DR3	2.7
Sjögren's disease	DR3	9.7
Grass pollinosis	DR3	4.7
Multiple sclerosis	DR2	4.8
Optic neuritis	DR2	2.4
Tuberculoid leprosy	DR2	8.1
Goodpasture's syndrome	DR2	13.1
Bürger disease	DR2	3.9
Rheumatoid arthritis	DR4	5.8

Data adapted from Ryder *et al.* (1979).

Disease	Associated HLA allele	Relative risk
Ankylosing spondylitis		
Caucasoids	B27	87.4
Japanese	B27	32.4
Post-Salmonella arthritis	B27	29.7
Post-Shigella arthritis	B27	20.7
Post-Yersinia arthritis	B27	17.6
Post-Gonorrhoeic arthritis	B27	14.0
Uveitis	B27	14.6
Reiter's disease	B27	37.0
Amyloidosis in rheumatoid arthritis	B27	8.2
Balanitis	B27	37.4
Psoriasis vulgaris	CW6	13.3
	DW11	5.9
	B17	4.8
	B13	4.8
	B37	4.4
Subacute thyroiditis	BW35	13.7
Manic depressive disorder (Bipolar)	B16	6.2
Idiopathic haemochromatosis	A3	8.2

Table 18.3. Diseases associated with HLA-A, -B and -C

Data adapted from Ryder *et al.* (1979).

systems including testis weight and dimensions of cranial bones (Iványi, 1978). It is not surprising, therefore, that some diseases associated with the MHS are due to defects in enzyme systems closely linked to the *HLA-A, -B, -C* and *-D* loci.

18.3.1 *Diseases associated with DR3*

Most of the diseases associated with DR3 have an autoimmune component (Table 18.2). It has been suggested that this allele leads to a general hyperresponsiveness (or reduced suppression) of the immune response. In the mixed lymphocyte response T lymphocytes from DR3-positive individuals are more responsive than T lymphocytes from DR3-negative persons (Osoba & Falk, 1978). Also the levels of some autoantibodies (rheumatoid factor and antibodies to the acetylcholine receptor) are often higher in DR3-positive patients than DR2 (Batchelor, 1981).

Recent studies have suggested that the increased antibody titres in DR3-positive individuals might be related to persisting antigen since macrophages from DR3-positive individuals degrade antigen more slowly than macrophages from DR3-negative individuals (Legrand *et al.*, 1980). From an evolutionary point of view the advantages to be gained from carrying alleles leading to hyperresponsiveness may outweigh the disadvantages of increased susceptibility to autoimmune disease.

Graves' disease is an interesting example of how the same disease can be associated with different alleles in different populations. In Caucasoid populations the disease is strongly associated with DR3 whereas in the Japanese populations this disease is found in association with DHO. This allele has similar properties to DR3 in that the gene frequency is the same and that the haplotype frequencies HLA-B8 DR3 and HLA-B35 DHO are similar in the two populations (Sasasuki et al., 1978).

18.3.2 Other diseases associated with DR

There are a number of clinically unrelated diseases which show strong association with the allele DR2. The suggestion has been made that DR2 is the counterpart of DR3 and is associated with immunological hyporesponsiveness (Batchelor, 1981). Patients with autoimmune diseases who are DR2 positive, have lower autoantibody titres. Further DR2-positive individuals are protected from the development of juvenile onset diabetes (relative risk <1·0). Again as with the DR3-associated diseases it seems unlikely that a specific immune response has been affected and more likely that there is some defect in the regulation of the immune response in patients who are DR2 positive.

18.3.3 Diseases associated with HLA-A, -B and -C

The most striking of all the HLA-associated diseases is ankylosing spondylitis (Brewerton et al., 1973). This disease has a very high association with HLA-B27. It is important to remember that there are patients with the disease who do not carry the B27 allele and it is possible that in these patients the aetiology of the disease may be different.

There is strong evidence that HLA-B27 acts in conjunction with bacterial infections since infections with Salmonella, Yersinia, Shigella and Gonococci in HLA-B27 individuals are often followed by arthritis. It would seem that the presence of the B27 allele may modify the host response to bacterial infections in an immuno-logically non-specific manner. It is not known whether it is the B27 allospecificity itself which predisposes to these diseases but in all populations tested so far ankylos-ing spondylitis is associated with B27. This is compatible with the B27 determinant being directly involved in the disease though it does not prove it. An intriguing recent finding is that the lymphocytes from all B27-positive individuals absorb a protein from the culture of certain strains of Klebsiella and B27-positive patients with akylosing spondylitis appear to have already absorbed this Klebsiella protein (Geczy et al., 1980). The relationship between these observations and the B27 arthropathies is far from clear.

18.4 MHS disease association and natural selection

An important question in the study of MHS and disease is whether particular MHS genes confer any survival advantage on individuals thereby leading to the selection for particular alleles in the remaining population. Most of the diseases in Tables 18.2 and 18.3 would not have much effect on the breeding potential of primitive man. Much more significant for selection would be if certain HLA alleles conferred resistance to common virulent pathogenic infections. This is hard to formally test in man but one retrospective study on Dutch immigrants to South America suggests that genes associated with HLA can influence survival in yellow fever and typhoid epidemics (De Vries *et al.*, 1979).

A clear case of selection of MHS through disease resistance is seen in chickens where a particular MHS type is associated with resistance to Marek's disease, a herpes virus-induced T-cell lymphoma. Breeding and selection of domestic fowls has shown that resistance is associated with the chicken MHS type B^{21}. This MHS type has been found in 12 out of 40 different populations of fowls including the Red Jungle fowl, the progenitor of the species where 75 per cent of the birds carry the B^{21} haplotype (Longenecker *et al.*, 1977).

18.5 Conclusion

The association of particular MHS haplotypes with certain diseases is not simply a sophisticated exercise in stamp collecting. As discussed in previous chapters (see Chapters 10, 11 and 12) we now know that the molecules of the *HLA-A, -B, -C* and *-D* loci play an important biological rôle in the regulation of the immune response particularly in relation to antigen presentation to T cells. Involvement of the *HLA-A, -B, -C* and *-D* loci in disease can therefore be interpreted in two ways. First, certain alleles may have a non-specific effect on the magnitude of the immune responses. This may be revealed either as hyper- or hyporesponsiveness to a number of bacterial or viral infections. Secondly, some of the products of these loci may have properties similar to the specific MHS-associated *Ir* genes or be in linkage disequilibrium with certain *Ir* genes. These two situations need not be mutually exclusive; for example, there appears to be an increased risk of diabetes with DR3/DR4 heterozygotes when compared to DR3 or DR4 homozygotes. Similarly DR7 in combination with DR3 may give an increased risk to coeliac disease. Undoubtedly as the biological functions of the MHS molecules becomes clarified then the particular nature of the defect and possible identification of the causal agent of each disease may become possible.

At present, studies on MHS disease association have shown that more diseases than originally expected have a genetic element in their aetiology. It has also been realized that what was previously regarded as one disease is in fact two or more showing different associations with the MHS.

Finally it is hoped that studies of MHS disease association will define individuals at risk to particular diseases. This would be particularly useful in family studies where at risk children could be identified, monitored and treated earlier if symptoms arise.

References

BATCHELOR R. (1981) In LACHMANN P.J. & PETERS D.K. (eds), *Clinical Aspects of Immunology*, 4th ed., Blackwell Scientific Publications, Oxford.

BODMER W.F. & BODMER J.G. (1978) Evolution and function of the HLA system. *Brit. Med. Bull.* 34, 309.

BREWERTON D.A., CAFFREY M., HART F.D., JAMES D.C.O., NICHOLLS A. & STURROCK R.D. (1973) Ankylosing spondylitis and HLA-27. *Lancet* i, 904.

DE VRIES R.R.P., MEERA KHAN P., BERNINI L.F., VAN LOGHEM E. & VAN ROOD J.J. (1979) Genetic control of survival in epidemics. *J. Immunogenet.* 6, 271.

DUPONT B., OBERFIELD S.E., SMITHWICK E.M., LEE T.D. & LEVINE L.S. (1977) Close genetic linkage between HLA and congenital adrenal hyperplasia (21-hydroxylase deficiency). *Lancet* ii, 1309.

GECZY A., ALEXANDER K., BASHIR H.V. & EDMONDS J. (1980) A factor(s) in *Klebsiella* culture filtrates specifically modifies an HLA-B27-associated cell-surface component. *Nature* 283, 782.

IVÁNYI P. (1978) Some aspects of the *H-2* system. *Proc. R. Soc. Lond. B.* 202, 117.

LEGRAND L., HORS J. & DAUSSET J. (1980) In: FOUGEREAU M. & DAUSSETT T. (eds.) *Proceedings of the Fourth International Congress of Immunology, Paris.* Academic Press, London.

LILLY F. (1966) The inheritance of susceptibility to the gross leukaemia virus in mice. *Genetics* 53, 529.

LIPINSKI M., HORS J., SALEUN H.P., SADDI R., PASSA P., LAFAURIE S., FEINGOLD N. & DAUSSET J. (1978) Idiopathic haemochromatosis: linkage with HLA. *Tissue Ant.* 11, 471.

LONGENECKER B.M., PAZDERKA F., GAVORA J.S., SPENCER J.L., STEPHENS E.A., WITTER R.L. & RUTH R.F. (1977) Role of the major histocompatibility complex in resistance to Marek's disease: restriction of the growth of JMV-MD tumour cells in genetically resistant birds. *Adv. Exp. Biol.* 88, 287.

MOURANT A.E., KOPEĆ A.C. & DOMANIEWSKI-SOBCZAK K. (1978) *Blood Groups and Diseases.* Oxford University Press, Oxford.

OSOBA D. & FALK J. (1978) HLA-B8 phenotype associated with an increased mixed leukocyte reaction. *Immunogenetics* 6, 425.

RYDER L.P., ANDERSEN E. & SVEJGAARD A. (1979) HLA and disease Registry 1979. *Tissue Ant.* Suppl.

SASASUKI T., KOHNO Y., IWAMOTO I. & TANIMURA M. (1978) HLA-B-D haplotypes associated with autoimmune diseases in Japanese population. *Tissue Ant.* 10, 218.

SVEJGAARD A. & RYDER L.P. (1977) In DAUSSET J. & SVEJGAARD A. (eds), *Associations Between HLA and Disease.* Munksgaard, Copenhagen.

VAN ROOD J.J., DE VRIES R.R.P. & BRADLEY B.A. (1980) Genetics and biology of the HLA system. In DORF M. & BENACERRAF B. (eds), *The Role of the Major Histocompatibility Complex in Immunobiology,* p. 238. Garland Press Publ. Inc., New York.

Further Reading

Histocompatibility Testing (1980). Terasaki P.I. (ed) UCLA Tissue Typing Laboratory Los Angeles California.

The HLA system. *Brit. Med. Bull.* 34, no. 3 (1978).

Chapter 19
Graft Rejection

19.1 Introduction

The immunological nature of graft rejection was only accepted after it had been shown that second grafts from the same donor were more rapidly rejected than the first grafts and that the accelerated response could occur at any site accessible to the lymphoid system of the recipient (Medawar, 1958). It was later shown that the reactivity for the accelerated rejection of certain grafts could be transferred to unprimed animals with lymphoid cells and that graft rejection could be prevented by the induction of neonatal tolerance to histocompatibility antigens (see Chapter 13).

19.2 Transplantation genetics

Grafts involving the transfer of tissue from one site to another within the same individual (autografts) or between genetically identical individuals (isografts or syngrafts) are in general accepted while grafts between genetically different individuals of the same species (allografts) or between different species (xenografts) are rejected.

In all species studied, the genes coding for the histocompatibility antigens can be divided into two categories. The first includes the major histocompatibility system (the MHS), a cluster of closely linked genes whose products are important in the induction of T cell responses (see Chapters 11 and 12) and where incompatibility generally leads to rapid graft rejection. The second category of histocompatibility genes codes for many different minor transplantation antigens which are scattered throughout the genome. In mice there are more than 30 such loci designated $H\text{-}1$, $H\text{-}3$, etc. ($H\text{-}2$ being the major histocompatibility system). A difference at one minor locus between the graft and the recipient leads to relatively slow graft rejection when compared to differences at $H\text{-}2$. The effects of minor histocompatibility antigens, however, are cumulative such that differences at multiple minor loci can evoke a rapid graft rejection. In man, skin grafts between identical twins are permanently accepted but skin grafts between HLA identical siblings are rejected, albeit more slowly than the grafts between siblings differing in HLA (Table 19.1).

Table 19.1. The effect of histocompatibility differences on skin graft survival

Species	Site of histoincompatibility		Skin graft rejection time (days)
	MHS	Minor loci	
Mouse	+	−	11
	−	H-1	25 -> 100*
	−	H-3	50
	−	H-10	71
	−	Multiple	11
Man (siblings)	−	Many	21
	+	Many	13

* The rejection time with H-1 and some other minor loci depends on the particular allelic differences between graft and recipient. (Adapted from Graff & Bailey, 1973; Ceppellini, 1971.)

19.2.1 Inheritance of histocompatibility antigens

Alleles of all the autosomal histocompatibility loci are expressed codominantly. Since the F_1 of two inbred strains expresses, and is tolerant to, all the histocompatibility antigens of both parental strains it will accept skin grafts from either of the parental strains. On the other hand, the parental strains will reject grafts from the F_1 in the same way that they reject grafts from each other (Fig. 19.1). There is evidence that an F_1 animal can express products of the MHS not found in either parent (see Chapter 12) but it is not known if these F_1 structures will serve as targets for graft rejection.

In addition to the histocompatibility loci on the autosomes there are histocompatibility loci, H-X and H-Y, on the sex chromosomes. H-Y is responsible for the rejection of male skin by female mice of the same strain. Female mice lack H-Y and hence are able to respond to this antigen. As far as is known, H-Y is invariant amongst the mouse strains.

19.3 Types of grafts

The cells, tissues or organs grafted and the site of the graft have an influence on the fate of the graft.

19.3.1 The blood supply to the graft

Organ grafts such as kidneys, liver and adult heart, require an immediate anastomosis with the host's blood supply and, consequently, the immunoglobulins in the

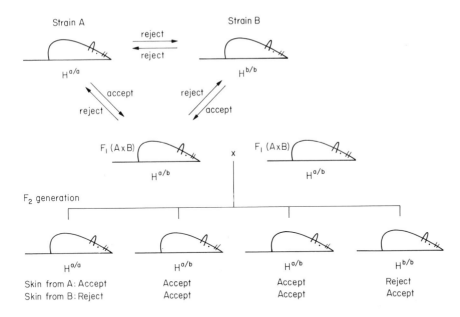

Strain A

Strain B

reject

reject

$H^{a/a}$

$H^{b/b}$

accept

reject

reject

accept

F_1 (A x B)

$H^{a/b}$

x

F_1 (A x B)

$H^{a/b}$

F_2 generation

$H^{a/a}$

$H^{a/b}$

$H^{a/b}$

$H^{b/b}$

Skin from A: Accept

Skin from B: Reject

Accept

Accept

Accept

Accept

Reject

Accept

Fig. 19.1 Rejection pattern of skin grafts between offspring of inbred strains. The rejection pattern of skin exchanged between two inbred strains of mice (A and B) and the F_1 hybrid. In the F_2 generation for each histocompatibility locus there are three types of mice $H^{a/a}$, $H^{a/b}$ and $H^{b/b}$ in the ratio $1:2:1$. If strains A and B differ from each other by a single histocompatibility locus, as would be the case if they were congenic strains for that H locus, then three-quarters of the F_2 mice accept skin from a parental strain. If there are N independently segregating H loci then $(\frac{3}{4})^N$ of the F_2 mice accept a parental graft.

host's circulation will come into contact with the endothelium of the blood vessels of the graft. With other grafts, such as tumour cells and heterotopic organ grafts in rodents, e.g. fetal hearts to the ear, the blood vessels to the graft develop over the first 2–3 days after grafting and are mainly of recipient tissue. Full thickness skin grafts are intermediate in the pattern of blood supply. Initially the graft has no direct connection to the blood vessels of the host but as these extend into the graft over the first few days after grafting they tend to form anastomoses with the blood vessels in the graft. These differences in blood supply influence the effects of antibody on graft survival (see 19.5.2 below).

19.3.2 *The site of the graft*

There are certain sites in the body which lack both lymphatic drainage and blood supply and grafts placed in these sites fail to activate the host's immune system. The effector mechanisms are also unable to migrate to and damage the graft. Examples of such sites are the anterior chamber of the eye and cornea. Providing vascularization of the graft does not occur then allogeneic grafts in these sites will survive. Similarly the survival of allogeneic chondrocytes in cartilage grafts depends on a physical barrier provided by the collagen matrix, preventing any interactions between the host's immune system and the allogeneic cells.

Other immunologically privileged sites seem to depend more on the failure to sensitize the host rather than forming a barrier to the host effector mechanisms. Hamster cheek pouch is one such tissue where grafts can survive in unsensitized animals but once the host is sensitized to the histocompatibility antigens in the graft then it is quickly rejected. Other apparently immunologically privileged sites include the brain, testis and the prostate.

19.3.3 The fetus as a graft

In an outbred population the fetus is histoincompatible with respect to its mother. The reason for the failure of the mother to reject the fetus is not known. The uterus, however, is not an immunologically privileged site and grafts embedded into the wall of the uterus will be rejected. One possibility is that the cells of the chorioallantoic membranes that come into contact with maternal lymphocytes express no histo-compatibility antigens and thus protect the rest of the fetus from the maternal immune system. (For a full discussion of the problem see Loke, 1978.)

19.3.4 Graft versus host reactions

When the graft consists of or contains immunocompetent cells, these recognize and respond to the major and minor histocompatibility antigens expressed on the recipient's tissues. If the host is incapable of reacting against the graft then the immunocompetent cells of the graft cause graft versus host disease. This is associated with damage to the host's epithelial cells, particularly of the gut and the skin which can be fatal. Graft versus host disease can occur if irradiated or genetically immuno-deficient recipients are reconstituted with histoincompatible lymphocytes. Similar reactions will also occur in normal recipients if they are tolerant to the histocompati-bility antigens on the graft, e.g. when parental lymphoid cells are injected into an unirradiated F_1. In the latter case if low numbers of parental lymphoid cells are used, then the graft versus host reaction is limited. This is possibly through a host response to the idiotypes of the receptors on the parental T cells proliferating in the host (see Chapter 9.8.2).

19.4 Induction of graft rejection

The induction of all forms of graft rejection depends upon the activation of T cells. Athymic nude mice will accept allogeneic and even xenogeneic grafts; nudes can grow feathers!

19.4.1 The MHS as alloantigens

In Chapters 11 and 12 we discussed the rôle of the products of the MHS in T cell activation in a syngeneic situation. In the abnormal situation of an allograft, if the donor and recipient are incompatible at the MHS then the MHS products on the graft become alloantigens and the T cell response to such antigens *in vivo* and *in vitro* has several characteristics.

(a) In unprimed animals the frequency of precursors to an allogeneic MHS can be as high as 1 in 10 (Ford *et al.*, 1974). This is several orders of magnitude higher than the frequency to minor transplantation antigens and is not due to cross-priming with microbial antigens since the same frequency is seen in germ free animals. The proliferative response of T cells to MHS antigens in a mixed lymphocyte reaction *in vitro* is presumably a consequence of the high frequency of precursors since the response to other antigens, including minor transplantation antigens, requires priming either *in vivo* or *in vitro* to obtain a measurable secondary response *in vitro*.

(b) The high frequency of precursors to an allogeneic MHS implies that cells responding to these antigens must also react with other antigens. In other words amongst the cells responding to conventional antigens, there will be cells that reconise allogeneic MHS molecules. This is well illustrated by the isolation from an H-2^b female mouse of a clone of cells that is cytotoxic for cells carrying H-Y in association with H-2^b but which also kills male or female cells expressing H-2^d (von Boehmer *et al.*, 1979).

(c) A further feature in the response of T cells to MHS antigens is that while the response to other antigens, including minor transplantation antigens, shows MHS restriction (see Chapter 11) this is not the case in the response to MHS antigens. It seems that when the antigen is itself a product of the MHS there is no longer a requirement for recognition of a further MHS product.

(d) Finally, the unique properties of the MHS molecules as antigens are only observed when the response is induced by live allogeneic cells. MHS products as purified molecules or on fragments of membrane are no longer potent stimulators of T cells and in these circumstances behave as other antigens (Batchelor *et al.*, 1978). For example they will fail to induce a primary proliferative response *in vitro*.

19.4.2 The rôle of antigen-presenting cells

In general, the induction of specific T cells requires the antigen to be presented on an antigen-presenting cell. It has been shown that Ia-positive macrophages and skin Langerhans cells (see Chapter 14.5.2) are able to present antigen to T cells but it is not known if there are other types of antigen-presenting cells or if different cells present antigens to different functional classes of T cells. However, if the graft does not contain antigen-presenting cells then the histocompatibility antigens on the graft must first be processed and presented to the host's T cells via the host's antigen-presenting mechanism. Even when the graft contains antigen-presenting cells one finds that the host's cells normally also become involved. The only exception so far is the reaction of F_1 female mice to male skin of one or other of the parental strains. If additional histocompatibilities are included in this system then both the host's and the graft's antigen-presenting cells present antigen (Table 19.2).

19.4.3 *The rôle of passenger cells in induction*

Most tissues contain migratory cells of the lymphoid series and it has been shown that these cells are sufficient to induce a specific response. Skin from bone-marrow radiation chimeras contains passenger cells derived from the donor bone marrow. This will prime animals syngeneic to the skin cells to give an accelerated second set rejection to grafts of the same tissue type as the bone-marrow donor (Fig. 19.2). It has also been suggested that passenger cells are implicated in the process of graft modification (see 19.6.3), but their importance in the induction of primary rejection has not been fully investigated.

19.4.4 *T cell help and allogeneic MHS*

In Chapter 10 we discussed the involvement of helper T cells in the induction of

Table 19.2. Response of female F_1 mice H-$2^{b/k}$ to male grafts

Source of male cells		Cytotoxicity to H-Y on target cells	
Priming cells	Boosting cells	H-2^b	H-2^k
H-2^b	H-2^b	+ +	–
H-2^b	H-2^k	–	–
H-2^k	H-2^k	–	+ +
H-2^k	H-2^b	–	–
H-2^d	H-2^b	+ +	–
H-2^d	H-2^k	–	+ +

Female (H-$2^b \times H$-2^k) F_1 mice are primed *in vivo* with male cells of different H-2 types and their spleen cells boosted *in vitro* prior to testing their cytotoxic activity on male target cells. When H-2^b or H-2^k cells are used to prime the animals there is no evidence of antigen presentation via the host's H-$2^{b/k}$ cells. Host antigen presentation only occurs when male cells histoincompatible at H-2 (H-2^d) are used. (Adapted from Simpson & Gordon, 1977.)

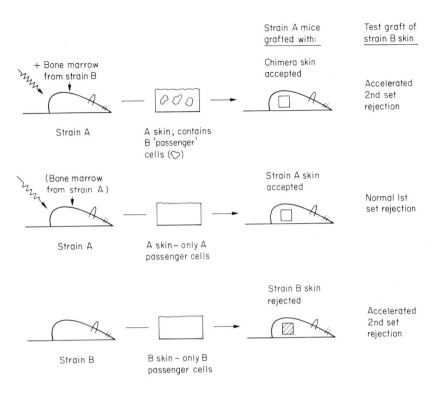

Fig. 19.2. Protocol to show that passenger cells from bone marrow can infiltrate skin and will prime an animal to give second set rejection. (Adapted from Steinmuller and Hart, 1971.)

cytotoxic T cells. When the helper T cells have been activated by differences in the *I* region of *H-2* or the *D* region of *HLA* then the help is non-specific, presumably mediated through non-specific lymphokines. Similar non-specific help can be seen in skin grafts in man where a second graft differing in the *D* region can accelerate the rejection of graft differing by HLA-A and -B alone (Jonkers *et al.*, 1979). Although these non-specific helper mechanisms are essential for the generation of cytotoxic cells in a primary MLR, and may bring forward the onset of rejection *in vivo*, they are not obligatory as grafts between MLR-compatible individuals are still rejected.

19.5 Mechanisms of graft rejection

As far as is known, the recognition of specific alloantigens in graft rejection is either through antibodies or specific T cells, there being no evidence that natural killer cells play any rôle.

19.5.1 T cell effector mechanisms

The histology of acute graft rejection seen typically with renal or skin grafts is of massive lymphocytic infiltration into the tissue of the graft. Graft rejection with this histology cannot be brought about by the passive administration of antibodies. There is convincing evidence that T cells alone are sufficient since bursectomized chickens will reject grafts. An obvious effector mechanism is direct attack by cytotoxic T cells. These cells can be obtained from the lymph nodes draining the site of an acute graft rejection. However, models of T cell responses *in vitro* to allo-antigens may be misleading; the response to the H-Y antigen as measured by graft rejection shows no correlation with *in vitro* assays for cytotoxic T cells specific for H-Y (Table 19.3). The other T cell effector mechanism likely to play an important part in rejection is the production of lymphokines by activated T cells that activate macrophages to bring about tissue damage (see Chapter 15).

19.5.2 Antibody-mediated damage

For grafts that require anastomosis to the host's blood supply, the presence in the recipient of complement-fixing, cytotoxic antibodies to the graft at the time of grafting, can lead to a hyperacute rejection. This is characterized by extensive vascular thrombosis brought about by the action of antibodies and complement interacting with platelets and clotting factors. In man, antibodies to the major blood groups and also to HLA-A and HLA-B can cause hyperacute kidney rejection. This is normally avoided by a cross-match procedure using the donor's lymphocytes and the patient's serum. Antibodies to other specificities can behave similarly; for example, antibodies to minor blood group antigens and antibodies specific to kidney tissue which are occasionally found in patients who have rejected one kidney (Ting *et al.*, 1978).

Antibodies are also extremely efficient at eliminating cells that have been

Table 19.3. Lack of correlation between syngeneic male skin graft rejection and generation of cytotoxic T cells specific for H-Y

Mouse strain	Median survival time (days)	Anti H-Y cytotoxicity *in vitro*
B10	40	Yes
B10 . A(5R)	21	No
CBA	>100	No
C3H . OH	>100	Yes

Adapted from Hurme *et al.* (1978).

introduced directly into the blood supply of the recipient. This occurs in bone marrow, granulocyte, platelet and blood transfusions. These reactions are induced by antibodies to a large number of different specificities including blood groups and the major transplantation antigens. Several tissue-specific antigenic systems have also been identified on platelets and granulocytes.

The importance to rejection of antibodies produced after grafting is less clear cut. Some antibodies help to maintain grafts (see 19.6.2) while others produce tissue damage of the type described above and in Chapter 15.4. In some cases it is possible to destroy long-standing skin grafts by injecting antibodies to the graft and antibodies are thought to be involved in the chronic rejection of renal allografts in man.

19.6 Attempts to prevent graft rejection

The major obstacle to graft acceptance is the difficulty of inducing tolerance in a fully developed immune system. Although the induction of classical transplantation tolerance is possible in a developing immune system, for example in neonates, this is of little practical value except perhaps in bone-marrow grafting (see 19.7.4).

19.6.1 Immunosuppressive drugs

The rationale behind immunosuppressive chemotherapy is to destroy cells responding to antigens. Most of the drugs used kill rapidly dividing cells but show only marginal, if any, preference for lymphocytes. Immunosuppressive chemotherapy in man is often a combination of steroids and cytotoxic drugs such as azathioprine but both have unfortunate side effects, particularly when used on children. High doses of steroids cause a general lymphocytolysis but this is not true for the maintenance doses used with established kidney grafts. Their mode of action at this dose is unknown. A further drawback with chemotherapy is that the drugs used at present cause a general suppression of the immune system and patients run the risk of overwhelming infections from organisms, many of which are not normally pathogenic.

Cyclosporin A, a cyclic undecapeptide from *Trichoderma polysporum*, may possibly be more specific in the target cells that it affects, although recent clinical trials show that this drug is not free of side effects (Calne *et al.*, 1979).

19.6.2 Immunosuppressive immunology

Antibodies to host lymphocytes have been used to improve the specificity of immunosuppressive regimes. If the recipient is pre-treated with xeno antisera specific for lymphocytes, particularly T cells, then graft rejection is delayed. The use of such reagents in man is complicated by the difficulty of obtaining a standard antiserum and the problem of the recipient's response to the foreign immunoglobulin giving rise to Arthus' reactions and serum sickness. In spite of these difficulties, antilymphocyte sera, in conjunction with chemotherapy, is used in heart grafts. This is clearly an area where monoclonal antisera to T cell subsets might usefully be applied.

Antibodies directed against the major histocompatibility antigens in the graft can, in some cases, prolong graft survival (Davies & Atkins, 1974). Antibodies specific for the I region products or its equivalent are usually most effective but in some experimental combinations antisera to K-D equivalent could produce complete acceptance (Gallico et al., 1979). The mode of action of these antibodies is not known but may be via destruction of antigen-presenting cells in the graft or by the removal by opsonization of antigen-specific T cells carrying antigen–antibody complex (Hutchinson & Zola, 1977).

Finally, in Chapter 13.4.1 we discussed the use of auto-anti-idiotypic reactions to produce prolongation of skin grafts in certain strains of rats. The generality of this type of reaction has not yet been established and its application to organ grafting in man would require living donors as the pre-treatment of the recipient takes several weeks.

19.6.3 Graft modification

It has been known for some time that tissues maintained in culture or held in an immunologically privileged site such as the anterior chamber of the eye, are subsequently rejected more slowly than tissue taken directly from a donor. In one case F_1 rat kidneys were grafted into one of the parental strains and the grafts induced to survive by the use of antisera (see 19.6.2). Kidneys that had survived in the parental environment were then regrafted into fresh untreated rats of the same parental strain and now the grafts were accepted without any immunosuppressive treatment (Batchelor et al., 1979). The reasons for graft modification in these systems is not known but may be due to the removal from the graft of passenger cells that play an important rôle in the induction of graft rejection.

19.7 Human allografts in practice

Over the last 20 years at least 20,000 renal allografts and some hundreds of heart and liver grafts have been performed. From the analysis of these data some facts have become clear.

19.7.1 Importance of immunosuppression

Even in grafts of HLA identical siblings immunosuppression is essential. Generally the greater the level of HLA mismatch the more immunosuppression is required, but with time the amounts of the immunosuppressive drugs can be reduced to maintenance doses. If the drugs are stopped altogether then a rejection crisis often ensues but there are a number of reports of successfully maintained grafts in individuals receiving no immunosuppression.

19.7.2 HLA matching

The success of kidney grafts depends on many non-immunological factors such as the condition of the donor kidney and the quality of the post-operative care. In addition, it is now generally accepted that the prognosis is related to the degree of mismatch at HLA between the donor and the recipient. Grafts between HLA identical siblings are most successful and have a greater chance of survival than HLA-A and -B match cadaver grafts. HLA-A and -B identical siblings are likely to be identical at all other loci in the MHS, while with unrelated donors this is not the case. Although matching for HLA-A and -B improves the prognosis of cadaver grafts (Fig. 19.3), these may not be the most important loci to match for. It is impractical at present to type for HLA-D by mixed lymphocyte reaction for kidney grafting but the serological HLA-DR typing may prove suitable and even more relevant for graft prognosis.

19.7.3 Blood transfusion and kidney graft survival

It was noticed that patients with kidney grafts who had received blood transfusion or who had had a previous pregnancy, had a better prognosis than patients who had

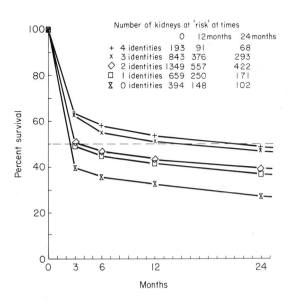

Number of kidneys at 'risk' at times

		0	12 months	24 months
+	4 identities	193	91	68
x	3 identities	843	376	293
◇	2 identities	1349	557	422
□	1 identities	659	250	171
⦻	0 identities	394	148	102

Fig. 19.3. Percentage survival of patients and kidney grafts at different times after grafting analysed with respect to the number of HLA-A and -B identities between the graft and the recipient. (Taken from the annual bulletin of the U.K. Transplant Service, 1979.)

received no blood transfusions (Opelz *et al.*, 1972). In experiments in monkeys this effect is only seen in animals who also receive immunosuppression, and blood transfusion on its own had no effect (van Es *et al.*, 1978). Further, one transfusion was enough to produce prolongation of kidney grafts in three-quarters of the monkeys tested. In man, leucocyte-free blood will not produce the effect (Persijn *et al.*, 1979).

Blood transfusion and pregnancy will induce cytotoxic anti-HLA antibodies that can lead to hyperacute graft rejection (see 19.5.2). Consequently, it has been argued that blood transfusion is merely dividing the recipients into poor or good responders to transplantation antigens. There will be a tendency not to graft the good responders in the transfused group as it will be harder to find a suitable kidney from a donor with a negative cross-match, while in the untransfused group both the good and the poor responders are grafted and the good responders will reject their grafts. This argument cannot adequately explain the experiments in monkeys and at present there is no satisfactory explanation for the apparently beneficial effects of blood transfusion.

19.7.4 Bone-marrow grafts

The difficulties with bone-marrow grafts are twofold: first the host may reject the graft and second the graft may lead to graft versus host disease. The first of these problems in some cases does not apply, for example with certain immunodeficient children. The host's immune response can be eliminated with combinations of cytotoxic drugs or by irradiation. Recently it has been found that total lymph node irradiation is preferable to whole body irradiation as the former reduces the frequency and severity of graft versus host reactions possible through the generation of suppressor cells (Strober *et al.*, 1979). Surprisingly bone-marrow grafts between identical twins can occasionally produce GVH-like reactions. The targets for this reaction are unknown but could be viral antigens. The induction of classical transplantation tolerance (see Chapter 13.2) in mice show that if the pluripotential stem cells develop in an allogeneic environment they give rise to mature cells that are tolerant to the recipient's alloantigens. The problem with human bone-marrow grafts is to separate the pluripotential stem cells from other more mature cells present in the donor bone marrow. With the recent developments of monoclonal antibodies to subsets of human lymphocyte and of assays for human stem cells there are now hopes that bone-marrow grafting may become more successful.

References

BATCHELOR J.R., WELSH K.I. & BURGOS H. (1978) Transplantation antigens *per se* are poor immunogens within a species. *Nature* **273**, 54.

BATCHELOR J.R., WELSH K.I., MAYNARD A. & BURGOS H. (1979) Failure of long-surviving passively-enhanced kidney allografts to provoke T-dependent alloimmunity. *J. exp. Med.* **150**, 455.

CEPPELLINI R. (1971) Old and new facts and speculations about transplantation antigens of man. In AMOS B. (ed.), *Progress in Immunology.* p. 973. Academic Press, New York.

CALNE R.Y. (1979) Cyclosporin A as the only immunosuppressant in 34 recipients of cadaveric organs. *Lancet* **ii**, 1033.

DAVIES A.J. & ATKINS R.C. (1974) What abrogates heart transplant rejection in immunological enhancement? *Nature* **247**, 294.

FORD W.L., SIMMONDS S.J. & ATKINS R.C. (1974) Estimates of the frequency of donor lymphocytes which respond to each Ag-B-determined antigenic complex. *J. exp. Med.* **141**, 681.

GALLICO G.G., BUTCHER G.W. & HOWARD J.C. (1979) The role of subregions of the rat MHC in the rejection and passive enhancement of renal allografts. *J. exp. Med.* **149**, 244.

GRAFF R.J. & BAILEY D.W. (1973) The non-*H-2* histocompatibility loci and their antigens. *Transplant. Rev.* **15**, 26.

HURME M., CHANDLER P.R., HETHERINGTON C.M. & SIMPSON E. (1978) Cytotoxic T-cell responses to H-Y: correlation with rejection of syngeneic male skin grafts. *J. exp. Med.* **147**, 768.

HUTCHINSON I.V. & ZOLA H. (1977) Antigen-reactive cell opsonization in passive enhancement of rat renal allografts. *Transplant. Proc.* **9**, 961.

JONKERS M., KOCH C.T., BLUSSÉ A., VAN OUEL A., FREDERIKS E. & VAN ROOD J.J. (1979) Human skin grafts from MLC-positive donors provide help for rejection of skin grafts from MLC-negative donors. *Transplantation* **27**, 231.

LOKE Y.W. (1978) *Immunology and Immunopathology of the Human Foetal–Maternal Interaction.* Elsevier-North Holland, Amsterdam.

MEDAWAR P.B. (1958) The immunology of transplantation. *Harvey Lectures Series* **52**, 144.

OPELZ G., MICKEY M.R. & TERASAKI P.I. (1972) Poor kidney transplant survival in receipients with frozen blood transfusion or no transfusion. *Lancet* **i**, 868.

PERSIJN G.G., COHEN B., LANSBERGEN Q. & VAN ROOD J.J. (1979) The effect of blood transfusion in renal transplantation in The Netherlands. *Transplantation* **28**, 396.

SIMPSON E. & GORDON R.D. (1977) Responsiveness to H-Y antigen. *Immunol. Rev.* **33**, 59.

STEINMULLER D. & HART E.A. (1971) Passenger leukocytes and induction of allograft immunity. *Transplant. Proc.* **3**, 673.

STROBER S. (1979) Allograft tolerance after total lymphoid irradiation. *Immunol. Rev.* **46**, 87.

TING A., WILLIAMS K.A. & MORRIS P.J. (1978) Transplantation immunological monitoring. *Brit. Med. Bull.* **34**, 263.

VAN ES A.A., MARQUET R.L., VAN ROOD J.J. & BALNER H. (1978) Influence of a single blood transfusion on kidney allograft survival in unrelated rhesus monkeys. *Transplantation* **26**, 325.

VON BOEHMER H. & HASS W. (1979) Distinct *Ir* genes for helper and killer cells in the cytotoxic response to H-Y antigen. *J. exp. Med.* **150**, 1134.

VON BOEHMER H., HEUGARTNER H., NABHOLZ M., LERNHARDT W., SCHREIER M.H. & HASS W. (1979) Fine specificity of a continuously growing killer cell clone specific for H-Y antigens. *Europ. J. Immunol.* **9**, 592.

Further reading

BILLINGHAM R.E. & SILVERS E.S. (1971) *The Immunobiology of Transplantation.* Prentice-Hall, Englewood Cliffs, N.J..

BARKER C.F. & BILLINGHAM R.E. (1977) Immunologically privileged sites. *Adv. Immunol.* **25**, 1.

BATCHELOR J.R. (1978) The riddle of kidney graft enhancement. *Transplantation* **26**, 139.

Glossary

Adjuvant: a substance which non-specifically enhances or modifies the response of the immune system to an antigen.

Affinity: a measure of the strength of binding, e.g. a single antibody combining site to a single antigenic determinant.

Affinity chromatography: method of purification of molecules by attaching substances for which they have affinity to an insoluble support medium and then using this as a chromatographic medium. Antibodies of high affinity may prove difficult to elute from an affinity column.

Allele: inherited variants at a genetic locus.

Allergic: pertaining to a state of altered reactivity. Commonly used to describe a state of hypersensitivity, i.e. allergic to strawberries or grass pollen. Although in the first edition we used the original sense of the word, in this edition we have not done so but rather used the common (but incorrect) usage of the word.

Allo: between genetically different members of the species.

Allogeneic: the differences in genes (or gene products) found by comparing different individuals of the same species.

Allotype: products of alleles, can be detected as inherited antigenic variants of a particular molecule.

Amino acid code: the one letter code for writing amino acid sequences is as follows:

alanine	A	methionine	M
arginine	R	phenylalanine	F
asparagine	N	proline	P
aspartic acid	D	serine	S
cysteine	C	threonine	T
glutamine	Q	tryptophan	W
glutamic acid	E	tyrosine	Y
glycine	G	valine	V
histidine	H		
isoleucine	I		
leucine	L		
lysine	K		

Amino acid sequenator: a machine which sequentially removes the amino terminal amino acid from a polypeptide chain and determines the nature of this residue, In this way the sequence of polypeptide can be rapidly determined.

Anaphylatoxin: proteins which cause release of mast cell granules and consequent increase in vascular permeability.

Antibody: molecule produced by animals in response to antigen (q.v.) which has the property of combining specifically with the antigen.

Antigen: molecule or particle which induces the formation of, and combines with antibody.

Antigen suicide: method of specifically destroying cells carrying receptors for antigens by exposing them to antigen of very high specific radioactivity. The local irradiation leads to the death of the cells.

Antiparallel: same as parallel but with directions opposite:

Parallel	Antiparallel
$-----\!>$	$--------\!>$
$-----\!>$	$<--------$

Ascertainment: the extent to which all relevant data is collected and its lack of bias.

Association: the phenomenon of two phenotypic markers being frequently found together. The association may be due to a causal relationship between the observed phenomena or to linkage disequilibrium between the genes which code for the phenotypic events (see chapter 6).

Ataxia-telangectasia: a complex syndrome with neurological and immunological abnormalities. Ataxia—imbalance of muscular control. Telangectasia—dilated capillary blood vessels.

Autosomes: chromosomes other than the X or Y sex chromosomes.

Avidity: net combining power of an antibody molecule with its antigen: related to both the affinity and the valencies of the antibody and the antigen.

$\beta_1 H$: the old name for Factor H of the complement system (see subsection 3.4.1).

β_2 *microglobulin*: a polypeptide component (11,000 m.w.) of the HL-A molecules (see chapter 6). Associated with certain membrane proteins including the HLA-A, -B, and -C molecules (see chapter 6).

BCG: bacille Calmette–Guérin. An attenuated strain of *Mycobacterium tuberculosis*, in general use as a vaccine, but also used as an adjuvant.

Bence-Jones proteins: 'free' light chains of immunoglobulin found in the urine of people (or mice) with multiple myeloma.

Bursa of Fabricius: lymphoepithelial organ unique to birds, located at the junction of the hind gut and cloaca.

B-mice: mice depleted of T-lymphocytes. A commonly used procedure is to thymectomize neonatal mice or adult mice. In the latter case the thymectomized mice are irradiated to destroy mature T-cells and then reconstituted with bone marrow.

C3b inactivator: the old name for Factor I of the complement system (see subsection 3.4.1). This has also been called KAF (conglutinin activating factor).

Capping: process of redistribution of cell-surface determinants to one small part of the cell surface. Usually accomplished by antibody which must be at least divalent.

Carrier: immunogenic molecule to which a hapten (q.v.) is coupled. See preamble to section II.

Cell cycle: the overall process of cell division. This is usually divided into four stages—G1, S, G2 and M. In S the DNA is undergoing replication and M is the period of mitoses.

Chemotactic: direction of the migration of cells such as polymorphs can be influenced by concentration gradients of certain substances known as chemotactic factors.

Chimerism: a situation in which cells from two genetically different individuals coexist in one body.

Clone: a family of cells (or organisms) of genetically identical constitution derived asexually from a single cell by repeated division.

Cobra venom factor (CVF): a complement component of the cobra corresponding to mammalian C3b. (see chapter 3).

Cold agglutinins: antibodies which form precipitates only at temperatures below 37°C.

Cogenic: animals which are constructed to differ at one particular locus (see chapter 6).

Crossing over: the breakage and repair of homologous DNA strands during meiosis. The mechanism of recombination between genes on a chromosome.

Cytophilic: having affinity for cells (i.e. cytophilic antibody). These antibodies bind to cells via the constant region, e.g. IgE to mast cells.

Cytotoxic: the ability to kill cells.

Deme: a breeding unit, a family unit, tribe or colony of mice with rigid social structure. Usually occupies a few square metres of territory.

Dizygotic twins: non-identical twins derived from two separate fusions of spermatozoa and ova.

DNP: dinitrophenol. A commonly used hapten, as is TNP or trinitrophenol.

Domain: a region of protein folded into a coherent three dimensional shape. The chains of immunoglobulin molecules can be divided into different domains consisting of about 110 amino acids and folded into a characteristic compact shape (see chapter 2).

Double diffusion: a method of analysis of antibody–antigen reaction taking place in agar pioneered by Ouchterlony.

Doubling time: time required for a population to double its numbers. Not simply related to the interval between divisions unless all the cells are dividing at the same rate.

ds-DNA: double stranded DNA.

Epstein–Barr virus: (E.B. virus) probable causal agent of Burkitt's lymphoma and able to transform human B cells into stable cell lines.

Effector cell: a useful concept in considering the maturation of lymphocytes. The effector cells are the end product of maturation and are the cells which actually produce the observed effect.

Endogenous: having origin within the organism.

Endothelium: the cells lining blood vessels and lymphatic vessels (from the Greek *endo*; within, *thele*; nipple).

Enhancement: the prolongation of graft survival by antibody to the graft, first observed with the increased growth of transplanted tumours.

Epithelium: closely packed sheet of cells covering the external surface of the entire body and lining all hollow structures within the body except blood vessels and lymphatics.

Epitope: single antigenic determinant. The portion of a molecule which will combine with a particular antibody combining site.

Forsmann antigen: a carbohydrate antigen with wide but non-uniform distribution in mammals. In some species (e.g. sheep) it is present on both tissue and red cells, but in others (e.g. guinea pigs) is present on tissue cells only. Antisera are classically raised by the injection of boiled horse kidney into rabbits (which wholly lack the antigen).

Freund's adjuvant: a water–oil emulsion of antigen (usually in aqueous phase) and killed *Mycobacteria tuberculosis* usually in the oily phase (complete Freund's adjuvant). Incomplete Freund's adjuvant contains no organisms in the oil phase.

Gamete: specialized cells which combine in sexual reproduction to form the zygote which will develop into the new individual. Ova and sperm in vertebrates.

Genome: the total complement of genetic material within a cell.

Genotype: the genetic characteristics inherited from parents, but not necessarily observable in the phenotype.

Germ line: genetic information which is passed from generation to generation in the conventional Mendelian way.

Giant cells: large multinucleated cells resulting from fusion of single cells (e.g. macrophages in chronic granulomas).

Glomerular basement membrane: the basement membrane of the kidney glomerulus which seems to have distinct antigenic structures from other basement membranes. Antibodies to it can be found in naturally occurring glomerulo-nephritis and can be raised experimentally.

Gluten: the storage protein of wheat. A dietary component involved in the patho-gensis of coeliac disease.

H-2: genetic region concerned with histocompatibility in mice (see chapters 6, 11 and 12).

Haplotype: set of genetic determinants located on a single chromosome.

Hapten: a small molecule which will combine with antibody but which is not capable of evoking an antibody response when injected alone.

Hapten-carrier: a hapten chemically bonded to a protein or other carrier. Hapten-carrier conjugates are used to evoke an immune response to a hapten.

Heterologous: foreign. Usually used to denote inter-species antigenic differences.

High endothelial venule: a small vein with characteristically 'plump' endothelial cells. The site of lymphocyte migration into lymph nodes and elsewhere.

Hinge region: the part of an immunoglobulin heavy chain that allows free movement of Fab arms with respect to Fc.

Histocompatibility: compatibility as determined by transplantation.

HLA: genetic region in man. Corresponding to murine *H-2*.

Homeostasis: the condition of equilibrium within the body.

Humoral: pertaining to the extracellular fluids.

Hybridoma: the name given to cell lines created by fusing B lymphocytes with a plasmacytoma. Hybridomas produce monoclonal antibodies.

Idiotope: see chapter 1.

Immune complex: term used to denote the products of antibody–antigen reactions and often refers to the small soluble complexes containing two or three antibody molecules associated with antigen.

Immunoconglutinins: antibodies (often autoantibodies) formed to complement components or their breakdown products.

Immunofluorescence: method involving the use of fluorochrome-labelled antibody.

Interferon: endogenous glycoproteins which have a non-specific anti-viral activity and require the synthesis of RNA and protein to establish resistance. There are at least three antigenically different interferons—IFN-α, IFN-β and IFN-γ which in man were formerly called Le-IF, F-IF and I-IF or type II-IF respectively.

Iso: same, of identical genetic constitution—isologous, isogeneic (synonym for syngeneic).

Isoantibody: antibody which reacts with an antigen present in another member of the same species but not in the animal itself—e.g. blood group antibodies (term now in the literature but not strictly correct—q.v. iso-).

Isoelectric focusing: high resolution electrophoretic separation in which molecules migrate to their isoelectric points (the pH at which the + ve and −ve charges on the molecule balance resulting in zero net charge) in a self-generating pH gradient.

Karyotype: the set of chromosomes isolated at mitosis. Can be used to distinguish male and female cells and follow inheritance of particular autosomes.

Kuppfer cells: phagocytic cells lining liver sinusoids.

LCM: lymphocytic chorio-meningitis. Viral disease of mice.

Ligand: a substance which links two molecules together.

Linkage: the coexistence of two genes in reasonable close proximity on a chromosome. Not to be confused with association.

Linkage disequilibrium: see chapter 6.

Locus: position on a chromosome at which a gene is to be found.

Lymphokine: generic term for molecules other than antibodies produced by or through the aid of lymphocytes. Kymphokines have a variety of biological activities (see chapter 10). It has recently been proposed to call them interleukins.

Migration inhibition factor (MIF): a generic term for any factor or complex of factors derived from lymphocytes which inhibit the migration of macrophages from capillary tubes *in vitro*.

Mitogen: substance which causes lymphocytes to undergo cell division, e.g. PHA (q.v.) endotoxin.

Mitomycin: a cell poison of plant origin which intercalates with DNA hence blocking cell division.

Molecular weight (m.w.): for proteins the only fully accurate method for determining molecular weight is the summation of the amino acid residues determined by sequences. Accurate molecular weight (±2 per cent) can be derived by painstaking experiments on highly purified material. Immunologists have a habit of making a single measurement of a physical parameter of a protein and announcing a molecular weight on the basis of this. Such an approach can be incorrect by a factor of two.

Monoclonal: derived from a single clone: monoclonal antibodies are homogenous.

Multigravid: having had numerous pregnancies.

Mutation: alteration in the genetic constitution of a cell.

Myeloma: see plasmacytoma.

NeF: nephritic factor; an auto-antibody to C3bB̄b̄ (see subsection 3.4.2).
Neoplasm: a cancer.
Non-covalent forces: chemical bonding forces weaker than covalent bonds, e.g. hydrogen bonds, non-polar (hydrophobic) and electrostatic bonds. These forces are of immense importance in maintaining the configuration of proteins and are disrupted by denaturing agents, e.g. detergents, urea etc.
Nude mouse: a genetically athymic mouse which also carries a closely linked defect in hair production.

Opsonization: process of coating an antigen which facilitates its phagocytosis.

PAF: platelet-aggregating factor. Released by basophils and causes platelets to aggregate.
Parabiosis: surgical creation of 'Siamese' twin arrangement brought about by connecting the blood circulations.
Pathogen: an organism which causes disease.
PHA: phytohaemagglutinin: a plant lectin which stimulates T lymphocytes to divide.
Phagoctosis: the process of ingestion of material into a cell by closing off an invagination of the protoplasm. This process requires the activity of the contractile elements in the cell and is energy dependent. Following ingestion the contents of the *phagosome* are digested by the discharge of cathepsins and other lysosomal enzymes into the phagosome.
Phenotype: individual characteristics as observed (cf. genotype).
Pinocytosis: the process of ingestion of liquids or very small particles into the cell.
Plasma cell: terminally differentated antibody forming cell with short half life (2–3 days).
Plasmacytoma: tumour of a plasma cell almost always secreting a homogeneous immunoglobulin.
Prime: to give first exposure to an antigen.
Pseudo alleles: variants of a gene which do not occupy homologous position on the chromosome. Pseudo alleles occur as a consequence of tandem duplication of genes.
Pyogenic: pus forming.

Radioautography: method of detecting radioactivity by allowing the radiation to blacken a photographic emulsion juxtaposed to the source. In this way the object 'takes its own photograph'.

Reagin: old term for IgE antibody.

Recombination: the process of rearrangement of genetic information which occurs during meiosis.

Reticuloendothelial system: a diffuse system of macrophages associated with the connective tissue framework of the liver, spleen, lymph nodes, serous cavities, lungs etc.

Rocket electrophoresis: electrophoresis of antigen into a gel containing antibody produces streaks of precipitation, the length of the streak or 'rocket' being proportional to the concentration of antigen.

S: Svedberg unit, a measure of the velocity of sedimentation of a molecule or particle in a gravitational field. Accurate measurements are referred to the behaviour of molecules at zero concentration (by extrapolation) in water at 20°C: $S°_{20w}$. A series of molecules of the same density and the same shape will have higher sedimentation rates as they increase in size, but highly asymmetric molecules (e.g. rods or branched structures) will have very much slower sedimentation characteristics than spherical molecules of the same mass. S values can only be derived from experiments in the ultra-centrifuge and alone do not give an estimate of molecular weight.

Sarcoma: malignant connective tissue tumour.

Segregation: distribution of genes among gametes.

SLE: system lupus erythematosus.

Somatic: pertaining to a single individual. Somatic mutation involves the alteration of the genetic potential of cells in an individual without altering the potential of the germ cells, so that the new potential is not passed from generation to generation.

Splenomegaly: increase in spleen size. Used as an assay for graft-versus host reactions.

Stoichiometric: occurring in a quantitatively fixed relationship, for instance the ability of one inhibitor molecule to react with one, and only one enzyme molecule.

Synergism: co-operative action.

Syngeneic: animals which have been produced by repeated brother-sister mating until homozygous at all measurable loci. All animals of a particular strain are thus almost identical in genetic constitution. Particularly important in experiments where cells are transferred from one animal to another.

T6: morphological chromosome marker in mice.

Tachyphylaxis: the phenomenon of increasing unreactivity to an external stimulus.

Tandem duplication: copies of genes lying in a linear array on a chromosome.

Thymoma: tumour of the thymus.

Tolerance: state of specific immunological unresponsiveness induced by exposure to antigen.

Transformation: morphological change in a cell used to signify changes associated with the stimulation of resting lymphocytes into cell division. Also the changes associated with infection by tumour viruses such as SV40.

Xeno: between species.

Index